MELVILLE'S
SOUTH SEAS

BOOKS BY A. GROVE DAY

Adventurers of the Pacific
Coronado and the Discovery of the Southwest
Coronado's Quest: The Discovery
of the Southwestern States
Explorers of the Pacific
Hawaii and Its People
Hawaii: Fiftieth Star
James A. Michener
Louis Becke
Pirates of the Pacific
The Sky Clears: Poetry of the American Indians
The Story of Australia
They Peopled the Pacific
Bluejacket (with F. J. Buenzle)
Hawaii: A History (with R. S. Kuykendall)
Rascals in Paradise (with James A. Michener)

EDITOR

Despatches of Hernando Cortes from Mexico
The Greatest American Short Stories
Mark Twain's Letters from Hawaii
Melville's South Seas: An Anthology
Stories of Hawaii by Jack London
Best South Sea Stories (with Carl Stroven)
A Hawaiian Reader (with Carl Stroven)
The Spell of Hawaii (with Carl Stroven)
The Spell of the Pacific: An Anthology
of Its Literature (with Carl Stroven)
True Tales of the South Seas (with Carl Stroven)

MELVILLE'S SOUTH SEAS

AN ANTHOLOGY

❀ ❀ ❀

*Edited with Introductions
and Notes by*

A. GROVE DAY

HAWTHORN BOOKS, INC.
Publishers
NEW YORK

MELVILLE'S SOUTH SEAS

1 2 3 4 5 6 7 8 9 10

End Papers:
Melville's voyaging in the South Seas, from a chart by Charles R. Anderson (Reprinted from Melville in the South Seas by permission of Columbia University Press)

PREFACE

❀ ❀ ❀

HERMAN MELVILLE, who was termed by his English biographer "the most powerful of all the great American writers,"[1] * spent more than three years roving the
Pacific Ocean and wrote his six best works about the South Seas.

The many valuable studies that have been made of Melville's writing do not
neglect the influence of this experience on his life and works, but none has
answered at length the question, What has been Melville's reflection in his
books of his life in the South Seas? This edited anthology attempts to reveal
the richness of Melville's presentation of Pacific life as it was seen during the
days of his romantic rovings among the exotic islands of that ocean, as well as
aboard various vessels that cruised its vast expanse.

Melville, whaleman from New York, may not have been the literary
Columbus of the Pacific, for many others since the days of Magellan have added
to the store of South Sea narratives; but Melville set a pattern for most of those
who followed. "I am tormented with an everlasting itch for things remote,"
Ishmael confesses in the opening chapter of *Moby Dick*. ". . . I love to sail
forbidden seas, and land on barbarous coasts." He adds in Chapter 57: "I
myself am a savage; owning no allegiance but to the King of the Cannibals."
Melville's yearning for summer isles of Eden and the Noble Savage of Rousseau
drove him, a young foremast hand and beachcomber, to erect in his volumes the
lasting archetypes of South Sea existence. Everyone who has since written about
those islands has sailed in Melville's widening wake.

The rise in the eighteenth century of the worldwide movement known as
Romanticism included as one of its strongest tenets a nostalgia for the primitive.
It is no accident that accounts of voyages and travels were high among the
favorite types of reading at that time. Jean Jacques Rousseau, who never left
crowded Europe, can be praised or blamed for preaching that the Golden Age
could be found among uncivilized tribes, who, he thought, were freer on the

* All of the editor's notes are numbered and appear at the end of the book. All other notes
have an asterisk and appear as they were included in Melville's original text.

v

whole than men in society. The hopes of the Romanticists that the Noble Savage could be found among the Indians of the New World were dashed by further acquaintance with the redmen. The last remaining region where primitive people, unspoiled by civilization, might be found was the Pacific Ocean of Samuel Wallis, Louis Antoine de Bougainville, and James Cook. Their descriptions of the free morality of the Tahitians seemed to give credence to the erotic dreams of Rousseau. Cook described in the report of his first, epoch-making voyage in 1769 how a young Polynesian lay with a girl of about twelve while a number of other Tahitians surrounded the scene and watched with approving interest.

The first great author to portray the authentic South Seas was, of course, Melville. He was the first man who lived the life of the sailor and beachcomber to transmute his observations into enduring literature. His first two books were advertised as sober travel accounts, although they are truly novels. They have theme, characterizations, plot, and lush settings—settings so vivid and richly embroidered that for years no one could see the South Seas through any eyes but Melville's. Some of his early readers accused him of making up everything in those books. We know today how faithful he tried to be in anthropological fact. He was, at the same time, drawing a very long bow indeed, exaggerating and inventing, exercising the novelist's need to transfigure fact into the truth that only fiction can give.

After Melville's day, his nostalgia for the primitive became the stock in trade of dozens of later fictionists—many of whom never saw a Pacific island—who exploited his patterns for a steady market of readers. "South Sea stuff" is still surefire. Each of us has his own Typee, his own Bali Ha'i. Solitude becomes more precious as our populations explode. The dream comprises natural beauty and a perfect climate—there are breakers on the reef and shady nooks by the lagoon, and it is always afternoon. Food is free; no need to punch a time clock or run to the supermarket. No need, either, for a modish wardrobe—a sarong suffices. All the irritations of urban existence vanish: no telephones, no subways, no smog, no strikes, no taxes. Most of all, the refuge hunters expect complete sex license, without remorse or alimony. The enduring image of the South Seas is that of Melville's golden-skinned Polynesian sweetheart Fayaway, her long brown tresses streaming, erect in his canoe on the Typee lake, spreading her robe of tapa to the trade winds to form a delightful sail. "Fayaway and Long Ago" might well be the theme song of all those who are escapists at heart. And all these dreams of the Pacific paradise-seekers must reveal some anguishing lacks in Western society.

Even though Melville was the first American of genius to make literary capital of the South Seas—he entered their waters as long ago as 1841—he is a writer modern in spirit. His greatest period of popularity is today, when he is probably studied more than any other American writer. Although somebody has always been reading Melville since 1846, and although the story of his neglect has been overstressed, Melville is the supreme example of the man ahead of his time, the overlooked author whose argosy sailed upstream years after his unremarked death. Interest was rearoused in 1919 on the centenary of Melville's birth. Half a century ago, few professors had ever heard of Herman Melville.[2] The revival markedly began with the publication in 1921 of Raymond Weaver's pioneering *Herman Melville, Mariner and Mystic,* belatedly followed in 1929 by Lewis Mumford's biography, *Herman Melville.* Significantly, the rediscovery of Melville came in the richest decade in American literature, comparable only to the decade in which that author had written his best books. Since 1921, the appeal of Melville to the readers of the world has been tremendous. *Moby Dick,* for example, is the only American novel to be included in the fifty-four-volume set of "Great Books of the Western World."

Melville still attracts readers, as has been said, because he is modern in his challenge. He is the great rebel, the doubter, the everlasting naysayer. He seeks absolute truth, and must strike through the mask of appearance. He is his own Ahab, the defiant captain who has been described as "modern man, and particularly American man, in his role as 'free' and 'independent' Individual, as self-sustaining and self-assertive Ego, of forcible will and unbending purpose all compact, inflexible, unpitying, and fell, but enlarged by both his vices and his strength to dimensions of legendary grandeur."[3]

Another attraction today, doubtless, is Melville's mysticism. More research has been performed during the past half century on Melville, according to a count of bibliographies, than on any other American literary man. His lightest word is weighed; the slightest scrap of his life treasured. Symbol-seekers pursue him madly. Scholars have been determinedly expounding him, but the last word probably will never be written. There are many Melvilles. He is a pool in which, perhaps, each critic sees his own image. But the Melville who at the age of twenty-two deserted a whale ship at the Polynesian island of Nuku-Hiva and explored the watery wastes and bowers of the South Seas was a real person, not a shadowy symbolist, and through his eyes we can see what the Pacific, America's ocean of the future, was like during America's past.

Melville's eyes were his most haunting feature. "He seems to see everything very accurately; and how he can do so with his small eyes, I cannot tell," Mrs. Nathaniel Hawthorne, a Massachusetts neighbor, wrote to her mother in 1850. "They are not keen eyes, either, but quite undistinguished in any way. . . . Once in a while, his animation gives place to a singularly quiet expression, out of these eyes to which I have objected: an indrawn, dim look, but which at the same time makes you feel that he is at that moment taking deepest note of what is before him. It is a strange, lazy glance, but with a power in it quite unique. It does not seem to penetrate through you, but to take you into itself."[4] Melville's small eyes were those of the born observer. He was, in the phrase of Henry James, a person upon whom nothing was lost. Part of his power as a great novelist was his power as a great reporter. Herein follow a selection of his reports from the Pacific, the ocean that has meant much to Americans in our century and will probably mean the most in the next century.

Melville's writings, as has been shown by several biographers, are far from trustworthy guides to his actual experiences. Many of the most exciting adventures never happened to him. He kept no notes during his Pacific years, and was careless of dates. He wrote from memory, aided by adept use of selected printed sources. An essay, "Herman Melville in the Pacific," has therefore been prepared as Part I, based on verifiable facts about his career. Among all the articles previously written, no one has put together the facts showing just where Herman was at what times, and what he was doing there. Introductory essays are also provided for the various parts of the book, to give some background for the sources, the circumstances of composition and publication, the reception of the various works, and the particular aspects of South Sea life that are there stressed.

"Benito Cereno," a long story by Melville, has not been included (although in 1928 Edward J. O'Brien in *The Fifteen Finest Short Stories* termed it "the noblest short story in American literature") because the action takes place not in the South Seas but off the coast of Chile.

This anthology is based upon my many pleasant years of reading Melville and of reading about him and the places he visited. The texts reproduced are in every case the best available. They have not been modernized or otherwise changed, because tampering with Melville's mechanics may sometimes distort his meanings. This edition may therefore be valuable to teachers and students. The book is directed mainly, however, to anyone who has enjoyed reading Melville or who has dreamed of cruising the world's oceans—especially the Pacific.

The spreading library of Melvilleana has been raided—as one can observe by looking at the Notes at the end—in order to prepare this collection. Most valuable have been *Melville in the South Seas* (New York: Columbia University Press, 1939; Dover, 1966) by Charles Roberts Anderson and *Journal of a Cruise in the Frigate "United States"* (Durham, N.C.: Duke University Press, 1937), which he located and edited. Dr. Anderson also kindly lent me a copy of an unpublished introduction to an edition of *Typee*. The most valuable general guides are, of course, Jay Leyda's *The Melville Log*, 2 vols. (New York: Harcourt, Brace & World, 1951) and Leon Howard's *Herman Melville: A Biography* (Berkeley and Los Angeles: University of California Press, 1951), based upon it. Other valuable sources were Newton Arvin's *Herman Melville*

(New York: Viking Press, 1950), James Baird's *Ishmael* (Baltimore: Johns Hopkins University Press, 1956), and *Herman Melville: Representative Selections,* edited by Willard Thorp (New York: American Book Company, 1938). In the introductory sections, place names have followed *Index to the Map of the Pacific Ocean,* published by the National Geographic Society in 1965. Thanks are due to all those who have kindly helped to obtain the illustrations included in the pictorial insert.

University of Hawaii   A. G. D.
May, 1970

CONTENTS

❀ ❀ ❀

A section of illustrations appears on pages 131–144.

THE PACIFIC

"To any meditative Magian rover, this serene Pacific, once beheld, must ever after be the sea of his adoption. It rolls the midmost waters of the world, the Indian Ocean and Atlantic being but its arms. The same waves wash the moles of the new-built California towns, but yesterday planted by the recentest race of men, and lave the faded but still gorgeous skirts of Asiatic lands, older than Abraham; while all between float milky-ways of coral isles, and low-lying, endless, unknown archipelagoes, and impenetrable Japans. Thus this mysterious, divine Pacific zones the world's whole bulk about; makes all coasts one bay to it; seems the tide-beating heart of earth."

—*Moby Dick*, Chapter III

MELVILLE'S
SOUTH SEAS

PART I

HERMAN MELVILLE
IN THE PACIFIC

A New York youth on the last day of 1840, as a "substitute for pistol and ball," signed ship's articles as an ordinary seaman on the whaler *Acushnet,* soon to sail on a maiden voyage of several years in the Pacific. Herman Melville, twenty-one, of a patrician British and Dutch family in financial straits, was unable to get a job at home and did not want to be a burden on others. Filled with a spirit of adventure and yearning for far places, he plunged into an enterprise that, unknown to him, was to lead to the creation of some of America's greatest books.

The ship, on this most famous of whaling voyages, was commanded by Captain Valentine Pease, Jr. The crew was not the mixed microcosm of the *Pequod* in *Moby Dick;* actually, the list showed twenty-one Americans, three Portuguese, and one Englishman. Melville and the other greenhorns learned the art of whale killing in the Atlantic, and the ship's cooper stored up one hundred fifty barrels of sperm oil. After a one-day stop at Rio de Janeiro to transfer this lading, the *Acushnet* headed for Cape Horn and the Pacific.

The whaler rounded the Horn, eastern gate of that ocean, with less anguish than that suffered by many ships. Captain William Bligh on his breadfruit voyage in the *Bounty,* for instance, struggled for a month against the fierce westerlies and then gave up, turning tail and heading around the world to get to Tahiti. Melville, almost half a century later, was luckier. One month out from Rio, on April 15, 1841, he sighted Staten Land to starboard through the haze, "like a pile of glaciers in Switzerland." The ship ran south for the Cape. Next day she fought a heavy squall, but on April 17 was only three leagues from the landmark island of Diego Ramírez.

Two days later Melville was initiated into the Pacific by a heavy gale, during which he saw his first albatross. Dashed upon the main hatches sat "a regal, feathery thing of unspotted whiteness, and with a hooked, Roman bill sublime." He had not yet read Coleridge's "Rime of the Ancient Mariner" and did not know that this "prodigy of plumage," the soaring sky-master of the Pacific wastes, was called an albatross. The sailor next to him told him it was a "goney."

Several days later the *Acushnet* was able to head north toward the quieter waters that had inspired Magellan to name this ocean "Pacific." She passed on May 7 between the two uninhabited islands of the Juan Fernández group. The easternmost one, Más a Tierra, was the usual stopping place of the early Pacific voyagers, who found there fresh vegetables, goat's meat, and a harbor which had been the favorite hangout of the buccaneers who preyed on the South American plate fleets. The *Acushnet* passed it by. She plowed north, after having spoken another whaler, the *William Wirt,* from her same home port of New Bedford, and reported a cargo of one hundred sixty barrels of oil.

The lookouts soon began seeing sperm whales, and men lowered the boats. The Peruvian coast was approached on June 9, and on the 23rd, Captain Pease dropped anchor for a ten-day stop at the harbor of Santa Marta. Here one of the crew deserted, but Melville wrote to his brother Gansevoort that he was in perfect health and not dissatisfied with his lot.

Soon Melville was to encounter men associated with the amazing event that was to yield him a stirring climax for his most famous book. He had been familiar with the legend of a ferocious, white-humped whale called Mocha Dick, who was alleged to have sunken three ships and stove in three others, causing the deaths of many sea hunters.[1] This "old bull whale, of prodigious size and strength," who was "white as wool," was to suggest Moby Dick, the "grand hooded phantom, like a snow hill in the air." Now Melville was to meet men who had known Owen Chase, one of the eight survivors of the celebrated wreck of the *Essex.*

The chief source of the catastrophe in *Moby Dick* was this encounter in 1820 on the equatorial cruising grounds of the Pacific. An enraged whale, apparently in revenge for the killing of three of his shoal, twice attacked the bows of the *Essex.* The ship sank within ten minutes. The crew, including First Mate Chase, took to the boats in black night, hanging over unknown waters, and embarked on a lengthy open-boat voyage to South America that brought "unparalleled suffering" and even cannibalism. Melville chatted aboard the *Acushnet* with the second mate, an Englishman named John Hall, who had twice sailed with Chase. Cruising west of the Galápagos Islands not far from the scene of the attack on the *Essex,* the *Acushnet* met a Nantucket whaler (probably the *Lima,* on July 23), and the men got together for a "gam." As Melville recalled, "In the forecastle I made the acquaintance of a fine lad of sixteen or thereabouts, a son [William Henry] of Owen Chase! I questioned him concerning his father's adventure; and when I left his ship to return again the next morning (for the two vessels were to sail in company for a few days) he went to his chest and handed me a complete copy . . . of the Narrative. . . . The reading of this wondrous story upon the landless sea, and close to the very latitude of the shipwreck, had a surprising effect upon me."[2] The effect was deepened when the *Acushnet* visited with another Nantucketer, the *Charles Carroll,* and the captain, whom Melville mistakenly believed was Owen Chase in person, came aboard. As a "mere foremast-hand," Melville had no chance to converse with this man, but thought him "the most prepossessing-looking whale-hunter" he had ever seen.[3]

The first Pacific islands visited by Melville were not the lush Edens of his dreams, but a heap of dried, volcanic masses of clinkers reminiscent of nether Hell. These were the equatorial Galápagos Islands (the name, appearing on Abraham Ortelius' map of Peru in 1574, means "tortoise" in Spanish). They had more poetically been called *Las Encantadas,* or The Enchanted Islands, because they seemed to disappear from the sight of early navigators in the haze of the broad ocean, as strange currents swirled around their scattered shores. On the opening page of his novel *Mardi,* Melville attributes the name to "the many wild currents and eddies there met."

A well-known whaling ground, the waters of the Galápagos group showed no fins for the *Acushnet,* now eleven months at sea. The vessel was spoken by the *Rousseau* of Nantucket on November 3 off Albemarle, largest and westernmost of the islands.[4] After twenty days, Captain Pease decided to return to the coast of South America to recruit men and resupply his ship. Before leaving the group, however, Pease anchored for six days at Chatham's Isle, probably to obtain a cargo of the giant tortoises that most ships entering that region, ever since the days of the buccaneers, had captured. These primordial, lumbering creatures, who survived on the sparse herbiage of the rocks, could easily be overtaken, hauled aboard, and stowed upside down in the ship, to provide the crew with fresh meat and soup stock for weeks. Melville's recollections of this visit to the islands of the tortoises were to result in the publication thirteen years later of the series of sketches he called *Las Encantadas.*

Who was this young escapist, rebel against Western civilization, who eagerly listened to the yarns of his fellow seamen and viewed scenes that were to be transmuted into world literature? His writings, as some scholars have shown, are not a reliable guide to his life, and some critics have gone badly astray by taking his novels as autobiography. A brief factual essay on his actual experiences, especially in the South Seas, can help his admirers to better appreciate his creativity.

Melville never took a college course in fiction writing—as he said, a whale ship was his Harvard College and his Yale. Virtually self-educated, he had done almost everything else before, almost casually, he began at the age of twenty-six to write down stories drawing upon his wanderings. Son of an unsuccessful businessman, academy student who failed to graduate, handyman in a family fur company, bank clerk and messenger boy, farmhand, sailor on a North Atlantic trading ship, country schoolteacher, unemployed surveyor, whaleman, deserter, harpooner, mutineer, pinsetter in a Honolulu bowling alley, clerk in a general store in that port, and foremast seaman in the American Navy, he perhaps looked upon the inky trade as another job to be tackled with all the cheerfulness a good maintopman could muster.

Baptized Herman Melvill, the child was born in New York City on August 1, 1819. His mother, of Dutch descent, was the only daughter of General Peter Gansevoort, Revolutionary defender of Fort Stanwix. Herman's father was the second son of another Revolutionary officer, Thomas Melvill, a Scotch-Irishman who had been an "Indian" at the Boston Tea Party and who became the valetudinarian celebrated in "The Last Leaf," the poem by Oliver Wendell Holmes.

Herman grew up with four brothers and four sisters. When his father, Allan, failed in business, he moved his family up the Hudson River to Albany, where he died heavily in debt on January 28, 1832. Twelve-year-old Herman was taken out of the Albany Academy after not much more than a year of schooling and given a job in a bank. Two years later he left to work on his uncle's farm and then served as a clerk in the store of his brother Gansevoort. This business, mainstay of the fatherless family, failed in the panic of 1837.

With the idea of becoming a schoolteacher, Herman had taken some courses at Albany Classical School and for three months, during his first assignment, in a one-room school outside Pittsfield, Massachusetts, had found a little time for "occasional writting & reading." The family, to save expenses, moved to rural Lansingburgh, where Herman studied engineering and surveying at the local academy in the hope of being hired on the construction of the Erie Canal, a great enterprise that would help to open the Middle West to commerce. Failing to get a place, Herman signed on as a seaman on a trading vessel, the *St. Lawrence,* for a summer voyage to Liverpool in 1839. From her mainmast he loosened a skysail by starlight, and caught his first glimpse of a pod of whales. His view of the seamy side of the Industrial Revolution in a British port did nothing to increase his admiration for European culture, and again he turned his face westward, where lay the course of empire.

Employers at his next school neglected to pay his salary, and closed the place before the end of the term. Accompanied by an Albany friend, Herman headed, in the summer of 1840, by way of the Canal and the Great Lakes to Illinois, where his uncle Thomas Melvill had settled at Galena. But the Middle West was not what Herman was seeking. The whaling industry—which at that time supplied oil for the lamps of the world, spermaceti for its finest candles, ambergris for its perfumes, and whalebone for its crinolines—was the arena where an active lad could find adventure if not profit. Thus Herman-Ishmael, when he felt a damp, drizzly November in his soul, quietly took his place on a pallet in the *Acushnet*'s fo'c'sle. He was not to return to America for almost four years.

The young Melville who went to sea in order to drive off the spleen and regulate his constitution was hardly a suicidal misanthrope, and certainly not the solemn patriarch of the textbook illustrations. At twenty-one, he was outgoing, friendly, eager to see the world, and willing to listen to anybody with a story to tell. He probably wore a light beard—whalemen and beachcombers seldom found it comfortable to shave, and despite naval regulations, homeward-bound sailors often grew masses of fancy herbiage. Herman was stocky, with a height of five feet nine and one-half inches. His complexion was fair, but he had been tanned by work in the hayfields and on the deck of the *St. Lawrence*. A fine head covered by thick, wavy, dark-brown hair was somewhat marred by large ears and small, green-blue eyes, beneath wide arching brows. His nose was straight and his lips firm. All in all, his visage could be deemed quite suitable for foreign travel. He was nimble, strong, and able to withstand the hardships of the whaler's briny, greasy existence. But as time went on, that life came to pall upon Herman.

He had his first chance to view the versatile coconut tree of the Pacific during the thirteen December days in 1841 when the *Acushnet* lay outside the breakers in the harbor of Tumbes, port of the town of Paita on the north coast of Peru. Captain Pease then made a determined Christmas cruise for whales that took the ship back to the equatorial grounds, passing in sight of Hood's Isle and Charles's Isle in the southern Galápagos on January 6, 1842. Ships were more numerous and whales were getting scarcer. At the present rate, there was no prospect that the *Acushnet* would fill all her casks for several more years.

"Six months at sea! Yes, reader, as I live, six months out of sight of land; cruising after the sperm whale beneath the scorching sun of the Line, and tossed on the billows of the wide-rolling Pacific—the sky above, the sea around, and nothing else! Weeks and weeks ago our fresh provisions were all exhausted." So Melville was to write. Threatened by the dread approach of scurvy, Captain Pease headed on June 17 for the wild Marquesas Islands for food and recruiting.

Life on the crowded whaler was beginning to arouse conflicts. The captain was probably showing signs of the irritation and bad health that caused his first and third mates to leave the *Acushnet* at the first civilized port. Herman's own decision to go over the side was heightened by his first views of the Marquesas.

The southern islands of the group had been discovered by the Álvaro de Mendaña fleet of 1595, attempting to return to the Solomons, which their leader had found almost thirty years before. Mendaña had named them Marquesas, with his patron, the Marquis of Cañete, Viceroy of Peru, in mind. The inhabitants of the Marquesas were the first Polynesian people ever to be seen by Europeans, and the Spanish thought the dusky women equal in physical charm to the ladies of Lima, Peru, who were noted for their beauty. Herman had probably heard stories about the Marquesas from the Galena family of his cousin, Thomas Wilson Melville, who had visited the group as a midshipman on the U.S.S. *Vincennes* thirteen years earlier. Herman's reading of travel books could not have prepared him for what he saw as the *Acushnet* cruised close to the shore of the island of Nuku-Hiva on the morning of June 23. Heading for the main anchorage, she passed below tree-fringed headlands, and one of the sailors said: "There—there's Typee. Oh, the bloody cannibals . . . !"

Toward noon, in squally weather, the ship passed between two pinnacles and entered the harbor of Taï-o-Haé, horseshoe-shaped and nine miles wide, surrounded by wooded ridges rising nearly half a mile in the sky. Ahead was a curving, sandy beach at the mouth of a bosky valley, cut by the gashes of mountain-born streams. Ashore, as the ship anchored in nine fathoms, the crew could see the bamboo houses of the natives.

An Irish lad of Melville's own age named Richard Tobias Greene, but who on board went only by the nickname of Toby, described in 1854 his recollection of the effect of this sight on one ocean-weary whaleman: "When we entered that bay, and saw its almost unearthly beauties break, as if by magic, on our bewildered eyes—the smooth surface of that lovely sheet of water, undisturbed save by some tiny canoe, as it shot forth from a fairy cavern, half concealed by the luxuriant foliage which hung in graceful festoons from the rocks above—we too were seized with the romantic."[5]

Melville's enjoyment of the scene faded as he saw with indignation the black hulls of a fleet of six French vessels, whose Rear Admiral, A. de Dupetit-Thouars, had recently proclaimed at Taï-o-Haé or Anna Maria Bay a French protectorate over the group. (The admiral was trying at about this same time to annex the Hawaiian Islands as well.)

The "lovely houris" who had headed Melville's list of South Sea delights did not wait for his vessel to anchor but swam out in a shoal to board at every quarter. In the evening, the deck was illuminated with lanterns, and the nymphs, "tricked out with flowers, and dressed in robes of variegated tapa," began dancing, and as the sea-weary sailor recalled, "the wild grace and spirit of their style excel everything that I have ever seen." Fortunately, no animals were on deck who might strip the girls of even their scant, leafy garb. Such an episode had happened on the staid first London Missionary Society ship in the South Seas when some native girls had come aboard. "The knavish goats," reported the chronicler, ". . . would not leave them even the little clothing they had: they flocked round them to get at the green leaves, till most of them were left entirely in their native beauty."

The night that followed may have shocked the young American sailor. "Our ship was now wholly given up to every species of riot and debauchery," he wrote. "Not the feeblest barrier was interposed between the unholy passions of the crew and their unlimited gratification. The grossest licentiousness and the most shameful inebriety prevailed, with occasional and but short-lived interruptions, through the whole period of her stay."

During the next fortnight, Melville decided that he might expect favorable treatment from these Polynesian people should he desert the *Acushnet* and find refuge in one of the valleys away from the port. He learned that, to the east, the nearest of the three valleys leading into Comptroller Bay was occupied by a tribe called Hapaas, or Happars, who were friendly and docile, but that the central valley was held by the Taipis, or Typees, notorious for their ferocity and cannibalism. He did not realize that the Haapa Valley was merely a shallow extension of the shoreline, whereas the deeper valley of the Taipis was one which cut far inland and would be encountered by any venturer seeking to cross the mountains of the center.

Herman discovered on the night of July 8 that his friend Toby, another of the starboard watch, was also meditating desertion. The two agreed to escape together. Next morning, on shore leave shortly before the *Acushnet* was about to sail, the pair headed, through drenching downpours, for the mountains of the interior.

Three hours before sunset, the deserters stood on what seemed to be the highest land on Nuku-Hiva, an immense overhanging cliff of basalt several thousand feet above the sea. "The lonely bay of Nuku-Hiva, dotted here and there with the black hulls of the vessels composing the French squadron, lay reposing at the base of a circular range of elevations, whose verdant sides, perforated with deep glens or diversified with smiling valleys, formed altogether the loveliest view I ever beheld, and were I to live a hundred years, I should never forget the feeling of admiration which I then experienced."

The *Acushnet,* hoping to capture the missing men, stayed an extra day in port and then hid out behind a nearby island for another day in a vain attempt to give the men a chance to return to the town, as they sensibly should have done. The whaler then departed, but Melville was destined not to be free of the threat of punishment for his desertion.

Melville in *Typee* devotes many thrilling pages to the five days he and Toby spent scrambling through the rain forest of Nuku-Hiva.[6] From July 9 until August 9 there is no record of their activities except those in *Typee* and in the recollections of Toby. As Melville says in his preface to *Omoo,* "No journal was kept by the author during his wanderings in the South Seas." Any scraps of information about the facts of his visit to Nuku-Hiva are precious. According to later gossip, Melville had a child by his sweetheart Fayaway; if so, descendants of the roving New Yorker may have survived the depopulation of the Marquesas and dwell there today.[7]

Thirteen years after Melville's stay, A. G. Jones visited Nuku-Hiva. His interpreter had lived on that island for twenty-five years and remembered Melville, but not Fayaway. "Mr. Jones met the king, Te Moana, and his wife, Queen Vaekuhu, who came aboard the *St. Mary's* as they had visited previously the frigate *United States* when Melville was a member of the crew of that ship. He learned that the 'noble Mehevi,' chief of all the Taipis, had been killed by Te Moana; and he obtained evidence that such persons as Kory-Kory, Melville's personal attendant, Tinor, and the one-eyed chief, Mow-Mow, had once existed; but had passed away. He was convinced that the Taipis were cannibals until a very late period and concluded that Melville had a truthful basis for his book but that his imagination was very largely drawn upon for the attractive features of the same."[8]

An American archaeologist, Robert C. Suggs, researching on Nuku-Hiva in recent years, states that Melville (called Merivi by the people of Taipi Valley) is still remembered there, and was held prisoner on a temple platform called Te'ivi'ohou, often referred to as "Melville's *paepae.*" The story told Suggs by one of the Marquesan women followed the novel closely. The narrator, who was supposed to be descended from Melville's sweetheart Fayaway (Pe'ue in Marquesan), correctly dated the arrival of Melville with the warships of the *ferani* or French. Variations on this story, repeated by other natives, deviated into myth when some volunteered that Melville had hauled a great treasure of gold and jewels over the mountains and buried it at the *paepae.*[9]

Toby Greene, according to his account, left about July 27 to seek help for Melville, who was incapacitated by a swollen leg suffered while making the painful journey into the valley of Taipi. Greene paid Jimmy Fitch, a beach-comber, five dollars to extricate Melville from the clutches of the tribe, and then went overland to Taï-o-haé, where he was taken aboard a ship, the *London Packet.* The captain refused to go to Melville's aid, but Toby got a boat and went back to the beach at Comptroller's Bay. He found Fitch, but Melville had not been rescued. Angrily, Toby threatened Fitch if the escape was not achieved. He then had to return to his new ship and sail, with anguish in his heart, for a four-month cruise of the islands.[10]

The days Melville spent in the valley of Taipi, reached presumably on July 14 (the day, incidentally, most heavily celebrated in French Polynesia—Bastille Day), may have seemed to him like weeks. He claimed in *Typee* to have lived for four months in this Marquesan paradise. Actually he passed only twenty-six nights there. He was limited to the upper part of the deep valley, inhabited by one of the three occupying tribes. Nevertheless, the recollections he gives in *Typee* have been accepted by many anthropologists, including Sir James George Fraser, as quite authentic accounts of the lives of these primitive people at a time before the French occupation began the decline and degradation of the proud Marquesan natives.

Melville's escape from his friendly hosts—he never claimed to have had evidence that they were cannibals—is described sensationally at the climax of *Typee.*[11] Again it appears that a need to supply exciting fiction caused him to heighten the facts. The desire to enjoy an erotic Eden in the South Seas was rapidly replaced by a determination to escape from it—if necessary, with violence against his native friends. What really happened? "Unless a band of barefoot savages dashed furiously over a mile of coral along a coast so rocky that for generations it had kept them separated from the neighboring Happars," comments Leon Howard, "they did not swim out from the headland to intercept their escaping prisoner and so give Melville the chance to make the Byronic gesture of thrusting his boat hook into the throat of the ferocious one-eyed chieftain."[12] The facts of the escape may reside in a line in the final chapter of *Typee:* "It was at this agonizing moment, when I thought all hope was ended, that a new contest arose between the two parties who had accompanied me to the shore." Presumably a quarrel had broken out between members of his own band and those of another of the three tribes that kept the valley in a continual state of skirmishing. In the confusion Melville could have fled to the boat of a ship seeking to recruit the man they had heard was in Taipi Valley.

At any rate, Melville was taken aboard an Australian whaler, the 213-ton bark *Lucy Ann,* which had sailed from Sydney on February 14. He shipped on August 9 as an able seaman and was promised a "lay" of one-120th part of the profits, but allowed no advance.

The adventures fictionized in *Omoo* begin at this point. Henry Ventom, master, may not have been as feeble a figure as Captain Guy, his counterpart in the novel, but conditions aboard this ship were even more notorious than those of other Australian whalers. The *Lucy Ann* was not a new vessel. She had served, among other duties, to transport in 1831 the colonists from Pitcairn Island to Tahiti, when these descendants of the *Bounty* mutineers became too populous on Pitcairn. Now the *Lucy Ann* had a bad record. Rebelling against crowded conditions and a harsh, drunken mate named James German, nine crewmen had deserted a short time before at Resolution Bay, and two sailors had been delivered to *La Reine Blanche,* French flagship, to be sent in irons to Valparaiso to be tried as mutineers. Three more had attempted to desert at Taï-o-haé, as Melville had done, and had been ignobly captured and returned. Among these was John B. Troy, steward, who had been in charge of the ship's medicine chest and had embezzled some of the supplies to sell ashore. Two other men had been enlisted at Taï-o-Haé the day before Melville was rescued. Others were sought at Santa Cristina or Tahuata (Melville spells it Hytyhoo), and at the island of La Dominica or Hiva Oa (Hivarhoo) three others were taken on, including William Bunnell, a beachcomber from New England whom Melville remembered as Salem. The *Lucy Ann* (called *Julia* in the novel) left the Marquesas group on August 20 with a full crew of men but lacking a second mate. Five of the sixteen seamen, according to the captain's testimony, were "ailing and ill of the venereal." This band of disaffected flotsam was sooner or later to drift into open rebellion.

Heading westward, the captain within a week began suffering from an abscess in the perineum and by September 4 was helpless in his cabin. The worried mate changed course for Tahiti, a decision confirmed by the captain.

Melville first saw the fabled amatory island of Tahiti on September 20. It had been discovered in June, 1767, by Captain Samuel Wallis of H.M.S. *Dolphin,* and independently, ten months later, by two French ships commanded by Louis Antoine de Bougainville. He had called it the New Cytherea, island of the love goddess Aphrodite, because of the enticing nymphs who swam out to his ships. Thereafter the French could not rest until they took over the group of the Society Islands and were achieving this aim when Melville arrived. The reputation of Tahiti as a paradise for seaworn, lovesick mariners had spread around the world, and at least one of the causes of the famed *Bounty* mutiny had been the charms the Polynesian maidens exerted upon Fletcher Christian and his friends during the breadfruit voyage. Now Herman Melville was himself to be involved in a South Sea mutiny.

To prevent the disgruntled crew from going ashore, the *Lucy Ann* lay off the port of Papeete. The account given by Melville in *Omoo* differs in many details from the discernible facts, the main outlines of which are now clear.[13] Mate German went ashore and returned in the afternoon with Dr. Francis Johnstone, local medical officer, who insisted that Captain Ventom be removed to the town. The next day (September 22, according to the Tahiti calendar, which was one day ahead of the ship's log), the captain was taken ashore, and the mate returned with Dr. Johnstone and the acting British consul, Charles B. Wilson. The five sick sailors were examined, along with Melville, whose leg gave him an excuse for hoping to be discharged from this hell ship. Two of the men were considered too ill for further cruising; the other four, including Melville and Troy, were judged capable of duty after a week or two of care. Four of the well men picked up in the Marquesas told Wilson they were unwilling to serve under Mate German in a proposed continuation of the whaling cruise, but they were ignored, and Wilson told Ventom that there was no objection to such a cruise provided two mates and two sailors were enlisted to fill the roster. Wilson replaced the six men the next day, taking them out in a boat rather than letting the unruly crew go ashore or stay on the ship without German in command.

The mutiny of the *Lucy Ann* was dramatized by Melville in his novel. No mention is made in official records of the famous "round robin" reproduced in *Omoo*. The six men on the sick list declined to join their watches. Three others, recruited in the Marquesas, refused duty and were joined by three members of the original Sydney crew, leaving only ten men to handle the ship. But on the next evening James Watts was back on duty, and at once had an altercation with Bembo. This was Benbow Byrne, the Maori harpooner who was in charge because, as even Wilson noted in his private journal, Mr. German was "not fit to take charge for continual drunkenness."

Next morning, disregarding his standing orders, German put the ship at anchor in Papeete harbor. When Wilson came aboard for a showdown, William Bunnell was accused of being a ringleader. Melville himself, instead of playing this rebel role as told in the novel, was safe with a medical certificate. He was not among the ten men who were sent in irons aboard *La Reine Blanche* for two nights. When this bluff failed to convince the men that they should sail with German, they were taken ashore and lodged at the "Calabooza Beretanee" or British jail. "Herman Melville also said that he would do no more duty," German testified on the 28th (Tahiti style), "and would share the same as the others who refused to do their duty." He voluntarily limped along with them, to live under the thatched shelter presided over by a genial Tahitian who let his prisoners roam at will in the hope of finding food to support themselves, for meals were not provided at the jail.

The men on shore were called once more on October 5 (Tahiti style) to hear depositions against them. Consul Wilson was given a final refusal, and in disgust sent the men back to the stocks to await the arrival of a British warship. Melville was probably not an official prisoner, but he remained with his companions when he was not making use of his time observing Tahitian life, as corrupted by Occidental "civilization," so graphically described in *Omoo*. The only nonnative person he was able to admire was a jolly Irish priest, Father Columba Murphy, a former carpenter who had achieved notoriety as an advance agent of French penetration of the Gambier, Society, and Hawaiian Islands.[14] Murphy was the only missionary Melville ever liked.

Herman's sojourn in the calaboose resulted in an attack on his repute, after he had become known as an author, by a South Sea trader named Edward Lucett. This British gentleman complained to Consul Wilson that on the night of November 16 (Tahiti style), he was seized by a number of native constables, maltreated, and placed in the stocks "where the seamen for revolt were confined." In his anonymous book,[15] Lucett states that Melville, "undoubtedly the ringleader of the mutineers," drew his sheath knife in an "un-

English" way and threw himself upon Lucett, a bound, defenseless man. Lucett undoubtedly was put in the stocks by the constables on a charge of violating the curfew law; thirteen of those responsible had to apologize and pay a fine of ten dollars each. He was mistaken in thinking that Melville was in the calaboose on that date, for the accused had shipped on a whaler early in the month; hence, Lucett's grudge was unfounded, and colored other remarks about Melville's character. The "dastardly ruffian of the bowie-knife genus" was probably the Yankee beachcomber Bunnell, alias Salem.

Melville's need for companionship ashore drew him closer to the ex-steward, John B. Troy, a tall, thin blond whose appearance had earned him the nickname of Doctor Long Ghost. This man is really the leading figure in the novel *Omoo*. With him Melville explored Tahiti and the nearby island of Mooréa, then called Eimeo (spelled Imeeo in the novel).

This strange pair departed from Papeete after the middle of October, sailing across the ten-mile channel in a boat along with their new employers, two partners who were trying to raise potatoes on Mooréa, in the valley of Maatea (Melville's Martair). According to *Omoo,* they were a cockney known as Shorty and a Maine backwoodsman named Zeke. Peter (Troy) and Paul (Melville), to give their assumed names, spent little time grubbing in the fields, because a day of rest, a hunting expedition in the hills, a visit to the mission church at Afareaitu on Sunday, October 23, and a trip to the village of Temae or Tamai took up almost a week. They were back in Maatea at the end of that time to obtain from Zeke a "certificate of discharge" that would protect them from arrest as they began wandering around the western beach to the village of Papetoi, where in the cove a lone whale ship was reported at anchor.

A true beachcomber enjoying the hospitality of a native, Melville visited another mission church at Papetoi on October 30, and found the people less spoiled than those of Europeanized Papeete. The two sailors then spent a day or two peeping around the "palace" of Queen Pomaré Vahine I, who had sought respite from French demands in this secluded seaside hideaway. Melville was, however, becoming less interested in Tahitian touring than in the whaler offshore, whose captain was seeking provisions and recruits. The captain was approached and agreed to consider Melville as a replacement for a dismissed boat-steerer or harpooner, but Long Ghost was rejected.[16]

Reluctantly deserting his friend Troy, Melville was taken on at Papetoi, about November 3, as a member of the crew of the *Charles and Henry* (named the *Leviathan* in the novel). When writing to his publisher about the first draft

of *Moby Dick,* Melville stated that it was "a romance of adventure . . . illustrated by the author's own personal experience of two years and more, as a
harpooneer."

Few clues to events during the seven months of Melville's third whaling
voyage can be found. The *Charles and Henry* (named for her owners, the
Coffin brothers of Nantucket) was reported off Tahiti on November 7. Captain
John B. Coleman may have finished recruiting by enlisting some Polynesians
at the islands of Rurutu and Raivavaé to the south. The ship went still farther
south, and then eastward, and was reported by the *Roscoe* of New Bedford
on January 27, 1843, at latitude 34°10′ S, longitude 87°40′ W, heading east
toward Más a Fuera. The young captain had not taken a single barrel of oil,
and decided to seek new grounds to the northwest, toward the "Sandwich
Islands" and the waters off Japan. The trade winds took him to the equatorial
regions by February 9, where with fifty barrels of new oil he was encouraged
to fish for nearly three months more.

The cruise covered one of the emptiest spots of the world, and the only
echoes of it are probably the whaling chapters of *Mardi* and *Moby Dick.* The
Charles and Henry was smaller than the *Acushnet* and crowded with a larger
crew (sixteen Americans and ten foreigners—most or all of them presumably
Polynesians), but Melville's status may have given him more privacy and
comfort. He never said anything against his crew mates, and in the opening
chapter of *Mardi* he described his skipper as a trump whose only defect was the
fickle desire to hunt the right whale on the Northwest Coast and in the Bay
of Kamchatka. "Sir, I did not ship for it," was his reply to such a project;
"put me somewhere ashore, I beseech." By mutual consent, Captain Coleman
discharged Melville, with two other crew members, on May 2, at the port of
Lahaina on the Hawaiian island of Maui, where the *Charles and Henry* had
arrived on April 27.

Beached at Lahaina, Melville wandered through this noted whaling port,
finding little to occupy him.[17] Even though King Kamehameha III and his
court were in residence, blue laws enforced by the missionaries and their
Hawaiian converts kept the atmosphere peaceful. Herman climbed the mountain
road to the mission school of Lahainaluna, founded in 1831 to train young
Hawaiian men to be Congregationalist ministers or teachers. There, as he
recalled in *Typee* (Chapter 30), he saw "a tabular exhibition of a Hawaiian
verb, conjugated through all its moods and tenses," which covered the side
of a considerable apartment.

Chances of employment were slight at Lahaina, and on May 18, with his money running low, Herman sailed to Honolulu, the commercial capital of the islands, on the schooner *Star,* along with other discharged seamen.

During this decade, Honolulu was the principal forward base for the whaling industry, for six sevenths of the world's whale ships were combing the new grounds in the Pacific. A Honolulu man told a newcomer in December, 1849, while talking about *Typee* and *Omoo,* that he had been well acquainted with Melville when he was "setting up pins in a ball alley."[18] If Herman had sunk to this unrespectable post among local bowlers, he did not remain in it long, for on June 1 he signed an indenture with a young English merchant, a Roman Catholic named Isaac Montgomery, promising to act as clerk and bookkeeper at a yearly salary of one hundred fifty dollars plus free board, lodging, and laundry. His employer was planning to open a general store on the first of July, when Melville received his initial quarterly salary of $37.50. Montgomery, who had arrived in 1838, had obtained operating capital mainly as an auctioneer, and his fluency had been admired by the king. Montgomery was a member of the British faction in the capital and an opponent of the Protestant American missionaries, headed by the powerful government adviser, Dr. Gerrit P. Judd.[19]

Melville stayed in Honolulu during a time of crisis in Hawaiian politics, for on the preceding February 25 the British naval frigate *Carysfort,* commanded by brash Lord George Paulet, had made heavy demands on the kingdom, under threat of bombardment of Honolulu. The king yielded to a provisional cession of the Sandwich Islands to Great Britain. Less than a week after Melville's discharge, Dr. Judd resigned in protest from the commission ruling the islands, and Paulet and his officers were left in full command of the life of the people. The archipelago was under the British flag until the end of July, when Paulet's domination was ended by the arrival on the 26th of Rear Admiral Richard Thomas in the *Dublin.* Dr. Judd's protests to Washington and London had resulted in the formal restoration of Hawaii to the Hawaiians, and the celebrations began. Melville's pro-British attitude in the Appendix to *Typee,* in which he describes the saturnalia on July 31 that followed the restoration, can be explained by his dislike of missionaries and his friendship with Montgomery, who was probably the gentleman he described as "much employed by his lordship."

Herman's status in Honolulu was lowly. He was still haunted by the *Acushnet,* which loomed up in Honolulu harbor on June 6. Valentine Pease had on June 2 sworn before the United States vice commercial agent at Lahaina, John Stetson, that Melville and Greene had deserted at Nuku-Hiva, and the captain might have been told that Melville was now lurking in

Honolulu.[20] The *Acushnet* returned to Hawaii for the third time as late as 1844. She foundered and was lost in the same year during which her former crewman composed *Moby Dick*.

Melville presumably wrote home that he intended to stay in Honolulu for some time, for letters addressed to him arrived there more than a year later. But when the American warship *United States* anchored after sunset on the night of the restoration, he may have had second thoughts about the life of a counterjumper in an isolated Polynesian port. He had been away for two and a half years, and here was a chance to work his way home and experience a new career at sea. Apparently, Montgomery did not try to hold him to his indenture. A few days before the vessel was to sail, Herman Melville again quietly took to ship. He enlisted on August 17 as an ordinary seaman in the United States Navy for a long voyage home.

Melville's career aboard the U.S.S. *United States,* which departed from Honolulu on August 21, was "the concluding episode, the graduation year, of his four years in the South Seas—a period out of which came the bulk of his writings, and the best."[21] This fine frigate had been launched at Philadelphia in 1797; she was reputed to be the swiftest ship in the Navy, and perhaps in the world. Herman was destined to spend fourteen months aboard this man-of-war, which in *White Jacket* he calls the *Neversink*. The places visited were Nuku-Hiva, Tahiti, Más a Tierra, Valparaiso, Callao, Mazatlán, Callao once more, Cape Horn, Rio de Janeiro, and Boston, where by special permission Melville was discharged on October 14, 1844, having completed the cruise for which he signed. Except for the first three offings, however, none of these places lay in Polynesia; and probably the only place where Melville was allowed ashore was at Callao, the port for Lima, Peru.

Aboard the *United States,* Melville again visited Taï-o-haé on October 6, 1843. In the harbor were *La Reine Blanche* and several other French ships, whose crews were building a fort and preparing to bring convicts to the lovely Marquesas. Melville describes in the opening chapter of *Typee* a state visit aboard his ship by the "king," Moana, and his young queen, a belle about fifteen years old. They were received with regal honors by the commodore. His Majesty wore a magnificent French uniform, and his consort "a gaudy tissue of scarlet cloth, trimmed with yellow silk, which, descending a little below the knees, exposed to view her bare legs, embellished with spiral tattooing, and somewhat resembling two miniature Trajan's columns. Upon her head was a fanciful turban of purple velvet, figured with silver sprigs, and surmounted by a tuft of variegated feathers." She singled out an old sailor and began comparing his blue and vermilion tattooing with her own. "All at once the royal lady, eager to display the hieroglyphics on her own sweet form, bent forward for a moment, and turning sharply round, threw up the skirts of her mantle, and revealed a sight from which the aghast Frenchmen retreated precipitately, and tumbling into their boat, fled the scene of so shocking a catastrophe."

Off Tahiti, reached on October 12, the ship anchored at Matavai Bay, reminiscent of Cook and Bligh. She was visited on the nineteenth by Queen Pomaré's consort, who was saluted with thirteen guns. The *United States* then departed from Tahiti, which the ship's scribe called "this Fairey Island which lies reposing on the bosom of the wide Pacific like some glittering gem on the brow of the beautiful."[22] With the ship becalmed on the south side of Mooréa, Herman had a chance to say a last farewell to the jagged peaks of the island where he had ranged with Long Ghost.

Heading for Valparaiso, the *United States* passed Más Afuera late one afternoon, and on the morning of November 19 ran close to Más a Tierra, the famed main island of Juan Fernández. Here, the sailors knew, was the place where that cranky Scot, Alexander Selkirk, had spent four years and four months alone; he had later given his story to Daniel Defoe to use for the yarn of Robinson Crusoe, monarch of all he surveyed.

The men had a good view of this pirate den, and the ship's scribe confessed that he had seldom seen a "more remarkable and picturesque view than it presented when seen from a short distance." The conspicuous Anvil Mountain rose three thousand feet "above a shore which is formed by an abrupt wall of dark-colored bare rock, eight or nine hundred feet in height, through whose wild ravines, broken by the mountain torrent, caught a view of verdant glades surrounded by luxuriant woodland. The higher parts of the island are in general thickly wooded, but in some places there are grassy plains of considerable extent, whose lively color contrasts agreeably with the dark foliage of the myrtle tree, which abounds on the island."[23] Melville's gentlemanly young shipmate, Ephraim Curtiss Hine, wrote about this view:

> The genius of Defoe has thrown
> Around the spot so wild and lone
> A robe that chains the raptured glance,
> Wove by the hand of fair romance!

Melville gives his own description of the Juan Fernández group in Sketch Fourth of *Las Encantadas.*

The value of Melville's naval career lay not in visits to islands but in his deep acquaintance with the men in that service and in his growing interest in literature. The period of fourteen months on the *United States* was telescoped in *White Jacket* to the three months during which the frigate was homeward bound. His first captain, James Armstrong, renamed Claret, is portrayed as a drunken tyrant, and his officers show up not much better. The finest man aboard, Melville considered, was a salty Englishman, John J. Chase, to whom he later dedicated *Billy Budd*. This fatherly figure had a literary bent and could quote long passages of the sea epic, the *Lusiad,* in the original Portuguese. Another literary friend, Hine, who appears in the book as Lemsford, was a fellow New Yorker who in 1848 was to publish *The Haunted Barque and Other Poems*. Melville's early interest in writing was revived by such company and by the chance to rove during quiet months through the library of the U.S.S. *United States.* Reading Morgan's *History of Algiers* and Knox's *Captivity in Ceylon* gave him some idea of how one's feelings could be aroused by travel books, and drowsing over the plays of Christopher Marlowe, Ben Jonson, and "the magnificent, mellow, old Beaumont and Fletcher" might well have deepened a delight in dramatic forms which preceded his immersion in Shakespeare. The future author had by now gathered better raw material than "Fragments from a Writing Desk"—the title of a piece he had written in 1839 for the Lansingburgh newspaper. Unconsciously, he was moving toward a writing career. The maintop and the library of a naval vessel, strangely, were the launching stocks of Melville's literary argosies.

Melville borrowed little from printed sources for *White Jacket;* he described "the world in a man-of-war" from his own recollection of the routines. But again he fictionized his narrative. Charles R. Anderson[24] has shown that the most exciting incidents never occurred: the great grog shortage, the Fourth of July theatricals, the brutal amputation of a seaman's leg at Rio by "Cadwallader Cuticle, M.D.," and the "massacre of the beards" and the "mutiny" that followed. The greatest inventions concerned Melville himself.

The recruit had scarcely been examined by the ship's surgeon off Honolulu when he was called to the gratings to witness punishment of two sailors, who were flogged with a dozen vigorous strokes of the cat-o'-nine-tails; two little apprentices, guilty of fighting, were whipped with the less excoriating "kitten." The dramatic scene in Chapter 67, in which Melville, threatened with a flogging for dereliction, decides to jump overboard and with him "drag Captain Claret from this earthly tribunal of his to that of Jehovah," is fiction. Any such charge would have been entered in the logbook of the frigate, and Melville never was officially reprimanded during the whole voyage. The final fiction in which Melville acts as protagonist is his fall from the topgallant yardarm just a few days before reaching the home port. The description given, which to most readers has the ring of terrible personal recollection, was the creative reworking of a passage in a book by a man who had preceded him in a South Sea cruise in the *United States*.[25]

Even the title of Melville's *White Jacket,* which one reviewer properly called "the best picture of life before the mast in a ship of war yet given to the world," was most likely based on an invention. When, instead of retaining the regulation blue jacket, the author clothed himself in an unpainted, white "lined frock" in the opening chapter, Melville was donning the artist's shirt of Nessus, and assuming the role of a white bird in a dark flock. In the penultimate chapter, the garment almost becomes his shroud and, cut away from his body, is harpooned for a shark; this passage culminates in memorable literature rather than mere autobiography.

Late in July, 1844, during the antarctic winter, the *United States* approached Cape Horn. In a squall on July 25 Herman saw the most glorious sight a voyager could expect: the full-rigged American ship *Natchez,* sixty-four days out from New York, flying westward under every inch of her canvas. The gale held off for three days, and then on July 28 the old wagon, as the frigate was called, was forced to lie to under storm staysails for six hours until the wind dropped and shifted. At last she rounded Cape Horn without a sight of land. Thus Melville departed from the Pacific by the same gate through which he had entered more than three years before. After his discharge in Boston in October, his life as a sailor was over, and he embarked on the even more stormy seas of authorship.

Melville's early adventures within the bounds of the Pacific Ocean actually extended for some three years and three months, but during most of this time he was at sea. He spent only five weeks at the Marquesas, about six at Tahiti and Mooréa, and about six more at Maui and Oahu. Less than a month had been passed in the company of unspoiled Polynesians, but the voyages in the Pacific were to become Melville's mainstay as a literary artist. As James Baird has shown, "It is not too much to say that everything he saw and felt is somewhere transposed to the framework of symbolic-artistic reference. Experience was not of itself experience; it was all emblematic to this mind, the token substance of a world which was itself protean, endlessly multiplex. . . . From 1842 to 1891 they proliferate in meaning; as imperishable images they render more and more symbols. . . . The permanent stamp [of Polynesia] was, indeed, imposed with such weight that it ordered the character of a new artistic personality. . . . This was the shaping time of Melville as artist. All that happened after the Pacific journey becomes a kind of exfoliation of youthful perception."[26]

Although Melville was to write to Nathaniel Hawthorne in 1851 that "Until I was twenty-five, I had no development at all," by August 1, 1844, his twenty-fifth birthday, passed on the ocean, young Herman had already formed his basic attitudes toward the world. "Life in the fo'c'sle," says Willard Thorp, "helped to make him a genuine democrat, a passionate hater of all forms of tyranny and shows of authority. . . . Unlike most of the previous voyagers to Tahiti and Honolulu he had nothing to sell and no gospel message to deliver. In consequence he had judged what he saw in the South Seas with impartial eyes."[27] No writer has better judged those scenes.

Melville was to return in his fortieth year to the Pacific, as a passenger. He left Boston on the American ship *Meteor*, commanded by his brother Thomas, on May 30, 1860, planning to go by way of Cape Horn to San Francisco and then to the Philippines and around the world. Herman was seasick the first night and queasy for several weeks thereafter, but faced the westerlies of Cape Horn with sturdy hope. The weather was the worst he had ever suffered at sea, and while rounding the Horn one sailor was injured on deck and another killed by falling from a yard. On peaceful days Herman wrote poems and read them to his sailor brother. But he was homesick for Pittsfield, Massachusetts, and his family. The attractions of San Francisco held him for only eight days. Having decided that his health would suffer from a round-the-world trip, he left the *Meteor* and embarked on the steamer *Cortes* on October 20 for Panama; after crossing the Isthmus, he joined another steamer, the *North Star,* for New York, and was home for Thanksgiving.

This later foray into the Pacific yielded up no literary trophies except a few poems, and thereafter Ishmael voyaged in that ocean no more. The Pacific experience, however, had fixed Melville's thought into an almost pious primitivist mold; to quote James Baird again: "The Pacific voyages were the religious confirmation of Ishmael. So, too, they confirmed other Ishmaels who followed him in these waters. For whether they were as devout as he, as poetic, as sensitive, or as purposive, they all belonged to the same communion."[28]

PART II

A PASSAGE TO THE MARQUESAS: *Typee* (1846)

⚜ ⚜ ⚜

INTRODUCTION

Melville's first book is a happy book. He lightheartedly made a novel out of his adventures in the Marquesas, and it immediately won the acclaim it deserved. It has delighted readers ever since—not primarily because it is a true account of one man's experiences, nor because it is a source book for archeologists, but mainly because the reader lingers with the storyteller for a while in a Pacific paradise that perhaps never existed but, if there be any poetic justice on earth, should have existed.

Impelled by his family to put down in writing some of the yarns he had been telling them, and having no other employment, young Herman in the late autumn of 1844 began to write his first book. He could add to his own recollections the stories he had heard from the Galena relatives concerning the adventures of his cousin, Midshipman Thomas Wilson Melville, who had visited the Marquesas on the U.S.S. *Vincennes* a dozen years earlier. He also drew upon forecastle yarns collected during almost four years at sea, as well as some printed books available to him.[1] Unaware of literary demands, in blissful ignorance of techniques, he went ahead and produced a minor masterpiece.[2]

Typee is often classed as a travel book or piece of autobiography by critics who neglect the fictional components with which it abounds. If *Moby Dick* is a novel—and it is—then *Typee* is likewise a novel. Melville's "peep at Polynesia" has all the dimensions of fiction—theme, characterization, plot, and setting.

The theme revolves around the contrasting values of orthodox "civilized" Christians and the natural man (and woman) of Jean Jacques Rousseau. In an early essay, Rousseau tried to show that primitive societies were, paradoxically, more moral and happy than other social organizations. Primitive men, he argued, were on the whole freer than any others, because the equality intended by God was spoiled by institutions. The greatest advantage of primitive life was

25

that the physical and moral aspects of sex were not at war, so that neither love nor jealousy troubled the innocent pagan.

Melville followed Rousseau to the point of declaring that in "the primitive state of society, the enjoyments of life, though few, and simple, are spread over a great extent, and are unalloyed; but civilization, for every advantage she imparts, holds a hundred evils in reserve" (Chapter 17). Paragraphs of *Typee* snipe at cruel colonizers, misguided missionaries, vicious traders and sailors—anyone who would disrupt the last remaining regions where a naturally virtuous and handsome people could be left in their tribal harmony.[3] Melville was working toward the end of a traditional literary type—the Noble Savage story—but he was able to assert boldly that the continued happiness of the Marquesan islanders sprang "principally from that all-pervading sensation which Rousseau has told us he at one time experienced, the mere buoyant sense of a healthful physical existence" (Chapter 17).

The joyousness of *Typee* derives in part from this zest of youth. Yet Tommo, as the narrator is called (a nickname perhaps inspired by Herman's cousin Thomas), after reveling in the hedonism of Paradise Regained, is plagued by the nudgings of a Faustian mind. The lack of intellectual stimulus has ever since his day led many dreaming invaders of the South Seas to eventual boredom, moral collapse, or escape. In Melville's case, it led to escape. As Ellery Sedgwick put it: "We have all been to Typee. . . . But it is a dark necessity of our being human that a time comes when we must escape from it for our lives. . . . For all its charms and its ingratiating ways, *Typee* is sub-human. A man cannot reside there but at the price of underdevelopment."[4]

Thus Melville wrote with youthful brashness, unworried about any structure beyond what he could find in the Pacific travel books that were popular in that decade. The unity of the book lies less in theme than in his chronological narrative of the adventures of a man in a place that few others have ever seen. Too young to be a philosopher, Herman appears inconsistent, revealing at different times the ferocity as well as the gentleness of his Polynesian hosts, and blaming their bad habits both on their culture and the intrusion of civilization. The final twist of his theme, however, should be underlined. This book shows that a young refugee from Occidental culture, by chance and hardship managing to escape to a South Sea Eden, shares the lives of noble savages. And after less than a month, he desperately flees back to the hell of a whaler's forecastle, even going so far in the act as to thrust a boathook into the throat of one of the friendly chiefs who was trying to keep him in Typee Valley.

Characterization in *Typee* is likewise close to that of a good novel. The narrator himself is, of course, the protagonist, on a pilgrimage to Arcadia, and nothing is brought into the book that he himself could not have seen or heard (with the exception of borrowings from the sources previously mentioned). The characters of Toby, as well as the aristocratic Marnoo, old Mehevi, and comic Kory-Kory, are drawn with a power unexpected in a young man who had never before written anything but fragments. Fayaway set a pattern for the South Sea dream girl of a hundred sarong romances.

The plot of the book is simple but suffices. The action is that of quest, escape, adventure among strangers, growing fear of being fattened for a cannibal oven, and escape to the same surroundings with which the book opened. The main suspense lies in the threat of cannibalism. Melville claims in Chapter 4 that the word "Typee" in the Marquesan dialect signifies a lover of human flesh. Anthropologists who have visited that group hold opposing views on whether or not the people actually used human beings as meat. Wrapped up in the novel, we are impelled to share Tommo's doubts, and shudder as we come at last to the "positive" evidence and his words in Chapter 32: "The last horrid revelation had now been made."

Above all, this is a book in which setting is paramount—a novel of atmosphere. Melville's best touches come from South Sea materials that he handles with relish. Perhaps the best way to read *Typee* is to forget scholarly puzzles and to regain a lost Eden through his eyes. The finest elements in the book are fictional scenes, moving landscapes, comic interludes, and confidential commentaries, in poetic tones, against a Polynesian background.

Melville created his early books without any desire for fame. "To go down to posterity is bad enough, any way," he wrote to his friend Nathaniel Hawthorne in June, 1851, "but to go down as a 'man who lived among cannibals!' " Yet he wondered wistfully whether the babies of the future might have *Typee* given to them with their gingerbread.

The printed text of Melville's first book may not be very close to what he really wanted to say. The story of its publication is almost as exciting as his description of the climb through the rain forest of Nuku-Hiva to Taipi Valley. Not until 1968 was the version published which follows, and hereafter should be the only one used for serious purposes.[5] The curious main point brought out by Dr. Leon Howard's "Historical Note" is that Melville had almost no hand in the publication of the earlier editions of *Typee*.

The manuscript was rejected in New York in 1845 by Harpers, although their reader compared it to *Robinson Crusoe,* on the grounds that "it was impossible that it could be true and therefore was without real value." A friend suggested that Herman's brother Gansevoort, who was leaving for England to become secretary of the American legation, might be able to find a publisher there. Some weeks later Gansevoort offered a portion of the manuscript to John Murray in London.

Murray was, quite rightly, suspicious that some of the events narrated had never happened precisely as told. Murray also believed that the manuscript was too well written to be the work of a common sailor. On request, Herman supplied additional factual material to lessen "the taint of fiction." Gansevoort proofread and probably revised the English edition, but Murray had hired one of his readers, Henry Milton, to spend almost two hundred hours rewriting the manuscript of this South Sea classic. Melville, only twenty-five at the time and new to publishing, was in no position to protest.

The first edition was issued by Murray in two parts in 1846, under the unwieldy title of *Narrative of a Four Months' Residence Among the Natives in a Valley of the Marquesas Islands*. It was an addition to Murray's Home and Colonial Library, supposedly authentic travel narratives. The first American edition, published in the same year by Wiley & Putnam of New York, was set from proofs of the English one, under the title of *Typee: A Peep at Polynesian Life*. Both these editions were issued by firms with different goals.

Murray was worried about authenticity. He was so delighted when Richard Tobias Greene, the original "Toby," popped up as a sign painter in Buffalo, New York, and confirmed Melville's adventures that his firm published as a pamphlet Melville's short sequel, "The Story of Toby," and added it to the second English edition.

Wiley feared that Melville would shock his American readers. The publisher, in a hurry to go to press, was, in the words of Dr. Howard, "torn between the fussy concern for propriety which made him begin the bowdlerization of the book and the frugality or fear of delay which evidently made him stop." Poor Herman hoped that the second American edition would call for only a few changes, which he made in May, 1846. But, at the request of Wiley, he did an extensive revision in July, removing about thirty pages of comment on the effect of Occidental impacts (especially those of missionaries) on the Pacific islanders, as well as the pro-British Appendix on the absentminded annexation of the Hawaiian kingdom by H.M.S. *Carysfort* in 1843. He also cut out much of the "raciness" that many early reviewers had admired.

The difficulty of finding out what Melville really wanted to say (or omit) is complicated by the fact that only a single sheet of the *Typee* manuscript remains. When compared with the first English edition, the two handwritten sides, presumably a second draft, reveal no less than sixty substantive changes between manuscript and book. The "Note on the Text" in the Northwestern-Newberry edition lists copious other material changes in the various earlier ones, including those in "The Story of Toby."

These scholarly texts now appearing permit the reader to get as close as possible to Melville's meanings, and their issuance should again encourage his admirers to plunge with delight into his early accounts of South Sea adventure.

❁ ❁ ❁

CHAPTER II

Various and conflicting were the thoughts which oppressed me during the silent hours that followed the events related in the preceding chapter. Toby, wearied with the fatigues of the day, slumbered heavily by my side; but the pain under which I was suffering effectually prevented my sleeping, and I remained distressingly alive to all the fearful circumstances of our present situation. Was it possible that, after all our vicissitudes, we were really in the terrible valley of Typee, and at the mercy of its inmates, a fierce and unrelenting tribe of savages?

Typee or Happar? I shuddered when I reflected that there was no longer any room for doubt; and that, beyond all hope of escape, we were now placed in those very circumstances from the bare thought of which I had recoiled with such abhorrence but a few days before. What might not be our fearful destiny? To be sure, as yet we had been treated with no violence; nay, had been even kindly and hospitably entertained. But what dependence could be placed upon the fickle passions which sway the bosom of a savage? His inconstancy and treachery are proverbial. Might it not be that beneath these fair appearances the islanders covered some perfidious design, and that their friendly reception of us might only precede some horrible catastrophe? How strongly did these forebodings spring up in my mind as I lay restlessly upon a couch of mats, surrounded by the dimly revealed forms of those whom I so greatly dreaded.

From the excitement of these fearful thoughts I sank towards morning into an uneasy slumber; and on awaking, with a start, in the midst of an appalling dream, looked up into the eager countenances of a number of the natives, who were bending over me.

It was broad day; and the house was nearly filled with young females, fancifully decorated with flowers, who gazed upon me as I rose with faces in which childish delight and curiosity were vividly pourtrayed. After waking Toby, they seated themselves round us on the mats, and gave full play to that prying inquisitiveness which time out of mind has been attributed to the adorable sex.

As these unsophisticated young creatures were attended by no jealous duennas, their proceedings were altogether informal, and void of artificial restraint. Long and minute was the investigation with which they honored us, and so uproarious their mirth, that I felt infinitely sheepish; and Toby was immeasurably outraged at their familiarity.

These lively young ladies were at the same time wonderfully polite and humane; fanning aside the insects that occasionally lighted on our brows; presenting us with food; and compassionately regarding me in the midst of my afflictions. But in spite of all their blandishments, my feelings of propriety were exceedingly shocked, for I could not but consider them as having overstepped the due limits of female decorum.

Having diverted themselves to their heart's content, our young visitants now withdrew, and gave place to successive troops of the other sex, who continued flocking towards the house until near noon; by which time I have no doubt that the greater part of the inhabitants of the valley had bathed themselves in the light of our benignant countenances.

At last, when their numbers began to diminish, a superb-looking warrior stooped the towering plumes of his head-dress beneath the low portal, and entered the house. I saw at once that he was some distinguished personage, the natives regarding him with the utmost deference, and making room for him as he approached. His aspect was imposing. The splendid long drooping tail-feathers of the tropical bird, thickly interspersed with the gaudy plumage of the cock, were disposed in an immense upright semicircle upon his head, their lower extremities being fixed in a crescent of guinea-beads which spanned the forehead. Around his neck were several enormous necklaces of boars' tusks, polished like ivory, and disposed in such a manner as that the longest and largest were upon his capacious chest. Thrust forward through the large apertures in his ears were two small and finely shaped sperm-whale teeth, presenting their cavities in front, stuffed with freshly-plucked leaves, and curiously wrought at the other end into strange little images and devices. These barbaric trinkets, garnished in this manner at their open extremities, and tapering and curving round to a point behind the ear, resembled not a little a pair of cornucopias.

The loins of the warrior were girt about with heavy folds of a dark-colored tappa, hanging before and behind in clusters of braided tassels, while anklets and bracelets of curling human hair completed his unique costume. In his right hand he grasped a beautifully carved paddle-spear, nearly fifteen feet in length, made of the bright koar-wood, one end sharply pointed, and the other flattened like an oar-blade. Hanging obliquely from his girdle by a loop of sinnate was a richly decorated pipe, the slender reed forming its stem was colored with a red pigment, and round it, as well as the idol-bowl, fluttered little streamers of the thinnest tappa.

But that which was most remarkable in the appearance of the splendid islander was the elaborated tattooing displayed on every noble limb. All imaginable lines and curves and figures were delineated over his whole body, and in their grotesque variety and infinite profusion I could only compare them to the crowded groupings of quaint patterns we sometimes see in costly pieces of lacework. The most simple and remarkable of all these ornaments was that which decorated the countenance of the chief. Two broad stripes of tattooing, diverging from the centre of his shaven crown, obliquely crossed both eyes—staining the lids—to a little below either ear, where they united with another stripe which swept in a straight line along the lips and formed the base of the triangle. The warrior, from the excellence of his physical proportions, might certainly have been regarded as one of Nature's noblemen, and the lines drawn upon his face may possibly have denoted his exalted rank.

This warlike personage, upon entering the house, seated himself at some distance from the spot where Toby and myself reposed, while the rest of the savages looked alternately from us to him, as if in expectation of something they were disappointed in not perceiving. Regarding the chief attentively, I thought his lineaments appeared familiar to me. As soon as his full face was turned upon me, and I again beheld its extraordinary embellishment, and met the strange gaze to which I had been subjected the preceding night, I immediately, in spite of the alteration in his appearance, recognised the noble Mehevi. On addressing him, he advanced at once in the most cordial manner, and, greeting me warmly, seemed to enjoy not a little the effect his barbaric costume had produced upon me.

I forthwith determined to secure, if possible, the good will of this individual, as I easily perceived he was a man of great authority in his tribe, and one who might exert a powerful influence upon our subsequent fate. In the endeavor I was not repulsed; for nothing could surpass the friendliness he manifested towards both my companion and myself. He extended his sturdy limbs by our side, and endeavored to make us comprehend the full extent of the kindly feelings by which he was actuated. The almost insuperable difficulty in communicating to one another our ideas affected the chief with no little mortification. He evinced a great desire to be enlightened with regard to the customs and peculiarities of the far-off country we had left behind us, and to which under the name of Maneeka he frequently alluded.

But that which more than any other subject engaged his attention was the late proceedings of the "Franee," as he called the French, in the neighboring bay of Nukuheva. This seemed a never-ending theme with him, and one concerning which he was never weary of interrogating us. All the information we succeeded in imparting to him on this subject was little more than that we had seen six men-of-war lying in the hostile bay at the time we had left it. When he received this intelligence, Mehevi, by the aid of his fingers, went through a long numerical calculation, as if estimating the number of Frenchmen the squadron might contain.

It was just after employing his faculties in this way that he happened to notice the swelling in my limb. He immediately examined it with the utmost attention, and after doing so despatched a boy who happened to be standing by with some message.

After the lapse of a few moments the stripling re-entered the house with an aged islander, who might have been taken for old Hippocrates himself. His head was as bald as the polished surface of a cocoa-nut shell, which article it precisely resembled in smoothness and color, while a long silvery beard swept almost to his girdle of bark. Encircling his temples was a bandeau of the twisted leaves of the Omoo tree, pressed closely over the brows to shield his feeble vision from the glare of the sun. His tottering steps were supported by a long slim staff, resembling the wand with which a theatrical magician appears on the stage, and in one hand he carried a freshly plaited fan of the green leaflets of the cocoa-nut tree. A flowing robe of tappa, knotted over the shoulder, hung loosely round his stooping form, and heightened the venerableness of his aspect.

Mehevi, saluting this old gentleman, motioned him to a seat between us, and then uncovering my limb, desired him to examine it. The leech gazed intently from me to Toby, and then proceeded to business. After diligently observing the ailing member, he commenced manipulating it; and on the supposition probably that the complaint had deprived the leg of all sensation, began to pinch and hammer it in such a manner that I absolutely roared with the pain. Thinking that I was as capable of making an application of thumps and pinches to the part as any one else, I endeavored to resist this species of medical treatment. But it was not so easy a matter to get out of the clutches of the old wizard; he fastened on the unfortunate limb as if it were something for which he had been long seeking, and muttering some kind of incantation continued his discipline, pounding it after a fashion that set me well nigh crazy; while Mehevi, upon the same principle which prompts an affectionate mother to hold a struggling child in a dentist's chair, restrained me in his powerful grasp, and actually encouraged the wretch in this infliction of torture.

Almost frantic with rage and pain, I yelled like a bedlamite; while Toby, throwing himself into all the attitudes of a posture-master, vainly endeavored to expostulate with the natives by signs and gestures. To have looked at my companion, as, sympathising with my sufferings, he strove to put an end to them, one would have thought that he was the deaf and dumb alphabet incarnated.

Whether my tormentor yielded to Toby's entreaties, or paused from sheer exhaustion, I do not know; but all at once he ceased his operations, and at the same time the chief relinquishing his hold upon me, I fell back, faint and breathless with the agony I had endured.

My unfortunate limb was now left much in the same condition as a rumpsteak after undergoing the castigating process which precedes cooking. My physician, having recovered from the fatigues of his exertions, as if anxious to make amends for the pain to which he had subjected me, now took some herbs out of a little wallet that was suspended from his waist, and moistening them in water, applied them to the inflamed part, stooping over it at the same time, and either whispering a spell, or having a little confidential chat with some imaginary demon located in the calf of my leg. My limb was now swathed in leafy bandages, and, grateful to Providence for the cessation of hostilities, I was suffered to rest.

Mehevi shortly after rose to depart; but before he went he spoke authoritatively to one of the natives whom he addressed as Kory-Kory; and from the little I could understand of what took place, pointed him out to me as a man whose peculiar business thenceforth would be to attend upon my person. I am not certain that I comprehended as much as this at the time, but the subsequent conduct of my trusty body-servant fully assured me that such must have been the case.

I could not but be amused at the manner in which the chief addressed me upon this occasion, talking to me for at least fifteen or twenty minutes as calmly as if I could understand every word that he said. I remarked this peculiarity very often afterwards in many other of the islanders.

Mehevi having now departed, and the family physician having likewise made his exit, we were left about sunset with the ten or twelve natives, who by this time I had ascertained composed the household of which Toby and I were members. As the dwelling to which we had been first introduced was the place of my permanent abode while I remained in the valley, and as I was necessarily placed upon the most intimate footing with its occupants, I may as well here enter into a little description of it and its inhabitants. This description will apply also to nearly all the other dwelling-places in the vale, and will furnish some idea of the generality of the natives.

Near one side of the valley, and about midway up the ascent of a rather abrupt rise of ground waving with the richest verdure, a number of large stones were laid in successive courses, to the height of nearly eight feet, and disposed in such a manner that their level surface corresponded in shape with the habitation which was perched upon it. A narrow space, however, was reserved in front of the dwelling, upon the summit of this pile of stones, (called by the natives a "pi-pi,") which being enclosed by a little picket of canes, gave it somewhat the appearance of a verandah. The frame of the house was constructed of large bamboos planted uprightly, and secured together at intervals by transverse stalks of the light wood of the habiscus, lashed with thongs of bark. The rear of the tenement—built up with successive ranges of cocoa-nut boughs bound one upon another, with their leaflets cunningly woven together—inclined a little from the vertical, and extended from the extreme edge of the "pi-pi" to about twenty feet from its surface; whence the shelving roof—thatched with the long tapering leaves of the palmetto—sloped steeply off to within about five feet of the floor; leaving the eaves drooping with tassel-like appendages over the front of the habitation. This was constructed of light and elegant canes, in a kind of open screen work, tastefully adorned with bindings of variegated sinnate, which served to hold together its various parts. The sides of the house were similarly built; thus presenting three quarters for the circulation of the air, while the whole was impervious to the rain.

In length this picturesque building was perhaps twelve yards, while in breadth it could not have exceeded as many feet. So much for the exterior; which with its wire-like reed-twisted sides, not a little reminded me of an immense aviary.

Stooping a little, you passed through a narrow aperture in its front; and facing you, on entering, lay two long, perfectly straight, and well-polished trunks of the cocoa-nut tree, extending the full length of the dwelling; one of them placed closely against the rear, and the other lying parallel with it some two yards distant, the interval between them being spread with a multitude of gaily-worked mats, nearly all of a different pattern. This space formed the common couch and lounging place of the natives, answering the purpose of a divan in Oriental countries. Here would they slumber through the hours of the night, and recline luxuriously during the greater part of the day. The remainder of the floor presented only the cool shining surfaces of the large stones of which the "pi-pi" was composed.

From the ridge pole of the house hung suspended a number of large packages enveloped in coarse tappa; some of which contained festival dresses, and various other matters of the wardrobe, held in high estimation. These were easily accessible by means of a line, which, passing over the ridge-pole, had one end attached to a bundle, while with the other, which led to the side of the dwelling and was there secured, the package could be lowered or elevated at pleasure.

Against the farther wall of the house were arranged in tasteful figures a variety of spears and javelins, and other implements of savage warfare. Outside of the habitation, and built upon the piazza-like area in its front, was a little shed used as a sort of larder or pantry, and in which were stored various articles of domestic use and convenience. A few yards from the pi-pi was a large shed built of cocoa-nut boughs, where the process of preparing the "poee-poee" was carried on, and all culinary operations attended to.

Thus much for the house, and its appurtenances; and it will be readily acknowledged that a more commodious and appropriate dwelling for the climate and the people could not possibly be devised. It was cool, free to admit the air, scrupulously clean, and elevated above the dampness and impurities of the ground.

But now to sketch the inmates; and here I claim for my tried servitor and faithful valet Kory-Kory the precedence of a first description. As his character will be gradually unfolded in the course of my narrative, I shall for the present content myself with delineating his personal appearance. Kory-Kory, though the most devoted and best natured serving-man in the world, was, alas! a hideous object to look upon. He was some twenty-five years of age, and about six feet in height, robust and well made, and of the most extraordinary aspect. His head was carefully shaven, with the exception of two circular spots, about the size of a dollar, near the top of the cranium, where the hair, permitted to grow of an amazing length, was twisted up in two prominent knots, that gave him the appearance of being decorated with a pair of horns. His beard, plucked out by the roots from every other part of his face, was suffered to droop in hairy pendants, two of which garnished his upper lip, and an equal number hung from the extremity of his chin.

Kory-Kory, with a view of improving the handiwork of nature, and perhaps prompted by a desire to add to the engaging expression of his countenance, had seen fit to embellish his face with three broad longitudinal stripes of tattooing, which, like those country roads that go straight forward in defiance of all obstacles, crossed his nasal organ, descended into the hollow of his eyes, and even skirted the borders of his mouth. Each completely spanned his physiognomy; one extending in a line with his eyes, another crossing the face in the vicinity of the nose, and the third sweeping along his lips from ear to ear. His countenance thus triply hooped, as it were, with tattooing, always reminded me of those unhappy wretches whom I have sometimes observed gazing out sentimentally from behind the grated bars of a prison window; whilst the entire body of my savage valet, covered all over with representations of birds and fishes, and a variety of most unaccountable-looking creatures, suggested to me the idea of a pictorial museum of natural history, or an illustrated copy of "Goldsmith's Animated Nature."

But it seems really heartless in me to write thus of the poor islander, when I owe perhaps to his unremitting attentions the very existence I now enjoy. Kory-Kory, I mean thee no harm in what I say in regard to thy outward adornings; but they were a little curious to my unaccustomed sight, and therefore I dilate upon them. But to underrate or forget thy faithful services is something I could never be guilty of, even in the giddiest moment of my life.

The father of my attached follower was a native of gigantic frame, and had once possessed prodigious physical powers; but the lofty form was now yielding to the inroads of time, though the hand of disease seemed never to have been laid upon the aged warrior. Marheyo—for such was his name—appeared to have retired from all active participation in the affairs of the valley, seldom or never accompanying the natives in their various expeditions; and employing the greater part of his time in throwing up a little shed just outside the house, upon which he was engaged to my certain knowledge for four months, without appearing to make any sensible advance. I suppose the old gentleman was in his dotage, for he manifested in various ways the characteristics which mark this particular stage of life.

I remember in particular his having a choice pair of ear-ornaments, fabricated from the teeth of some sea-monster. These he would alternately wear and take off at least fifty times in the course of the day, going and coming from his little hut on each occasion with all the tranquillity imaginable. Sometimes slipping them through the slits in his ears, he would seize his spear—which in length and slightness resembled a fishingpole—and go stalking beneath the shadows of the neighboring groves, as if about to give a hostile meeting to some cannibal knight. But he would soon return again, and hiding his weapon under the projecting eaves of the house, and rolling his clumsy trinkets carefully in a piece of tappa, would resume his more pacific operations as quietly as if he had never interrupted them.

But despite his eccentricities, Marheyo was a most paternal and warmhearted old fellow, and in this particular not a little resembled his son Kory-Kory. The mother of the latter was the mistress of the family, and a notable housewife, and a most industrious old lady she was. If she did not understand the art of making jellies, jams, custards, tea-cakes, and such like trashy affairs, she was profoundly skilled in the mysteries of preparing "amar," "poee-poee," and "kokoo," with other substantial matters. She was a genuine busy-body; bustling about the house like a country landlady at an unexpected arrival; for ever giving the young girls tasks to perform, which the little hussies as often neglected; poking into every corner, and rummaging over bundles of old tappa, or making a prodigious clatter among the calabashes. Sometimes she might have been seen squatting upon her haunches in front of a huge wooden basin, and kneading poee-poee with terrific vehemence, dashing the stone pestle about as if she would shiver the vessel into fragments; on other occasions, galloping about the valley in search of a particular kind of leaf, used in some of her recondite operations, and returning home, toiling and sweating, with a bundle, under which most women would have sunk.

To tell the truth, Kory-Kory's mother was the only industrious person in all the valley of Typee; and she could not have employed herself more actively had she been left an exceedingly muscular and destitute widow, with an inordinate supply of young children, in the bleakest part of the civilized world. There was not the slightest necessity for the greater portion of the labor performed by the old lady: but she seemed to work from some irresistible impulse; her limbs continually swaying to and fro, as if there were some indefatigable engine concealed within her body which kept her in perpetual motion.

Never suppose that she was a termagant or a shrew for all this; she had the kindliest heart in the world and acted towards me in particular in a truly maternal manner, occasionally putting some little morsel of choice food into my hand, some outlandish kind of savage sweetmeat or pastry, like a doting mother petting a sickly urchin with tarts and sugar-plums. Warm indeed are my remembrances of the dear, good, affectionate old Tinor!

Besides the individuals I have mentioned, there belonged to the household three young men, dissipated, good-for-nothing, roystering blades of savages, who were either employed in prosecuting love-affairs with the maidens of the tribe, or grew boozy on "arva" and tobacco in the company of congenial spirits, the scapegraces of the valley.

Among the permanent inmates of the house were likewise several lovely damsels, who instead of thrumming pianos and reading novels, like more enlightened young ladies, substituted for these employments the manufacture of a fine species of tappa; but for the greater portion of the time were skipping from house to house, gadding and gossiping with their acquaintances.

From the rest of these, however, I must except the beauteous nymph Fayaway, who was my peculiar favorite. Her free pliant figure was the very perfection of female grace and beauty. Her complexion was a rich and mantling olive, and when watching the glow upon her cheeks I could almost swear that beneath the transparent medium there lurked the blushes of a faint vermilion. The face of this girl was a rounded oval, and each feature as perfectly formed as the heart or imagination of man could desire. Her full lips, when parted with a smile, disclosed teeth of a dazzling whiteness; and when her rosy mouth opened with a burst of merriment, they looked like the milk-white seeds of the "arta," a fruit of the valley, which, when cleft in twain, shows them reposing in rows on either side, imbedded in the red juicy pulp. Her hair of the deepest brown, parted irregularly in the middle, flowed in natural ringlets over her shoulders, and whenever she chanced to stoop, fell over and hid from view her lovely bosom. Gazing into the depths of her strange blue eyes, when she was in a contemplative mood, they seemed most placid yet unfathomable; but when illuminated by some lively emotion, they beamed upon the beholder like stars. The hands of Fayaway were as soft and delicate as those of any countess; for an entire exemption from rude labor marks the girlhood and even prime of a Typee woman's life. Her feet, though wholly exposed, were as diminutive and fairly shaped as those which peep from beneath the skirts of a Lima lady's dress. The skin of this young creature, from continual ablutions and the use of mollifying ointments, was inconceivably smooth and soft.

I may succeed, perhaps, in particularising some of the individual features of Fayaway's beauty, but that general loveliness of appearance which they all contributed to produce I will not attempt to describe. The easy unstudied graces of a child of nature like this, breathing from infancy an atmosphere of perpetual summer, and nurtured by the simple fruits of the earth; enjoying a perfect freedom from care and anxiety, and removed effectually from all injurious tendencies, strike the eye in a manner which cannot be pourtrayed. This picture is no fancy sketch; it is drawn from the most vivid recollections of the person delineated.

Were I asked if the beauteous form of Fayaway was altogether free from the hideous blemish of tattooing, I should be constrained to answer that it was not. But the practitioners of this barbarous art, so remorseless in their inflictions upon the brawny limbs of the warriors of the tribe, seem to be conscious that it needs not the resources of their profession to augment the charms of the maidens of the vale.

The females are very little embellished in this way, and Fayaway, with all the other young girls of her age, were even less so than those of their sex more advanced in years. The reason of this peculiarity will be alluded to hereafter. All the tattooing that the nymph in question exhibited upon her person may be easily described. Three minute dots, no bigger than pin-heads, decorated either lip, and at a little distance were not at all discernible. Just upon the fall of the shoulder were drawn two parallel lines half an inch apart, and perhaps three inches in length, the interval being filled with delicately executed figures. These narrow bands of tattooing, thus placed, always reminded me of those stripes of gold lace worn by officers in undress, and which are in lieu of epaulettes to denote their rank.

Thus much was Fayaway tattooed—the audacious hand which had gone so far in its desecrating work stopping short, apparently wanting the heart to proceed.

But I have omitted to describe the dress worn by this nymph of the valley.

Fayaway—I must avow the fact—for the most part clung to the primitive and summer garb of Eden. But how becoming the costume! It showed her fine figure to the best possible advantage; and nothing could have been better adapted to her peculiar style of beauty. On ordinary occasions she was habited precisely as I have described the two youthful savages whom we had met on first entering the valley. At other times, when rambling among the groves, or visiting at the houses

of her acquaintances, she wore a tunic of white tappa, reaching from her waist
to a little below the knees; and when exposed for any length of time to the sun,
she invariably protected herself from its rays by a floating mantle of the same
material, loosely gathered about the person. Her gala dress will be described
hereafter.

As the beauties of our own land delight in bedecking themselves with fanciful
articles of jewellery, suspending them from their ears, hanging them about their
necks, and clasping them around their wrists; so Fayaway and her companions
were in the habit of ornamenting themselves with similar appendages.

Flora was their jeweller. Sometimes they wore necklaces of small carnation
flowers, strung like rubies upon a fibre of tappa, or displayed in their ears a
single white bud, the stem thrust backward through the aperture, and showing
in front the delicate petals folded together in a beautiful sphere, and looking
like a drop of the purest pearl. Chaplets too, resembling in their arrangement the
strawberry coronal worn by an English peeress, and composed of intertwined
leaves and blossoms, often crowned their temples; and bracelets and anklets of the
same tasteful pattern were frequently to be seen. Indeed, the maidens of the
island were passionately fond of flowers, and never wearied of decorating their
persons with them; a lovely trait in their character, and one that ere long will
be more fully alluded to.

Though in my eyes, at least, Fayaway was indisputably the loveliest female I
saw in Typee, yet the description I have given of her will in some measure
apply to nearly all the youthful portion of her sex in the valley. Judge ye then,
reader, what beautiful creatures they must have been.

CHAPTER 12

. . . On the afternoon of the day that I took my first bath in the valley, we received another visit from Mehevi. The noble savage seemed to be in the same
pleasant mood, and was quite as cordial in his manner as before. After remaining
about an hour, he rose from the mats, and motioning to leave the house, invited
Toby and myself to accompany him. I pointed to my leg; but Mehevi in his turn
pointed to Kory-Kory, and removed that objection; so, mounting upon the
faithful fellow's shoulders again—like the old man of the sea astride of Sindbad
—I followed after the chief.

The nature of the route we now pursued struck me more forcibly than anything I had yet seen, as illustrating the indolent disposition of the islanders. The
path was obviously the most beaten one in the valley, several others leading from
either side into it, and perhaps for successive generations it had formed the
principle avenue of the place. And yet, until I grew more familiar with its im-

pediments, it seemed as difficult to travel as the recesses of a wilderness. Part of it swept round an abrupt rise of ground, the surface of which was broken by frequent inequalities, and thickly strewn with projecting masses of rocks, whose summits were often hidden from view by the drooping foliage of the luxuriant vegetation. Sometimes directly over, sometimes evading these obstacles with a wide circuit, the path wound along;—one moment climbing over a sudden eminence smooth with continued wear, then descending on the other side into a steep glen, and crossing the flinty channel of a brook. Here it pursued the depths of a glade, occasionally obliging you to stoop beneath vast horizontal branches; and now you stepped over huge trunks and boughs that lay rotting across the track.

Such was the grand thoroughfare of Typee. After proceeding a little distance along it—Kory-Kory panting and blowing with the weight of his burden—I dismounted from his back, and grasping the long spear of Mehevi in my hand, assisted my steps over the numerous obstacles of the road; preferring this mode of advance to one which, from the difficulties of the way, was equally painful to myself and my wearied servitor.

Our journey was soon at an end; for, scaling a sudden height, we came abruptly upon the place of our destination. I wish that it were possible to sketch in words this spot as vividly as I recollect it.

Here were situated the Taboo groves of the valley—the scene of many a prolonged feast, of many a horrid rite. Beneath the dark shadows of the consecrated bread-fruit trees there reigned a solemn twilight—a cathedral-like gloom. The frightful genius of pagan worship seemed to brood in silence over the place, breathing its spell upon every object around. Here and there, in the depths of these awful shades, half screened from sight by masses of overhanging foliage, rose the idolatrous altars of the savages, built of enormous blocks of black and polished stone, placed one upon another, without cement, to the height of twelve or fifteen feet, and surmounted by a rustic open temple, enclosed with a low picket of canes, within which might be seen, in various stages of decay, offerings of bread-fruit and cocoa-nuts, and the putrefying relics of some recent sacrifice.

In the midst of the wood was the hallowed "hoolah hoolah" ground—set apart for the celebration of the fantastic religious ritual of these people—comprising an extensive oblong pi-pi, terminating at either end in a lofty terraced altar, guarded by ranks of hideous wooden idols, and with the two remaining sides flanked by ranges of bamboo sheds, opening towards the interior of the quadrangle thus formed. Vast trees, standing in the middle of this space, and throwing over it an umbrageous shade, had their massive trunks built round with slight stages, elevated a few feet above the ground, and railed in with canes, forming so many rustic pulpits, from which the priests harangued their devotees.

This holiest of spots was defended from profanation by the strictest edicts of the all-pervading "taboo," which condemned to instant death the sacrilegious female who should enter or touch its sacred precincts, or even so much as press with her feet the ground made holy by the shadows that it cast.

Access was had to the enclosure through an embowered entrance on one side, facing a number of towering cocoa-nut trees, planted at intervals along a level area of a hundred yards. At the further extremity of this space was to be seen a building of considerable size, reserved for the habitation of the priests and religious attendants of the groves.

In its vicinity was another remarkable edifice, built as usual upon the summit of a pi-pi, and at least two hundred feet in length, though not more than twenty in breadth. The whole front of this latter structure was completely open, and from one end to the other ran a narrow verandah, fenced in on the edge of the pi-pi with a picket of canes. Its interior presented the appearance of an immense lounging-place, the entire floor being strewn with successive layers of mats, lying between parallel trunks of cocoa-nut trees, selected for the purpose from the straightest and most symmetrical the vale afforded.

To this building, denominated in the language of the natives the "Ti," Mehevi now conducted us. Thus far we had been accompanied by a troop of the natives of both sexes; but as soon as we approached its vicinity, the females gradually separated themselves from the crowd, and standing aloof, permitted us to pass on. The merciless prohibitions of the taboo extended likewise to this edifice, and were enforced by the same dreadful penalty that secured the Hoolah Hoolah ground from the imaginary pollution of a woman's presence.

On entering the house, I was surprised to see six muskets ranged against the bamboo on one side, from the barrels of which depended as many small canvas pouches, partly filled with powder. Disposed about these muskets, like the cutlasses that decorate the bulkhead of a man-of-war's cabin, were a great variety of rude spears and paddles, javelins, and war-clubs. This then, said I to Toby, must be the armory of the tribe.

As we advanced further along the building, we were struck with the aspect of four or five hideous old wretches, on whose decrepit forms time and tattooing seemed to have obliterated every trace of humanity. Owing to the continued operation of this latter process, which only terminates among the warriors of the island after the figures sketched upon their limbs in youth have been blended together—an effect, however, produced only in cases of extreme longevity—the bodies of these men were of a uniform dull green color—the hue which the tattooing gradually assumes as the individual advances in age. Their skin had a frightful scaly appearance, which, united with its singular color, made their limbs not a little resemble dusty specimens of verde-antique. Their flesh, in parts, hung upon them in huge folds, like the overlapping plaits on the flank of a rhinoceros. Their heads were completely bald, whilst their faces were puckered into a thousand wrinkles, and they presented no vestige of a beard. But the most remarkable peculiarity about them was the appearance of the feet; the toes, like the radiating lines of the mariner's compass, pointed to every quarter of the horizon. This was doubtless attributable to the fact, that during nearly a hundred years of existence the said toes never had been subjected to any artificial confinement, and in their old age, being averse to close neighborhood, bid one another keep open order.

These repulsive-looking creatures appeared to have lost the use of their lower limbs altogether; sitting upon the floor cross-legged in a state of torpor. They never heeded us in the least, scarcely looking conscious of our presence, while Mehevi seated us upon the mats, and Kory-Kory gave utterance to some unintelligible gibberish.

In a few moments a boy entered with a wooden trencher of poee-poee; and in regaling myself with its contents I was obliged again to submit to the officious intervention of my indefatigable servitor. Various other dishes followed, the chief manifesting the most hospitable importunity in pressing us to partake, and to remove all bashfulness on our part, set us no despicable example in his own person.

The repast concluded, a pipe was lighted, which passed from mouth to mouth, and yielding to its soporific influence, the quiet of the place, and the deepening shadows of approaching night, my companion and I sank into a kind of drowsy repose, while the chief and Kory-Kory seemed to be slumbering beside us.

I awoke from an uneasy nap, about midnight, as I supposed; and, raising myself partly from the mat, became sensible that we were enveloped in utter darkness. Toby lay still asleep, but our late companions had disappeared. The only sound that interrupted the silence of the place was the asthmatic breathing of the old men I have mentioned, who reposed at a little distance from us. Beside them, as well as I could judge, there was no one else in the house.

Apprehensive of some evil, I roused my comrade, and we were engaged in a whispered conference concerning the unexpected withdrawal of the natives, when all at once, from the depths of the grove, in full view of us where we lay, shoots of flame were seen to rise, and in a few moments illuminated the surrounding trees, casting, by contrast, into still deeper gloom the darkness around us.

While we continued gazing at this sight, dark figures appeared moving to and fro before the flames; while others, dancing and capering about, looked like so many demons.

Regarding this new phenomenon with no small degree of trepidation, I said to my companion, "What can all this mean, Toby?"

"Oh, nothing," replied he; "getting the fire ready, I suppose."

"Fire!" exclaimed I, while my heart took to beating like a trip-hammer, "what fire?"

"Why, the fire to cook us, to be sure; what else would the cannibals be kicking up such a row about if it were not for that?"

"Oh, Toby! have done with your jokes; this is no time for them; something is about to happen, I feel confident."

"Jokes, indeed!' exclaimed Toby, indignantly. "Did you ever hear me joke? Why, for what do you suppose the devils have been feeding us up in this kind of style during the last three days, unless it were for something that you are too much frightened at to talk about? Look at that Kory-Kory there!—has he not been stuffing you with his confounded mushes, just in the way they treat swine before they kill them? Depend upon it, we will be eaten this blessed night, and there is the fire we shall be roasted by."

This view of the matter was not at all calculated to allay my apprehensions, and I shuddered when I reflected that we were indeed at the mercy of a tribe of cannibals, and that the dreadful contingency to which Toby had alluded was by no means removed beyond the bounds of possibility.

"There! I told you so! they are coming for us!" exclaimed my companion the next moment, as the forms of four of the islanders were seen in bold relief against the illuminated back-ground, mounting the pi-pi and approaching towards us.

They came on noiselessly, nay stealthily, and glided along through the gloom that surrounded us as if about to spring upon some object they were fearful of disturbing before they should make sure of it.—Gracious heaven! the horrible reflections which crowded upon me that moment.—A cold sweat stood upon my brow, and spell-bound with terror I awaited my fate!

Suddenly the silence was broken by the well-remembered tones of Mehevi, and at the kindly accents of his voice my fears were immediately dissipated. "Tommo, Toby, ki ki!" (eat).—He had waited to address us until he had assured himself that we were both awake, at which he seemed somewhat surprised.

"Ki ki! is it?" said Toby in his gruff tones; "well, cook us first, will you?—but what's this?" he added, as another savage appeared, bearing before him a large trencher of wood, containing some kind of steaming meat, as appeared from the odors it diffused, and which he deposited at the feet of Mehevi. "A baked baby, I dare say! but I will have none of it, never mind what it is.—A pretty fool I should make of myself, indeed, waked up here in the middle of the night, stuffing and guzzling, and all to make a fat meal for a parcel of bloody-minded cannibals one of these mornings!—No, I see what they are at very plainly, so I am resolved to starve myself into a bunch of bones and gristle, and then, if they serve me up, they are welcome! But I say, Tommo, you are not going to eat any of that mess there, in the dark, are you? Why, how can you tell what it is?"

"By tasting it, to be sure," said I, masticating a morsel that Kory-Kory had just put in my mouth; "and excellently good it is too, very much like veal."

"A baked baby, by the soul of Captain Cook!" burst forth Toby, with amazing vehemence; "Veal? why there never was a calf on the island till you landed. I tell you you are bolting down mouthfuls from a dead Happar's carcass, as sure as you live, and no mistake!"

Emetics and lukewarm water! What a sensation in the abdominal regions! Sure enough, where could the fiends incarnate have obtained meat? But I resolved to satisfy myself at all hazards; and turning to Mehevi I soon made the ready chief understand that I wished a light to be brought. When the taper came, I gazed eagerly into the vessel, and recognised the mutilated remains of a juvenile porker! "Puarkee!" exclaimed Kory-Kory, looking complacently at the dish; and from that day to this I have never forgotten that such is the designation of a pig in the Typee lingo . . . .

CHAPTER 14

. . . Kory-Kory never for one moment left my side, unless it were to execute my wishes. The faithful fellow, twice every day, in the cool of the morning and in the evening, insisted upon carrying me to the stream, and bathing me in its refreshing water.

Frequently in the afternoon he would carry me to a particular part of the stream, where the beauty of the scene produced a soothing influence upon my mind. At this place the waters flowed between grassy banks, planted with enormous bread-fruit trees, whose vast branches interlacing overhead, formed a leafy canopy; near the stream were several smooth black rocks. One of these, projecting several feet above the surface of the water, had upon its summit a shallow cavity, which, filled with freshly-gathered leaves, formed a delightful couch.

Here I often lay for hours, covered with a gauze-like veil of tappa, while Fayaway, seated beside me, and holding in her hand a fan woven from the leaflets of a young cocoa-nut bough, brushed aside the insects that occasionally lighted on my face, and Kory-Kory, with a view of chasing away my melancholy, performed a thousand antics in the water before us.

As my eye wandered along this romantic stream, it would fall upon the half-immersed figure of a beautiful girl, standing in the transparent water, and catching in a little net a species of diminutive shell-fish, of which these people are extravagantly fond. Sometimes a chattering group would be seated upon the edge of a low rock in the midst of the brook, busily engaged in thinning and polishing the shells of cocoa-nuts, by rubbing them briskly with a small stone in the water, an operation which soon converts them into a light and elegant drinking vessel, somewhat resembling goblets made of tortoiseshell.

But the tranquillizing influences of beautiful scenery, and the exhibition of human life under so novel and charming an aspect, were not my only sources of consolation.

Every evening the girls of the house gathered about me on the mats, and after chasing away Kory-Kory from my side—who, nevertheless, retired only to a little distance and watched their proceedings with the most jealous attention— would anoint my whole body with a fragrant oil, squeezed from a yellow root, previously pounded between a couple of stones, and which in their language is denominated "aka." And most refreshing and agreeable are the juices of the "aka," when applied to one's limbs by the soft palms of sweet nymphs, whose bright eyes are beaming upon you with kindness; and I used to hail with delight the daily recurrence of this luxurious operation, in which I forgot all my troubles, and buried for the time every feeling of sorrow.

Sometimes in the cool of the evening my devoted servitor would lead me out upon the pi-pi in front of the house, and seating me near its edge, protect my body from the annoyances of the insects which occasionally hovered in the air, by wrapping me round with a large roll of tappa. He then bustled about, and employed himself at least twenty minutes in adjusting everything to secure my personal comfort.

Having perfected his arrangements, he would get my pipe, and, lighting it, would hand it to me. Often he was obliged to strike a light for the occasion, and as the mode he adopted was entirely different from what I had ever seen or heard of before, I will describe it.

A straight, dry, and partly decayed stick of the Habiscus, about six feet in length, and half as many inches in diameter, with a smaller bit of wood not more than a foot long, and scarcely an inch wide, is as invariably to be met with in every house in Typee as a box of lucifer matches in the corner of a kitchen cupboard at home.

The islander, placing the larger stick obliquely against some object, with one end elevated at an angle of forty-five degrees, mounts astride of it like an urchin about to gallop off upon a cane, and then grasping the smaller one firmly in both hands, he rubs its pointed end slowly up and down the extent of a few inches on the principal stick, until at last he makes a narrow groove in the wood, with an abrupt termination at the point furthest from him, where all the dusty particles which the friction creates are accumulated in a little heap.

At first Kory-Kory goes to work quite leisurely, but gradually quickens his pace, and waxing warm in the employment, drives the stick furiously along the smoking channel, plying his hands to and fro with amazing rapidity, the perspiration starting from every pore. As he approaches the climax of his effort, he pants and gasps for breath, and his eyes almost start from their sockets with the violence of his exertions. This is the critical stage of the operation; all his previous labors are vain if he cannot sustain the rapidity of the movement until the reluctant spark is produced. Suddenly he stops, becomes perfectly motionless. His hands still retain their hold of the smaller stick, which is pressed convulsively against the further end of the channel among the fine powder there accumulated, as if he had just pierced through and through some little viper that was wriggling and struggling to escape from his clutches. The next moment a delicate wreath of smoke curls spirally into the air, the heap of dusty particles glows with fire, and Kory-Kory almost breathless, dismounts from his steed.

This operation appeared to me to be the most laborious species of work performed in Typee; and had I possessed a sufficient intimacy with the language to have conveyed my ideas upon the subject, I should certainly have suggested to the most influential of the natives the expediency of establishing a college of vestals to be centrally located in the valley, for the purpose of keeping alive the indispensable article of fire; so as to supersede the necessity of such a vast outlay of strength and good temper, as were usually squandered on these occasions. There might, however, be special difficulties in carrying this plan into execution.

What a striking evidence does this operation furnish of the wide difference between the extreme of savage and civilized life. A gentleman of Typee can bring up a numerous family of children and give them all a highly respectable cannibal education, with infinitely less toil and anxiety than he expends in the simple process of striking a light; whilst a poor European artisan, who through the instrumentality of a lucifer performs the same operation in one second, is put to his wits' end to provide for his starving offspring that food which the children of a Polynesian father, without troubling their parent, pluck from the branches of every tree around them.

CHAPTER 17

. . . The term "Savage" is, I conceive, often misapplied, and indeed when I consider the vices, cruelties, and enormities of every kind that spring up in the tainted atmosphere of a feverish civilization, I am inclined to think that so far as the relative wickedness of the parties is concerned, four or five Marquesan Islanders sent to the United States as Missionaries might be quite as useful as an equal number of Americans despatched to the Islands in a similar capacity.

I once heard it given as an instance of the frightful depravity of a certain tribe in the Pacific, that they had no word in their language to express the idea of virtue. The assertion was unfounded; but were it otherwise, it might be met by stating that their language is almost entirely destitute of terms to express the delightful ideas conveyed by our endless catalogue of civilized crimes.

In the altered frame of mind to which I have referred, every object that presented itself to my notice in the valley struck me in a new light, and the opportunities I now enjoyed of observing the manners of its inmates, tended to strengthen my favorable impressions. One peculiarity that fixed my admiration was the perpetual hilarity reigning through the whole extent of the vale. There seemed to be no cares, griefs, troubles, or vexations, in all Typee. The hours tripped along as gaily as the laughing couples down a country dance.

There were none of those thousand sources of irritation that the ingenuity of civilized man has created to mar his own felicity. There were no foreclosures of mortgages, no protested notes, no bills payable, no debts of honor in Typee; no unreasonable tailors and shoemakers, perversely bent on being paid; no duns of any description; no assault and battery attorneys, to foment discord, backing their clients up to a quarrel, and then knocking their heads together; no poor relations, everlastingly occupying the spare bed-chamber, and diminishing the elbow room at the family table; no destitute widows with their children starving on the cold charities of the world; no beggars; no debtors' prisons; no proud and hard-hearted nabobs in Typee; or to sum up all in one word—no Money! That "root of all evil" was not to be found in the valley.

In this secluded abode of happiness there were no cross old women, no cruel step-dames, no withered spinsters, no love-sick maidens, no sour old bachelors, no inattentive husbands, no melancholy young men, no blubbering youngsters, and no squalling brats. All was mirth, fun, and high good humor. Blue devils, hypochondria, and doleful dumps, went and hid themselves among the nooks and crannies of the rocks.

Here you would see a parcel of children frolicking together the live-long day, and no quarreling, no contention, among them. The same number in our own land could not have played together for the space of an hour without biting or scratching one another. There you might have seen a throng of young females, not filled with envyings of each other's charms, not displaying the ridiculous affectations of gentility, nor yet moving in whalebone corsets, like so many automatons, but free, inartificially happy, and unconstrained.

There were some spots in that sunny vale where they would frequently resort to decorate themselves with garlands of flowers. To have seen them reclining beneath the shadows of one of the beautiful groves; the ground about them strewn with freshly gathered buds and blossoms, employed in weaving chaplets and necklaces, one would have thought that all the train of Flora had gathered together to keep a festival in honor of their mistress.

With the young men there seemed almost always some matter of diversion or business on hand that afforded a constant variety of enjoyment. But whether fishing, or carving canoes, or polishing their ornaments, never was there exhibited the least sign of strife or contention among them.

As for the warriors, they maintained a tranquil dignity of demeanor, journeying occasionally from house to house, where they were always sure to be received with the attention bestowed upon distinguished guests. The old men, of whom there were many in the vale, seldom stirred from their mats, where they would recline for hours and hours, smoking and talking to one another with all the garrulity of age.

But the continual happiness, which so far as I was able to judge appeared to prevail in the valley, sprung principally from that all-pervading sensation which Rousseau has told us he at one time experienced, the mere buoyant sense of a healthful physical existence. And indeed in this particular the Typees had ample reason to felicitate themselves, for sickness was almost unknown. During the whole period of my stay I saw but one invalid among them; and on their smooth clear skins you observed no blemish or mark of disease. . . .

CHAPTER 18

Returning health and peace of mind gave a new interest to everything around me. I sought to diversify my time by as many enjoyments as lay within reach. Bathing in company with troops of girls formed one of my chief amusements. We sometimes enjoyed the recreation in the waters of a miniature lake, into which the central stream of the valley expanded. This lovely sheet of water was almost circular in figure, and about three hundred yards across. Its beauty was indescribable. All around its banks waved luxuriant masses of tropical foliage, soaring high above which were to be seen, here and there, the symmetrical shaft of the cocoa-nut tree, surmounted by its tuft of graceful branches, drooping in the air like so many waving ostrich plumes.

The ease and grace with which the maidens of the valley propelled themselves through the water, and their familiarity with the element, were truly astonishing. Sometimes they might be seen gliding along, just under the surface, without apparently moving hand or foot—then throwing themselves on their sides, they darted through the water, revealing glimpses of their forms, as, in the course of their rapid progress, they shot for an instant partly into the air—at one moment they dived deep down into the water and the next they rose bounding to the surface.

I remember upon one occasion plunging in among a parcel of these river-nymphs, and counting vainly upon my superior strength, sought to drag some of them under the water, but I quickly repented my temerity. The amphibious young creatures swarmed about me like a shoal of dolphins, and seizing hold of my devoted limbs, tumbled me about and ducked me under the surface, until from the strange noises which rang in my ears, and the supernatural visions dancing before my eyes, I thought I was in the land of spirits. I stood indeed as little chance among them as a cumbrous whale attacked on all sides by a legion of sword-fish. When at length they relinquished their hold of me, they swam away in every direction, laughing at my clumsy endeavors to reach them.

There was no boat on the lake; but at my solicitation and for my special use, some of the young men attached to Marheyo's household, under the direction of the indefatigable Kory-Kory, brought up a light and tastefully-carved canoe from the sea. It was launched upon the sheet of water, and floated there as gracefully as a swan. But, melancholy to relate, it produced an effect I had not anticipated. The sweet nymphs, who had sported with me before in the lake, now all fled its vicinity. The prohibited craft, guarded by the edicts of the "taboo," extended the prohibition to the waters in which it lay.

For a few days, Kory-Kory, with one or two other youths, accompanied me in my excursions to the lake, and while I paddled about in my light canoe, would swim after me shouting and gambolling in pursuit. But I was ever partial to what is termed in the "Young Men's Own Book"—"the society of virtuous and intelligent young ladies;" and in the absence of the mermaids, the amusement became dull and insipid. One morning I expressed to my faithful servitor my desire for the return of the nymphs. The honest fellow looked at me bewildered for a moment, and then shook his head solemnly, and murmured "*taboo! taboo!*" giving me to understand that unless the canoe was removed, I could not expect to have the young ladies back again. But to this procedure I was averse; I not only wanted the canoe to stay where it was, but I wanted the beauteous Fayaway to get into it, and paddle with me about the lake. This latter proposition completely horrified Kory-Kory's notions of propriety. He inveighed against it, as something too monstrous to be thought of. It not only shocked their established notions of propriety, but was at variance with all their religious ordinances.

However, although the "taboo" was a ticklish thing to meddle with, I determined to test its capabilities of resisting an attack. I consulted the chief Mehevi, who endeavored to dissuade me from my object: but I was not to be repulsed; and accordingly increased the warmth of my solicitations. At last he entered into a long, and I have no doubt a very learned and eloquent exposition of the history and nature of the "taboo" as affecting this particular case; employing a variety of most extraordinary words, which, from their amazing length and sonorousness, I have every reason to believe were of a theological nature. But all that he said failed to convince me: partly, perhaps, because I could not comprehend a word that he uttered; but chiefly, that for the life of me I could not understand why a woman should not have as much right to enter a canoe as a man. At last he became a little more rational, and intimated that, out of the abundant love he bore me, he would consult with the priests and see what could be done.

How it was that the priesthood of Typee satisfied the affair with their consciences, I know not; but so it was, and Fayaway's dispensation from this portion of the taboo was at length procured. Such an event I believe never before had occurred in the valley; but it was high time the islanders should be taught a little gallantry, and I trust that the example I set them may produce beneficial effects. Ridiculous, indeed, that the lovely creatures should be obliged to paddle about in the water, like so many ducks, while a parcel of great strapping fellows skimmed over its surface in their canoes.

The first day after Fayaway's emancipation I had a delightful little party on the lake—the damsel, Kory-Kory, and myself. My zealous body-servant brought from the house a calabash of poee-poee, half a dozen young cocoa-nuts—stripped of their husks—three pipes, as many yams, and me on his back a part of the way. Something of a load; but Kory-Kory was a very strong man for his size, and by no means brittle in the spine. We had a very pleasant day; my trusty valet plied the paddle and swept us gently along the margin of the water, beneath the shades of the overhanging thickets. Fayaway and I reclined in the stern of the canoe, on the very best terms possible with one another; the gentle nymph occasionally placing her pipe to her lip, and exhaling the mild fumes of the tobacco, to which her rosy breath added a fresh perfume. Strange as it may seem, there is nothing in which a young and beautiful female appears to more advantage than in the act of smoking. How captivating is a Peruvian lady, swinging in her gaily-woven hammock of grass, extended between two orange trees, and inhaling the fragrance of a choice cigarro! But Fayaway, holding in her delicately formed olive hand the long yellow reed of her pipe, with its quaintly carved bowl, and every few moments languishingly giving forth light wreaths of vapor from her mouth and nostrils, looked still more engaging.

We floated about thus for several hours, when I looked up to the warm, glowing, tropical sky, and then down into the transparent depths below; and when my eye, wandering from the bewitching scenery around, fell upon the grotesquely-tattooed form of Kory-Kory, and finally encountered the pensive gaze of Fayaway, I thought I had been transported to some fairy region, so unreal did everything appear.

This lovely piece of water was the coolest spot in all the valley, and I now made it a place of continual resort during the hottest period of the day. One side of it lay near the termination of a long gradually expanding gorge, which mounted to the heights that environed the vale. The strong trade wind, met in its course by these elevations, circled and eddied about their summits, and was sometimes driven down the steep ravine and swept across the valley, ruffling in its passage the otherwise tranquil surface of the lake.

One day, after we had been paddling about for some time, I disembarked Kory-Kory, and paddled the canoe to the windward side of the lake. As I turned the canoe, Fayaway, who was with me, seemed all at once to be struck with some happy idea. With a wild exclamation of delight, she disengaged from her person the ample robe of tappa which was knotted over her shoulder (for the purpose of shielding her from the sun), and spreading it out like a sail, stood erect with upraised arms in the head of the canoe. We American sailors pride ourselves upon our straight clean spars, but a prettier little mast than Fayaway made was never shipped a-board of any craft.

In a moment the tappa was distended by the breeze—the long brown tresses of Fayaway streamed in the air—and the canoe glided rapidly through the water, and shot towards the shore. Seated in the stern, I directed its course with my paddle until it dashed up the soft sloping bank, and Fayaway, with a light spring, alighted on the ground; whilst Kory-Kory, who had watched our manœuvres with admiration, now clapped his hands in transport, and shouted like a madman. Many a time afterwards was this feat repeated.

If the reader have not observed ere this that I was the declared admirer of Miss Fayaway, all I can say is that he is little conversant with affairs of the heart, and I certainly shall not trouble myself to enlighten him any farther. Out of the calico I had brought from the ship I made a dress for this lively girl. In it she looked, I must confess, something like an opera dancer. The drapery of the latter damsel generally commences a little above the elbows, but my island beauty's began at the waist, and terminated sufficiently far above the ground to reveal the most bewitching ankle in the universe. . . .

CHAPTER 19

. . . In my various wanderings through the vale, and as I became better acquainted with the character of its inhabitants, I was more and more struck with the light-hearted joyousness that everywhere prevailed. The minds of these simple savages, unoccupied by matters of graver moment, were capable of deriving the utmost delight from circumstances which would have passed unnoticed in more intelligent communities. All their enjoyment, indeed, seemed to be made up of the little trifling incidents of the passing hour; but these diminutive items swelled altogether to an amount of happiness seldom experienced by more enlightened individuals, whose pleasures are drawn from more elevated but rarer sources.

What community, for instance, of refined and intellectual mortals would derive the least satisfaction from shooting pop-guns? The mere supposition of such a thing being possible would excite their indignation, and yet the whole population of Typee did little else for ten days but occupy themselves with that childish amusement, fairly screaming, too, with the delight it afforded them.

One day I was frolicking with a little spirited urchin, some six years old, who chased me with a piece of bamboo about three feet long, with which he occasionally belabored me. Seizing the stick from him, the idea happened to suggest itself, that I might make for the youngster, out of the slender tube, one of those nursery muskets with which I had sometimes seen children playing. Accordingly, with my knife I made two parallel slits in the cane several inches in length, and cutting loose at one end the elastic strip between them, bent it back and slipped the point into a little notch made for the purpose. Any small substance placed against this would be projected with considerable force through the tube, by merely springing the bent strip out of the notch.

Had I possessed the remotest idea of the sensation this piece of ordnance was destined to produce, I should certainly have taken out a patent for the invention. The boy scampered away with it, half delirious with ecstacy, and in twenty minutes afterwards I might have been seen surrounded by a noisy crowd— venerable old greybeards—responsible fathers of families—valiant warriors— matrons—young men—girls and children, all holding in their hand bits of bamboo, and each clamoring to be served first.

For three or four hours I was engaged in manufacturing pop-guns, but at last made over my good-will and interest in the concern to a lad of remarkable quick parts, whom I soon initiated into the art and mystery.

Pop, Pop, Pop, Pop, now resounded all over the valley. Duels, skirmishes, pitched battles, and general engagements were to be seen on every side. Here, as you walked along a path which led through a thicket, you fell into a cun- ningly-laid ambush, and became a target for a body of musketeers whose tattooed limbs you could just see peeping into view through the foliage. There, you were assailed by the intrepid garrison of a house, who levelled their bamboo rifles at you from between the upright canes which composed its sides. Farther on you were fired upon by a detachment of sharpshooters, mounted upon the top of a pi-pi.

Pop, Pop, Pop, Pop! green guavas, seeds, and berries were flying about in every direction, and during this dangerous state of affairs I was half afraid that, like the man and his brazen bull, I should fall a victim to my own ingenuity. Like everything else, however, the excitement gradually wore away, though ever after occasional pop-guns might be heard at all hours of the day. . . .

CHAPTER 20

Nothing can be more uniform and undiversified than the life of the Typees; one tranquil day of ease and happiness follows another in quiet succession; and with these unsophisticated savages the history of a day is the history of a life. I will, therefore, as briefly as I can, describe one of our days in the valley.

To begin with the morning. We were not very early risers—the sun would be shooting his golden spikes above the Happar mountain, ere I threw aside my tappa robe, and girding my long tunic about my waist, sallied out with Fayaway and Kory-Kory, and the rest of the household, and bent my steps towards the stream. Here we found congregated all those who dwelt in our section of the valley; and here we bathed with them. The fresh morning air and the cool flowing waters put both soul and body in a glow, and after a half-hour employed in this recreation, we sauntered back to the house—Tinor and Marheyo gathering dry sticks by the way for fire-wood; some of the young men laying the cocoa-nut trees under contribution as they passed beneath them; while Kory-Kory played his outlandish pranks for my particular diversion, and Fayaway and I, not arm in arm to be sure, but sometimes hand in hand, strolled along, with feelings of perfect charity for all the world, and especial good-will towards each other.

Our morning meal was soon prepared. The islanders are somewhat abstemious at this repast; reserving the more powerful efforts of their appetite to a later period of the day. For my own part, with the assistance of my valet, who, as I have before stated, always officiated as spoon on these occasions, I ate sparingly from one of Tinor's trenchers of poee-poee; which was devoted exclusively for my own use, being mixed with the milky meat of ripe cocoa-nut. A section of a roasted bread-fruit, a small cake of "Amar," or a mess of "Cokoo," two or three bananas, or a Mawmee apple; an annuee, or some other agreeable and nutricious fruit served from day to day to diversify the meal, which was finished by tossing off the liquid contents of a young cocoa-nut or two.

While partaking of this simple repast, the inmates of Marheyo's house, after the style of the indolent Romans, reclined in sociable groups upon the divan of mats, and digestion was promoted by cheerful conversation.

After the morning meal was concluded, pipes were lighted; and among them my own especial pipe, a present from the noble Mehevi. The islanders, who only smoke a whiff or two at a time, and at long intervals, and who keep their pipes going from hand to hand continually, regarded my systematic smoking of four or five pipefuls of tobacco in succession, as something quite wonderful. When two or three pipes had circulated freely, the company grad-ually broke up. Marheyo went to the little hut he was for ever building. Tinor began to inspect her rolls of tappa, or employed her busy fingers in plaiting grass-mats. The girls anointed themselves with their fragrant oils, dressed their hair, or looked over their curious finery, and compared together their ivory trinkets, fashioned out of boar's tusks or whale's teeth. The young men and warriors produced their spears, paddles, canoe-gear, battle-clubs, and war-conchs, and occupied themselves in carving all sorts of figures upon them with pointed bits of shell or flint, and adorning them, especially the war-conchs, with tassels of braided bark and tufts of human hair. Some, immediately after eating, threw themselves once more upon the inviting mats, and resumed the employment of the previous night, sleeping as soundly as if they had not closed their eyes for a week. Others sallied out into the groves, for the purpose of gathering fruit or fibres of bark and leaves; the last two being in constant requisition, and applied to a hundred uses. A few, perhaps, among the girls, would slip into the woods after flowers, or repair to the stream with small calabashes and cocoa-nut shells, in order to polish them by friction with a smooth stone in the water. In truth these innocent people seemed to be at no loss for something to occupy their time; and it would be no light task to enumerate all their employ-ments, or rather pleasures.

My own mornings I spent in a variety of ways. Sometimes I rambled about from house to house, sure of receiving a cordial welcome wherever I went; or from grove to grove, and from one shady place to another, in company with Kory-Kory and Fayaway, and a rabble rout of merry young idlers. Sometimes I was too indolent for exercise, and accepting one of the many invitations I was continually receiving, stretched myself out on the mats of some hospitable dwell-ing, and occupied myself pleasantly either in watching the proceedings of those around me or taking part in them myself. Whenever I chose to do the latter, the delight of the islanders was boundless; and there was always a throng of com-petitors for the honor of instructing me in any particular craft. I soon became quite an accomplished hand at making tappa—could braid a grass sling as well as the best of them—and once, with my knife, carved the handle of a javelin so exquisitely, that I have no doubt, to this day, Karnoonoo, its owner, preserves it as a surprising specimen of my skill. As noon approached, all those who had wandered forth from our habitation, began to return; and when mid-day was fairly come scarcely a sound was to be heard in the valley: a deep sleep fell upon all. The luxurious siesta was hardly ever omitted, except by old Marheyo, who was so eccentric a character, that he seemed to be governed by no fixed principles whatever; but acting just according to the humor of the moment, slept, ate, or tinkered away at his little hut, without regard to the proprieties of time or place. Frequently he might have been seen taking a nap in the sun at noon-day, or a bath in the stream at mid-night. Once I beheld him perched eighty feet from the ground, in the tuft of a cocoa-nut tree, smoking; and often I saw him standing up to the waist in water, engaged in plucking out the stray hairs of his beard, using a piece of mussel-shell for tweezers.

The noon-tide slumber lasted generally an hour and a half; very often longer; and after the sleepers had arisen from their mats they again had recourse to their pipes, and then made preparations for the most important meal of the day.

I, however, like those gentlemen of leisure who breakfast at home and dine at their club, almost invariably, during my intervals of health, enjoyed the afternoon repast with the bachelor chiefs of the Ti, who were always rejoiced to see me, and lavishly spread before me all the good things which their larder afforded. Mehevi generally produced among other dainties a baked pig, an article which I have every reason to suppose was provided for my sole gratification.

The Ti was a right jovial place. It did my heart, as well as my body, good to visit it. Secure from female intrusion, there was no restraint upon the hilarity of the warriors, who, like the gentlemen of Europe after the cloth is drawn and the ladies retire, freely indulged their mirth.

After spending a considerable portion of the afternoon at the Ti, I usually found myself, as the cool of the evening came on, either sailing on the little lake with Fayaway, or bathing in the waters of the stream with a number of the savages, who, at this hour, always repaired thither. As the shadows of night approached Marheyo's household were once more assembled under his roof: tapers were lit, long and curious chants were raised, interminable stories were told (for which one present was little the wiser), and all sorts of social festivities served to while away the time.

The young girls very often danced by moonlight in front of their dwellings. There are a great variety of these dances, in which, however, I never saw the men take part. They all consist of active, romping, mischievous evolutions, in which every limb is brought into requisition. Indeed, the Marquesan girls dance all over, as it were; not only do their feet dance, but their arms, hands, fingers, ay, their very eyes, seem to dance in their heads. In good sooth, they so sway their floating forms, arch their necks, toss aloft their naked arms, and glide, and swim, and whirl, that it was almost too much for a quiet, sober-minded, modest young man like myself.

The damsels wear nothing but flowers and their compendious gala tunics; and when they plume themselves for the dance, they look like a band of olive-colored Sylphides on the point of taking wing.

Unless some particular festivity was going forward, the inmates of Marheyo's house retired to their mats rather early in the evening; but not for the night, since, after slumbering lightly for a while, they rose again, relit their tapers, partook of the third and last meal of the day, at which poee-poee alone was eaten, and then, after inhaling a narcotic whiff from a pipe of tobacco, disposed themselves for the great business of night, sleep. With the Marquesans it might almost be styled the great business of life, for they pass a large portion of their time in the arms of Somnus. The native strength of their constitutions is no way shown more emphatically than in the quantity of sleep they can endure. To many of them, indeed, life is little else than an often interrupted and luxurious nap.

CHAPTER 22

. . . The following morning, awaking rather late, I perceived the whole of Marheyo's family busily engaged in preparing for the festival. The old warrior himself was arranging in round balls the two grey locks of hair that were suffered to grow from the crown of his head; his earrings and spear, both well polished, lay beside him, while the highly decorative pair of shoes hung suspended from a projecting cane against the side of the house. The young men were similarly employed; and the fair damsels, including Fayaway, were anointing themselves with "aka," arranging their long tresses, and performing other matters connected with the duties of the toilet.

Having completed their preparations, the girls now exhibited themselves in gala costume; the most conspicuous feature of which was a necklace of beautiful white flowers, with the stems removed, and strung closely together upon a single fibre of tappa. Corresponding ornaments were inserted in their ears, and woven garlands upon their heads. About their waist they wore a short tunic of spotless white tappa, and some of them superadded to this a mantle of the same material, tied in an elaborate bow upon the left shoulder, and falling about the figure in picturesque folds.

Thus arrayed, I would have matched the charming Fayaway against any beauty in the world.

People may say what they will about the taste evinced by our fashionable ladies in dress. Their jewels, their feathers, their silks, and their furbelows would have sunk into utter insignificance beside the exquisite simplicity of attire adopted by the nymphs of the vale on this festive occasion. I should like to have seen a gallery of coronation beauties, at Westminster Abbey, confronted for a moment by this band of Island girls; their stiffness, formality, and affectation contrasted with the artless vivacity and unconcealed natural graces of these savage maidens. It would be the Venus de' Medici placed beside a milliner's doll.

It was not long before Kory-Kory and myself were left alone in the house, the rest of its inmates having departed for the Taboo Groves. My valet was all impatience to follow them; and was as fidgety about my dilatory movements as a diner out waiting hat in hand at the bottom of the stairs for some lagging com-

panion. At last, yielding to his importunities, I set out for the Ti. As we passed
the houses peeping out from the groves through which our route lay, I noticed
that they were entirely deserted by their inhabitants.

When we reached the rock that abruptly terminated the path, and concealed
from us the festive scene, wild shouts and a confused blending of voices assured
me that the occasion, whatever it might be, had drawn together a great multitude. Kory-Kory, previous to mounting the elevation, paused for a moment, like
a dandy at a ball-room door, to put a hasty finish to his toilet. During this short
interval, the thought struck me that I ought myself perhaps to be taking some
little pains with my appearance. But as I had no holiday raiment, I was not a
little puzzled to devise some means of decorating myself. However, as I felt
desirous to create a sensation, I determined to do all that lay in my power; and
knowing that I could not delight the savages more than by conforming to their
style of dress, I removed from my person the large robe of tappa which I was
accustomed to wear over my shoulders whenever I sallied into the open air, and
remained merely girt about with a short tunic descending from my waist to my
knees.

My quick-witted attendant fully appreciated the compliment I was paying to
the costume of his race, and began more sedulously to arrange the folds of the
one only garment which remained to me. Whilst he was doing this, I caught
sight of a knot of young lasses, who were sitting near us on the grass surrounded
by heaps of flowers which they were forming into garlands. I motioned to them
to bring some of their handywork to me; and in an instant a dozen wreaths
were at my disposal. One of them I put round the apology for a hat which I
had been forced to construct for myself out of palmetto-leaves, and some of the
others I converted into a splendid girdle. These operations finished, with the slow
and dignified step of a full-dressed beau I ascended the rock.

CHAPTER 23

The whole population of the valley seemed to be gathered within the precincts
of the grove. In the distance could be seen the long front of the Ti, its immense
piazza swarming with men, arrayed in every variety of fantastic costume, and
all vociferating with animated gestures; while the whole interval between it and
the place where I stood was enlivened by groups of females fancifully decorated,
dancing, capering, and uttering wild exclamations. As soon as they descried me
they set up a shout of welcome; and a band of them came dancing towards me
chanting as they approached some wild recitative. The change in my garb
seemed to transport them with delight, and clustering about me on all sides,
they accompanied me towards the Ti. When however we drew near it these

joyous nymphs paused in their career, and parting on either side, permitted me to pass on to the now densely thronged building.

So soon as I mounted to the pi-pi I saw at a glance that the revels were fairly under way.

What lavish plenty reigned around!—Warwick feasting his retainers with beef and ale was a niggard to the noble Mehevi!—All along the piazza of the Ti were arranged elaborately carved canoe-shaped vessels, some twenty feet in length, filled with newly made poee-poee, and sheltered from the sun by the broad leaves of the banana. At intervals were heaps of green bread-fruit, raised in pyramidical stacks, resembling the regular piles of heavy shot to be seen in the yard of an arsenal. Inserted into the interstices of the huge stones which formed the pi-pi were large boughs of trees; hanging from the branches of which, and screened from the sun by their foliage, were innumerable little packages with leafy coverings, containing the meat of the numerous hogs which had been slain, done up in this manner to make it more accessible to the crowd. Leaning against the railing of the piazza were an immense number of long, heavy bamboos, plugged at the lower end, and with their projecting muzzles stuffed with a wad of leaves. These were filled with water from the stream, and each of them might hold from four to five gallons.

The banquet being thus spread, nought remained but for every one to help himself at his pleasure. Accordingly not a moment passed but the transplanted boughs I have mentioned were rifled by the throng of the fruit they certainly had never borne before. Calabashes of poee-poee were continually being replenished from the extensive receptacle in which that article was stored, and multitudes of little fires were kindled about the Ti for the purpose of roasting the bread-fruit.

Within the building itself was presented a most extraordinary scene. The immense lounge of mats lying between the parallel rows of the trunks of cocoa-nut trees, and extending the entire length of the house, at least two hundred feet, was covered by the reclining forms of a host of chiefs and warriors, who were eating at a great rate, or soothing the cares of Polynesian life in the sedative fumes of tobacco. The smoke was inhaled from large pipes, the bowls of which, made out of small cocoa-nut shells, were curiously carved in strange heathenish devices. These were passed from mouth to mouth by the recumbent smokers, each of whom, taking two or three prodigious whiffs, handed the pipe to his neighbor; sometimes for that purpose stretching indolently across the body of some dozing individual whose exertions at the dinner-table had already induced sleep.

The tobacco used among the Typees was of a very mild and pleasing flavor, and as I always saw it in leaves, and the natives appeared pretty well supplied with it, I was led to believe that it must have been the growth of the valley.

Indeed Kory-Kory gave me to understand that this was the case; but I never saw a single plant growing on the island. At Nukuheva, and, I believe, in all the other valleys, the weed is very scarce, being only obtained in small quantities from foreigners, and smoking is consequently with the inhabitants of these places a very great luxury. How it was that the Typees were so well furnished with it I cannot divine. I should think them too indolent to devote any attention to its culture; and, indeed, as far as my observation extended, not a single atom of the soil was under any other cultivation than that of shower and sunshine. The tobacco-plant, however, like the sugar-cane, may grow wild in some remote part of the vale.

There were many in the Ti for whom the tobacco did not furnish a sufficient stimulus, and who accordingly had recourse to "arva," as a more powerful agent in producing the desired effect.

"Arva" is a root very generally dispersed over the South Seas, and from it is extracted a juice, the effects of which upon the system are at first stimulating in a moderate degree; but it soon relaxes the muscles, and exerting a narcotic influence produces a luxurious sleep. In the valley this beverage was universally prepared in the following way:—Some half-dozen young boys seated themselves in a circle around an empty wooden vessel, each one of them being supplied with a certain quantity of the roots of the "arva," broken into small bits and laid by his side. A cocoa-nut goblet of water was passed around the juvenile company, who rinsing their mouths with its contents, proceeded to the business before them. This merely consisted in thoroughly masticating the "arva," and throwing it mouthful after mouthful into the receptacle provided. When a sufficient quantity had been thus obtained water was poured upon the mass, and being stirred about with the forefinger of the right-hand, the preparation was soon in readiness for use. The "arva" has medicinal qualities.

Upon the Sandwich Islands it has been employed with no small success in the treatment of scrofulous affections, and in combating the ravages of a disease for whose frightful inroads the ill-starred inhabitants of that group are indebted to their foreign benefactors. But the tenants of the Typee valley, as yet exempt from these inflictions, generally employ the "arva" as a minister to social enjoyment, and a calabash of the liquid circulates among them as the bottle with us.

Mehevi, who was greatly delighted with the change in my costume, gave me a cordial welcome. He had reserved for me a most delectable mess of "cokoo," well knowing my partiality for that dish; and had likewise selected three or four young cocoa-nuts, several roasted bread-fruit, and a magnificent bunch of bananas, for my especial comfort and gratification. These various matters were at once placed before me; but Kory-Kory deemed the banquet entirely insufficient for my wants until he had supplied me with one of the leafy packages of pork,

which, notwithstanding the somewhat hasty manner in which it had been prepared, possessed a most excellent flavor, and was surprisingly sweet and tender.

Pork is not a staple article of food among the people of the Marquesas, consequently they pay little attention to the breeding of the swine. The hogs are permitted to roam at large in the groves, where they obtain no small part of their
nourishment from the cocoa-nuts which continually fall from the trees. But it is
only after infinite labor and difficulty, that the hungry animal can pierce the
husk and shell so as to get at the meat. I have frequently been amused at seeing
one of them, after crunching the obstinate nut with his teeth for a long time
unsuccessfully, get into a violent passion with it. He would then root furiously
under the cocoa-nut, and, with a fling of his snout, toss it before him on the
ground. Following it up, he would crunch at it again savagely for a moment, and
the next knock it on one side, pausing immediately after, as if wondering how
it could so suddenly have disappeared. In this way the persecuted cocoa-nuts
were often chased half across the valley.

The second day of the Feast of Calabashes was ushered in by still more uproarious noises than the first. The skins of innumerable sheep seemed to be resounding to the blows of an army of drummers. Startled from my slumbers by
the din, I leaped up, and found the whole household engaged in making preparations for immediate departure. Curious to discover of what strange events
these novel sounds might be the precursors, and not a little desirous to catch a
sight of the instruments which produced the terrific noise, I accompanied the
natives as soon as they were in readiness to depart for the Taboo Groves.

The comparatively open space that extended from the Ti toward the rock, to
which I have before alluded as forming the ascent to the place was, with the
building itself, now altogether deserted by the men, the whole distance being
filled by bands of females, shouting and dancing under the influence of some
strange excitement.

I was amused at the appearance of four or five old women who, in a state
of utter nudity, with their arms extended flatly down their sides, and holding
themselves perfectly erect, were leaping stiffly into the air, like so many sticks
bobbing to the surface, after being pressed perpendicularly into the water. They
preserved the utmost gravity of countenance, and continued their extraordinary
movements without a single moment's cessation. They did not appear to attract
the observation of the crowd around them, but I must candidly confess that,
for my own part, I stared at them most pertinaciously.

Desirous of being enlightened with regard to the meaning of this peculiar
diversion, I turned inquiringly to Kory-Kory; that learned Typee immediately
proceeded to explain the whole matter thoroughly. But all that I could comprehend from what he said was, that the leaping figures before me were be-

reaved widows, whose partners had been slain in battle many moons previously; and who, at every festival, gave public evidence in this manner of their calamities. It was evident that Kory-Kory considered this an all-sufficient reason for so indecorous a custom; but I must say that it did not satisfy me as to its propriety.

Leaving these afflicted females, we passed on to the Hoolah-Hoolah ground. Within the spacious quadrangle, the whole population of the valley seemed to be assembled, and the sight presented was truly remarkable. Beneath the sheds of bamboo which opened towards the interior of the square, reclined the principal chiefs and warriors, while a miscellaneous throng lay at their ease under the enormous trees which spread a majestic canopy overhead. Upon the terraces of the gigantic altars, at either end, were deposited green bread-fruit in baskets of cocoa-nut leaves, large rolls of tappa, bunches of ripe bananas, clusters of mammee-apples, the golden-hued fruit of the artu-tree, and baked hogs, laid out in large wooden trenchers, fancifully decorated with freshly plucked leaves, whilst a variety of rude implements of war were piled in confused heaps before the ranks of hideous idols. Fruits of various kinds were likewise suspended in leafen baskets, from the tops of poles planted uprightly, and at regular intervals, along the lower terraces of both altars. At their base were arranged two parallel rows of cumbersome drums, standing at least fifteen feet in height, and formed from the hollow trunks of large trees. Their heads were covered with shark skins, and their barrels were elaborately carved with various quaint figures and devices. At regular intervals they were bound round by a species of sinnate of various colors, and strips of native cloth flattened upon them here and there. Behind these instruments were built slight platforms, upon which stood a number of young men who, beating violently with the palms of their hands upon the drum-heads, produced those outrageous sounds which had awakened me in the morning. Every few minutes these musical performers hopped down from their elevation into the crowd below, and their places were immediately supplied by fresh recruits. Thus an incessant din was kept up that might have startled Pandemonium.

Precisely in the middle of the quadrangle were placed perpendicularly in the ground, a hundred or more slender, fresh-cut poles, stripped of their bark, and decorated at the end with a floating pennon of white tappa; the whole being fenced about with a little picket of canes. For what purpose these singular ornaments were intended I in vain endeavored to discover.

Another most striking feature of the performance was exhibited by a score of old men, who sat cross-legged in the little pulpits, which encircled the trunks of the immense trees growing in the middle of the enclosure. These venerable gentlemen, who I presume were the priests, kept up an uninterrupted monotonous chant, which was nearly drowned in the roar of drums. In the right hand they held a finely woven grass fan, with a heavy black wooden handle curiously chased: these fans they kept in continual motion.

But no attention whatever seemed to be paid to the drummers or to the old priests; the individuals who composed the vast crowd present being entirely taken up in chatting and laughing with one another, smoking, drinking arva, and eating. For all the observation it attracted, or the good it achieved, the whole savage orchestra might, with great advantage to its own members and the company in general, have ceased the prodigious uproar they were making.

In vain I questioned Kory-Kory and others of the natives, as to the meaning of the strange things that were going on; all their explanations were conveyed in such a mass of outlandish gibberish and gesticulation that I gave up the attempt in despair. All that day the drums resounded, the priests chanted, and the multitude feasted and roared till sunset, when the throng dispersed, and the Taboo Groves were again abandoned to quiet and repose. The next day the same scene was repeated until night, when this singular festival terminated.

CHAPTER 25

Although I had been unable during the late festival to obtain information on many interesting subjects which had much excited my curiosity, still that important event had not passed by without adding materially to my general knowledge of the islanders.

I was especially struck by the physical strength and beauty which they displayed, by their great superiority in these respects over the inhabitants of the neighboring bay of Nukuheva, and by the singular contrasts they presented among themselves in their various shades of complexion.

In beauty of form they surpassed anything I had ever seen. Not a single instance of natural deformity was observable in all the throng attending the revels. Occasionally I noticed among the men the scars of wounds they had received in battle; and sometimes, though very seldom, the loss of a finger, an eye, or an arm, attributable to the same cause. With these exceptions, every individual appeared free from those blemishes which sometimes mar the effect of an otherwise perfect form. But their physical excellence did not merely consist in an exemption from these evils; nearly every individual of their number might have been taken for a sculptor's model.

When I remembered that these islanders derived no advantage from dress, but appeared in all the naked simplicity of nature, I could not avoid comparing them with the fine gentlemen and dandies who promenade such unexceptionable figures in our frequented thoroughfares. Stripped of the cunning artifices of the tailor, and standing forth in the garb of Eden,—what a sorry set of round-shouldered, spindle-shanked, crane-necked varlets would civilized men appear! Stuffed calves, padded breasts, and scientifically cut pantaloons would then avail them nothing, and the effect would be truly deplorable.

Nothing in the appearance of the islanders struck me more forcibly than the whiteness of their teeth. The novelist always compares the masticators of his heroine to ivory; but I boldly pronounce the teeth of the Typees to be far more beautiful than ivory itself. The jaws of the oldest greybeards among them were much better garnished than those of most of the youths of civilized countries; while the teeth of the young and middle-aged, in their purity and whiteness, were actually dazzling to the eye. This marvellous whiteness of the teeth is to be ascribed to the pure vegetable diet of these people, and the uninterrupted healthfulness of their natural mode of life.

The men, in almost every instance, are of lofty stature, scarcely ever less than six feet in height, while the other sex are uncommonly diminutive. The early period of life at which the human form arrives at maturity in this generous tropical climate, likewise deserves to be mentioned. A little creature, not more than thirteen years of age, and who in other particulars might be regarded as a mere child, is often seen nursing her own baby; whilst lads who, under less ripening skies, would be still at school, are here responsible fathers of families.

On first entering the Typee Valley, I had been struck with the marked contrast presented by its inhabitants with those of the bay I had previously left. In the latter place, I had not been favorably impressed with the personal appearance of the male portion of the population; although with the females, excepting in some truly melancholy instances, I had been wonderfully pleased. I had observed that even the little intercourse Europeans had carried on with the Nukuheva natives had not failed to leave its traces amongst them. One of the most dreadful curses under which humanity labors had commenced its havocks, and betrayed, as it ever does among the South Sea islanders, the most aggravated symptoms. From this, as from all other foreign inflictions, the yet uncontaminated tenants of the Typee Valley were wholly exempt; and long may they continue so. Better will it be for them for ever to remain the happy and innocent heathens and barbarians that they now are, than, like the wretched inhabitants of the Sandwich Islands, to enjoy the mere name of Christians without experiencing any of the vital operations of true religion, whilst, at the same time, they are made the victims of the worst vices and evils of civilized life. . . .

CHAPTER 27

. . . There was one admirable trait in the general character of the Typees which, more than any thing else, secured my admiration: it was the unanimity of feeling they displayed on every occasion. With them there hardly appeared to be any difference of opinion upon any subject whatever. They all thought and acted alike. I do not conceive that they could support a debating society for a single night: there would be nothing to dispute about; and were they to call a convention to take into consideration the state of the tribe, its session would be a remarkably short one. They showed this spirit of unanimity in every action of life: every thing was done in concert and good fellowship. I will give an instance of this fraternal feeling.

One day, in returning with Kory-Kory from my accustomed visit to the Ti, we passed by a little opening in the grove; on one side of which, my attendant informed me, was that afternoon to be built a dwelling of bamboo. At least a hundred of the natives were bringing materials to the ground, some carrying in their hands one or two of the canes which were to form the sides, others slender rods of the habiscus, strung with palmetto leaves, for the roof. Every one contributed something to the work; and by the united, but easy, and even indolent, labors of all, the entire work was completed before sunset. The islanders, while employed in erecting this tenement, reminded me of a colony of beavers at work. To be sure, they were hardly as silent and demure as those wonderful creatures, nor were they by any means as diligent. To tell the truth, they were somewhat inclined to be lazy, but a perfect tumult of hilarity prevailed; and they worked together so unitedly, and seemed actuated by such an instinct of friendliness, that it was truly beautiful to behold.

Not a single female took part in this employment: and if the degree of consideration in which the ever-adorable sex is held by the men be—as the philosophers affirm—a just criterion of the degree of refinement among a people, then I may truly pronounce the Typees to be as polished a community as ever the sun shone upon. The religious restrictions of the taboo alone excepted, the women of the valley were allowed every possible indulgence. Nowhere are the ladies more assiduously courted; nowhere are they better appreciated as the contributors to our highest enjoyments; and nowhere are they more sensible of their power. Far different from their condition among many rude nations, where the women are made to perform all the work while their ungallant lords and masters lie buried in sloth, the gentle sex in the valley of Typee were exempt from toil, if toil it might be called that, even in that tropical climate, never distilled one drop of perspiration. Their light household occupations, together with the manufacture of tappa, the platting of mats, and the polishing of drinking-vessels, were the only employments pertaining to the women. And even these resembled those pleasant avocations which fill up the elegant morning leisure of our fashionable ladies at home. But in these occupations, slight and agreeable though they were, the giddy young girls very seldom engaged. Indeed these wilful, care-killing damsels were averse to all useful employment. Like so many spoiled beauties, they ranged through the groves—bathed in the stream—danced—flirted—played all manner of mischievous pranks, and passed their days in one merry round of thoughtless happiness.

During my whole stay on the island I never witnessed a single quarrel, nor any thing that in the slightest degree approached even to a dispute. The natives appeared to form one household, whose members were bound together by the ties of strong affection. The love of kindred I did not so much perceive, for it seemed blended in the general love; and where all were treated as brothers and sisters, it was hard to tell who were actually related to each other by blood.

Let it not be supposed that I have overdrawn this picture. I have not done so. Nor let it be urged, that the hostility of this tribe to foreigners, and the hereditary feuds they carry on against their fellow-islanders beyond the mountains, are facts which contradict me. Not so: these apparent discrepancies are easily reconciled. By many a legendary tale of violence and wrong, as well as by events which have passed before their eyes, these people have been taught to look upon white men with abhorrence. The cruel invasion of their country by Porter has alone furnished them with ample provocation; and I can sympathize in the spirit which prompts the Typee warrior to guard all the passes to his valley with the point of his levelled spear, and, standing upon the beach, with his back turned upon his green home, to hold at bay the intruding European.

As to the origin of the enmity of this particular clan towards the neighboring tribes, I cannot so confidently speak. I will not say that their foes are the aggressors, nor will I endeavor to palliate their conduct. But surely, if our evil passions must find vent, it is far better to expend them on strangers and aliens, than in the bosom of the community in which we dwell. In many polished countries civil contentions, as well as domestic enmities, are prevalent, at the same time that the most atrocious foreign wars are waged. How much less guilty, then, are our islanders, who of these three sins are only chargeable with one, and that the least criminal!

The reader will ere long have reason to suspect that the Typees are not free from the guilt of cannibalism; and he will then, perhaps, charge me with admiring a people against whom so odious a crime is chargeable. But this only enormity in their character is not half so horrible as it is usually described. According to the popular fictions, the crews of vessels, shipwrecked on some barbarous coast, are eaten alive like so many dainty joints by the uncivil inhabitants; and unfortunate voyagers are lured into smiling and treacherous bays; knocked in the head with outlandish warclubs; and served up without any preliminary dressing. In truth, so horrific and improbable are these accounts, that many sensible and well-informed people will not believe that any cannibals exist; and place every book of voyages which purports to give any account of them, on the same shelf with Blue Beard and Jack the Giant-Killer; while others, implicitly crediting the most extravagant fictions, firmly believe that there are people in the world with tastes so depraved that they would infinitely prefer a single mouthful of material humanity to a good dinner of roast beef and plum pudding. But here, Truth, who loves to be centrally located, is again found between the two extremes; for cannibalism to a certain moderate extent is practised among several of the primitive tribes in the Pacific, but it is upon the bodies of slain enemies alone; and horrible and fearful as the custom is, immeasurably as it is to be abhorred and condemned, still I assert that those who indulge in it are in other respects humane and virtuous.

CHAPTER 29

I think I must enlighten the reader a little about the natural history of the valley.

Whence, in the name of Count Buffon and Baron Cuvier, came those dogs that I saw in Typee? Dogs!—Big hairless rats rather; all with smooth, shining, speckled hides—fat sides, and very disagreeable faces. Whence could they have come? That they were not the indigenous production of the region, I am firmly convinced. Indeed they seemed aware of their being interlopers, looking fairly ashamed, and always trying to hide themselves in some dark corner. It was plain enough they did not feel at home in the vale—that they wished themselves well out of it, and back to the ugly country from which they must have come.

Scurvy curs! they were my abhorrence; I should have liked nothing better than to have been the death of every one of them. In fact, on one occasion, I intimated the propriety of a canine crusade to Mehevi; but the benevolent king would not consent to it. He heard me very patiently; but when I had finished, shook his head, and told me, in confidence, that they were "taboo."

As for the animal that made the fortune of the ex-lord-mayor Whittington: I shall never forget the day that I was lying in the house about noon, everybody else being fast asleep; and happening to raise my eyes, met those of a big black spectral cat, which sat erect in the doorway, looking at me with its frightful goggling green orbs, like one of those monstrous imps that torment some of Teniers' saints! I am one of those unfortunate persons to whom the sight of these animals is at any time an insufferable annoyance.

Thus constitutionally averse to cats in general, the unexpected apparition of this one in particular utterly confounded me. When I had a little recovered from the fascination of its glance, I started up; the cat fled, and emboldened by this, I rushed out of the house in pursuit; but it had disappeared. It was the only time I ever saw one in the valley, and how it got there I cannot imagine. It is just possible that it might have escaped from one of the ships at Nukuheva. It was in vain to seek information on the subject from the natives; since none of them had seen the animal, the appearance of which remains a mystery to me to this day.

Among the few animals which are to be met with in Typee, there were none which I looked upon with more interest than a beautiful golden-hued species of lizard. It measured perhaps five inches from head to tail, and was most gracefully proportioned. Numbers of these creatures were to be seen basking in the sunshine upon the thatching of the houses, and multitudes at all hours of the day showed their glittering sides as they ran frolicking between the spears of grass or raced in troops up and down the tall shafts of the cocoa-nut trees. But the remarkable beauty of these little animals and their lively ways were not their only claims upon my admiration. They were perfectly tame and insensible to fear. Frequently, after seating myself upon the ground in some shady place during the heat of the day, I would be completely overrun with them. If I brushed one off my arm, it would leap perhaps into my hair: when I tried to frighten it away by gently pinching its leg, it would turn for protection to the very hand that attacked it.

The birds are also remarkably tame. If you happened to see one perched upon a branch within reach of your arm, and advanced towards it, it did not fly away immediately, but waited quietly looking at you, until you could almost touch it, and then took wing slowly, less alarmed at your presence, it would seem, than desirous of removing itself from your path. Had salt been less scarce in the valley than it was, this was the very place to have gone birding with it.

I remember that once, on an uninhabited island of the Gallipagos, a bird alighted on my outstretched arm, while its mate chirped from an adjoining tree. Its tameness, far from shocking me, as a similar occurrence did Selkirk, imparted to me the most exquisite thrill of delight I ever experienced; and with somewhat of the same pleasure did I afterwards behold the birds and lizards of the valley show their confidence in the kindliness of man.

Among the numerous afflictions which the Europeans have entailed upon some of the natives of the South Seas, is the accidental introduction among them of that enemy of all repose and ruffler of even tempers—the Mosquito. At the Sandwich Islands and at two or three of the Society group there are now thriving colonies of these insects, who promise ere long to supplant altogether the aboriginal sand-flies. They sting, buzz, and torment, from one end of the year to the other, and by incessantly exasperating the natives materially obstruct the benevolent labors of the missionaries.

From this grievous visitation, however, the Typees are as yet wholly exempt; but its place is unfortunately in some degree supplied by the occasional presence of a minute species of fly, which, without stinging, is nevertheless productive of no little annoyance. The tameness of the birds and lizards is as nothing when compared to the fearless confidence of this insect. He will perch upon one of your eye-lashes, and go to roost there, if you do not disturb him, or force his way through your hair, or along the cavity of the nostril, till you almost fancy he is resolved to explore the very brain itself. On one occasion I was so inconsiderate as to yawn while a number of them were hovering around me. I never repeated the act. Some half-dozen darted into the open apartment, and began walking about its ceiling; the sensation was dreadful. I involuntarily closed my mouth, and the poor creatures being enveloped in inner darkness, must in their consternation have stumbled over my palate, and been precipitated into the gulf beneath. At any rate, though I afterwards charitably held my mouth open for at least five minutes, with a view of affording egress to the stragglers, none of them ever availed themselves of the opportunity.

There are no wild animals of any kind on the island, unless it be decided that the natives themselves are such. The mountains and the interior present to the eye nothing but silent solitudes, unbroken by the roar of beasts of prey, and enlivened by few tokens even of minute animated existence. There are no venomous reptiles, and no snakes of any description to be found in any of the valleys.

In a company of Marquesan natives the weather affords no topic of conversation. It can hardly be said to have any vicissitudes. The rainy season, it is true, brings frequent showers, but they are intermitting and refreshing. When an islander bound on some expedition rises from his couch in the morning, he is never solicitous to peep out and see how the sky looks, or ascertain from what quarter the wind blows. He is always sure of a "fine day," and the promise of a few genial showers he hails with pleasure. There is never any of that "remarkable weather" on the island which from time immemorial has been experienced in America, and still continues to call forth the wondering conversational exclamations of its elderly citizens. Nor do there ever occur any of those eccentric meteorological changes which elsewhere surprise us. In the valley of Typee ice-creams would never be rendered less acceptable by sudden frosts, nor would picnic parties be deferred on account of inauspicious snow-storms: for there day follows day in one unvarying round of summer and sunshine, and the whole year is one long tropical month of June just melting into July.

It is this genial climate which causes the cocoa-nuts to flourish as they do. This invaluable fruit, brought to perfection by the rich soil of the Marquesas, and borne aloft on a stately column more than a hundred feet from the ground, would seem at first almost inaccessible to the simple natives. Indeed the slender, smooth, and soaring shaft, without a single limb or protuberance of any kind to assist one in mounting it, presents an obstacle only to be overcome by the surprising agility and ingenuity of the islanders. It might be supposed that their indolence would lead them patiently to await the period when the ripened nuts, slowly parting from their stems, fall one by one to the ground. This certainly would be the case, were it not that the young fruit, encased in a soft green husk, with the incipient meat adhering in a jelly-like pellicle to its sides, and containing a bumper of the most delicious nectar, is what they chiefly prize. They have at least twenty different terms to express as many progressive stages in the growth of the nut. Many of them reject the fruit altogether except at a particular period of its growth, which, incredible as it may appear, they seemed to me to be able to ascertain within an hour or two. Others are still more capricious in their tastes; and after gathering together a heap of the nuts of all ages, and ingeniously tapping them, will sip first from one and then from another, as fastidiously as some delicate wine-bibber experimenting glass in hand among his dusty demijohns of different vintages.

Some of the young men, with more flexible frames than their comrades, and perhaps with more courageous souls, had a way of walking up the trunk of the cocoa-nut trees which to me seemed little less than miraculous; and when looking at them in the act, I experienced that curious perplexity a child feels when he beholds a fly moving feet uppermost along a ceiling.

I will endeavor to describe the way in which Narnee, a noble young chief, sometimes performed this feat for my peculiar gratification; but his preliminary performances must also be recorded. Upon my signifying my desire that he should pluck me the young fruit of some particular tree, the handsome savage, throwing himself into a sudden attitude of surprise, feigns astonishment at the apparent absurdity of the request. Maintaining this position for a moment, the strange emotions depicted on his countenance soften down into one of humorous resignation to my will, and then looking wistfully up to the tufted top of the tree, he stands on tip-toe, straining his neck and elevating his arm, as though endeavoring to reach the fruit from the ground where he stands. As if defeated in this childish attempt, he now sinks to the earth despondingly, beating his breast in well-acted despair; and then, starting to his feet all at once, and throwing back his head, raises both hands, like a school-boy about to catch a falling ball. After continuing this for a moment or two, as if in expectation that the fruit was going to be tossed down to him by some good spirit in the tree-top, he turns wildly round in another fit of despair, and scampers off to the distance of thirty or forty yards. Here he remains awhile, eyeing the tree, the very picture of misery; but the next moment, receiving, as it were, a flash of inspiration, he rushes again towards it, and clasping both arms about the trunk, with one elevated a little above the other, he presses the soles of his feet close together against the tree, extending his legs from it until they are nearly horizontal, and his body becomes doubled into an arch; then, hand over hand and foot after foot, he rises from the earth with steady rapidity, and almost before you are aware of it, has gained the cradled and embowered nest of nuts, and with boisterous glee flings the fruit to the ground.

This mode of walking the tree is only practicable where the trunk declines considerably from the perpendicular. This, however, is almost always the case; some of the perfectly straight shafts of the trees leaning at an angle of thirty degrees.

The less active among the men, and many of the children of the valley, have another method of climbing. They take a broad and stout piece of bark, and secure either end of it to their ankles; so that when the feet thus confined are extended apart, a space of little more than twelve inches is left between them. This contrivance greatly facilitates the act of climbing. The band pressed against the tree, and closely embracing it, yields a pretty firm support; while with the arms clasped about the trunk, and at regular intervals sustaining the body, the feet are drawn up nearly a yard at a time, and a corresponding elevation of the hands immediately succeeds. In this way I have seen little children, scarcely five years of age, fearlessly climbing the slender pole of a young cocoa-nut tree, and while hanging perhaps fifty feet from the ground, receive the plaudits of their parents beneath, who clapped their hands, and encouraged them to mount still higher.

What, thought I, on first witnessing one of these exhibitions, would the nervous mothers of America and England say to a similar display of hardihood in any of their children? The Lacedemonian matrons might have approved of it, but most modern dames would have gone into hysterics at the sight. . . .

CHAPTER 30

In one of my strolls with Kory-Kory, in passing along the border of a thick growth of bushes, my attention was arrested by a singular noise. On entering the thicket I witnessed for the first time the operation of tattooing as performed by these islanders.

I beheld a man extended flat upon his back on the ground, and, despite the forced composure of his countenance, it was evident that he was suffering agony. His tormentor bent over him, working away for all the world like a stone-cutter with mallet and chisel. In one hand he held a short slender stick, pointed with a shark's tooth, on the upright end of which he tapped with a small hammer-like piece of wood, thus puncturing the skin, and charging it with the coloring matter in which the instrument was dipped. A cocoa-nut shell containing this fluid was placed upon the ground. It is prepared by mixing with a vegetable juice the ashes of the "armor," or candle-nut, always preserved for the purpose. Beside the savage, and spread out upon a piece of soiled tappa, were a great number of curious black-looking little implements of bone and wood, used in the various divisions of his art. A few terminated in a single fine point, and, like very delicate pencils, were employed in giving the finishing touches, or in operating upon the more sensitive portions of the body, as was the case in the present instance. Others presented several points distributed in a line, somewhat resembling the teeth of a saw. These were employed in the coarser parts of the work, and particularly in pricking in straight marks. Some presented their points disposed in small figures, and being placed upon the body, were, by a single blow of the hammer, made to leave their indelible impression. I observed a few the handles of which were mysteriously curved, as if intended to be introduced into the orifice of the ear, with a view perhaps of beating the tattoo upon the tympanum. Altogether, the sight of these strange instruments recalled to mind that display of cruel-looking mother-of-pearl-handled things which one sees in their velvet-lined cases at the elbow of a dentist.

The artist was not this time engaged on an original sketch, his subject being a venerable savage, whose tattooing had become somewhat faded with age and needed a few repairs, and accordingly he was merely employed in touching up the works of some of the old masters of the Typee school, as delineated upon the human canvas before him. The parts operated upon were the eyelids, where a longitudinal streak, like the one which adorned Kory-Kory, crossed the countenance of the victim.

In spite of all the efforts of the poor old man, sundry twitchings and screwings of the muscles of the face denoted the exquisite sensibility of these shutters to the windows of his soul, which he was now having repainted. But the artist, with a heart as callous as that of an army surgeon, continued his performance, enlivening his labors with a wild chant, tapping away the while as merrily as a woodpecker.

So deeply engaged was he in his work, that he had not observed our approach, until, after having enjoyed an unmolested view of the operation, I chose to attract his attention. As soon as he perceived me, supposing that I sought him in his professional capacity, he seized hold of me in a paroxysm of delight, and was all eagerness to begin the work. When, however, I gave him to understand that he had altogether mistaken my views, nothing could exceed his grief and disappointment. But recovering from this, he seemed determined not to credit my assertion, and grasping his implements, he flourished them about in fearful vicinity to my face, going through an imaginary performance of his art, and every moment bursting into some admiring exclamation at the beauty of his designs.

Horrified at the bare thought of being rendered hideous for life if the wretch were to execute his purpose upon me, I struggled to get away from him, while Kory-Kory, turning traitor, stood by, and besought me to comply with the outrageous request. On my reiterated refusals the excited artist got half beside himself, and was overwhelmed with sorrow at losing so noble an opportunity of distinguishing himself in his profession.

The idea of engrafting his tattooing upon my white skin filled him with all a painter's enthusiasm: again and again he gazed into my countenance, and every fresh glimpse seemed to add to the vehemence of his ambition. Not knowing to what extremities he might proceed, and shuddering at the ruin he might inflict upon my figure-head, I now endeavored to draw off his attention from it, and holding out my arm in a fit of desperation, signed to him to commence operations. But he rejected the compromise indignantly, and still continued his attack on my face, as though nothing short of that would satisfy him. When his fore-finger swept across my features, in laying out the borders of those parallel bands which were to encircle my countenance, the flesh fairly crawled upon my bones. At last, half wild with terror and indignation, I succeeded in breaking away from the three savages, and fled towards old Marheyo's house, pursued by the indomitable artist, who ran after me, implements in hand. Kory-Kory, however, at last interfered, and drew him off from the chace.

This incident opened my eyes to a new danger; and I now felt convinced that in some luckless hour I should be disfigured in such a manner as never more to have the *face* to return to my countrymen, even should an opportunity offer.

These apprehensions were greatly increased by the desire which King Mehevi and several of the inferior chiefs now manifested that I should be tattooed. The pleasure of the king was first signified to me some three days after my casual encounter with Karky the artist. Heavens! what imprecations I showered upon that Karky! Doubtless he had plotted a conspiracy against me and my countenance, and would never rest until his diabolical purpose was accomplished. Several times I met him in various parts of the valley, and, invariably, whenever he descried me, he came running after me with his mallet and chisel, flourishing them about my face as if he longed to begin. What an object he would have made of me!

When the king first expressed his wish to me, I made known to him my utter abhorrence of the measure, and worked myself into such a state of excitement, that he absolutely stared at me in amazement. It evidently surpassed his majesty's comprehension how any sober-minded and sensible individual could entertain the least possible objection to so beautifying an operation.

Soon afterwards he repeated his suggestion, and meeting with a like repulse, showed some symptoms of displeasure at my obduracy. On his a third time renewing his request, I plainly perceived that something must be done, or my visage was ruined for ever; I therefore screwed up my courage to the sticking point, and declared my willingness to have both arms tattooed from just above the wrist to the shoulder. His majesty was greatly pleased at the proposition, and I was congratulating myself with having thus compromised the matter, when he intimated that as a thing of course my face was first to undergo the operation. I was fairly driven to despair; nothing but the utter ruin of my "face divine," as the poets call it, would, I perceived, satisfy the inexorable Mehevi and his chiefs, or rather, that infernal Karky, for he was at the bottom of it all.

The only consolation afforded me was a choice of patterns: I was at perfect liberty to have my face spanned by three horizontal bars, after the fashion of my serving-man's; or to have as many oblique stripes slanting across it; or if, like a true courtier, I chose to model my style on that of royalty, I might wear a sort of freemason badge upon my countenance in the shape of a mystic triangle. However, I would have none of these, though the king most earnestly impressed upon my mind that my choice was wholly unrestricted. At last, seeing my unconquerable repugnance, he ceased to importune me.

But not so some other of the savages. Hardly a day passed but I was subjected to their annoying requests, until at last my existence became a burden to me; the pleasures I had previously enjoyed no longer afforded me delight, and all my former desire to escape from the valley now revived with additional force.

A fact which I soon afterwards learned augmented my apprehension. The whole system of tattooing was, I found, connected with their religion; and it was evident, therefore, that they were resolved to make a convert of me. . . .

CHAPTER 32

. . . It was during the period I was in this unhappy frame of mind that the painful malady under which I had been laboring—after having almost completely subsided—began again to show itself, and with symptoms as violent as ever. This added calamity nearly unmanned me; the recurrence of the complaint proved that without powerful remedial applications all hope of cure was futile; and when I reflected that just beyond the elevations which bound me in, was the medical relief I needed, and that, although so near, it was impossible for me to avail myself of it, the thought was misery.

In this wretched situation, every circumstance which evinced the savage nature of the beings at whose mercy I was, augmented the fearful apprehensions that consumed me. An occurrence which happened about this time affected me most powerfully.

I have already mentioned that from the ridge-pole of Marheyo's house were suspended a number of packages enveloped in tappa. Many of these I had often seen in the hands of the natives, and their contents had been examined in my presence. But there were three packages hanging very nearly over the place where I lay, which from their remarkable appearance had often excited my curiosity. Several times I had asked Kory-Kory to show me their contents; but my servitor, who in almost every other particular had acceded to my wishes, always refused to gratify me in this.

One day, returning unexpectedly from the "Ti," my arrival seemed to throw the inmates of the house into the greatest confusion. They were seated together on the mats, and by the lines which extended from the roof to the floor I immediately perceived that the mysterious packages were for some purpose or other under inspection. The evident alarm the savages betrayed filled me with forebodings of evil, and with an uncontrollable desire to penetrate the secret so jealously guarded. Despite the efforts of Marheyo and Kory-Kory to restrain me, I forced my way into the midst of the circle, and just caught a glimpse of three human heads, which others of the party were hurriedly enveloping in the coverings from which they had been taken.

One of the three I distinctly saw. It was in a state of perfect preservation, and, from the slight glimpse I had of it, seemed to have been subjected to some smoking operation which had reduced it to the dry, hard, and mummy-like appearance it presented. The two long scalp-locks were twisted up into balls upon the crown of the head in the same way that the individual had worn them during life. The sunken cheeks were rendered yet more ghastly by the rows of glistening teeth which protruded from between the lips, while the sockets of the eyes—filled with oval bits of mother-of-pearl shell, with a black spot in the centre—heightened the hideousness of its aspect.

Two of the three were heads of the islanders; but the third, to my horror, was that of a white man. Although it had been quickly removed from my sight, still the glimpse I had of it was enough to convince me that I could not be mistaken.

Gracious God! what dreadful thoughts entered my mind! In solving this mystery perhaps I had solved another, and the fate of my lost companion might be revealed in the shocking spectacle I had just witnessed. I longed to have torn off the folds of cloth, and satisfied the awful doubts under which I labored. But before I had recovered from the consternation into which I had been thrown, the fatal packages were hoisted aloft and once more swung over my head. The natives now gathered round me tumultuously, and labored to convince me that what I had just seen were the heads of three Happar warriors, who had been slain in battle. This glaring falsehood added to my alarm, and it was not until I reflected that I had observed the packages swinging from their elevation before Toby's disappearance, that I could at all recover my composure.

But although this horrible apprehension had been dispelled, I had discovered enough to fill me, in my present state of mind, with the most bitter reflections. It was plain that I had seen the last relic of some unfortunate wretch, who must have been massacred on the beach by the savages, in one of those perilous trading adventures which I have before described.

It was not, however, alone the murder of the stranger that overcame me with gloom. I shuddered at the idea of the subsequent fate his inanimate body might have met with. Was the same doom reserved for me? Was I destined to perish like him—like him, perhaps, to be devoured, and my head to be preserved as a fearful memento of the event? My imagination ran riot in these horrid speculations, and I felt certain that the worst possible evils would befal me. But whatever were my misgivings, I studiously concealed them from the islanders, as well as the full extent of the discovery I had made.

Although the assurances which the Typees had often given me, that they never eat human flesh, had not convinced me that such was the case, yet, having been so long a time in the valley without witnessing anything which indicated the existence of the practice, I began to hope that it was an event of very rare occurrence, and that I should be spared the horror of witnessing it during my stay among them; but, alas! these hopes were soon destroyed. . . .

The sound of the drums continued, without intermission, the whole day, and falling continually upon my ear, caused me a sensation of horror which I am unable to describe. On the following day hearing none of those noisy indications of revelry, I concluded that the inhuman feast was terminated; and feeling a kind of morbid curiosity to discover whether the Ti might furnish any evidence of what had taken place there, I proposed to Kory-Kory to walk there. To this proposition he replied by pointing with his finger to the newly risen sun, and then up to the zenith, intimating that our visits must be deferred until noon. Shortly after that hour we accordingly proceeded to the Taboo Groves, and as soon as we entered their precincts, I looked fearfully round in quest of some memorial of the scenes which had so lately been acted there; but everything appeared as usual. On reaching the Ti, we found Mehevi and a few chiefs reclining on the mats, who gave me as friendly a reception as ever. No allusions of any kind were made by them to the recent events; and I refrained, for obvious reasons, from referring to them myself.

After staying a short time I took my leave. In passing along the piazza, previously to descending from the pi-pi, I observed a curiously carved vessel of wood, of considerable size, with a cover placed over it, of the same material, and which resembled in shape a small canoe. It was surrounded by a low railing of bamboos, the top of which was scarcely a foot from the ground. As the vessel had been placed in its present position since my last visit, I at once concluded that it must have some connection with the recent festival; and, prompted by a curiosity I could not repress, in passing it I raised one end of the cover; at the same moment the chiefs, perceiving my design, loudly ejaculated, "Taboo! taboo!" But the slight glimpse sufficed; my eyes fell upon the disordered members of a human skeleton, the bones still fresh with moisture, and with particles of flesh clinging to them here and there!

Kory-Kory, who had been a little in advance of me, attracted by the exclamations of the chiefs, turned round in time to witness the expression of horror on my countenance. He now hurried towards me, pointing at the same time to the canoe, and exclaiming rapidly, "Puarkee! puarkee!" (Pig, pig). I pretended to yield to the deception, and repeated the words after him several times, as though acquiescing in what he said. The other savages, either deceived by my conduct or unwilling to manifest their displeasure at what could not now be remedied, took no further notice of the occurrence, and I immediately left the Ti.

All that night I lay awake, revolving in my mind the fearful situation in which I was placed. The last horrid revelation had now been made, and the full sense of my condition rushed upon my mind with a force I had never before experienced.

Where, thought I, desponding, is there the slightest prospect of escape? The only person who seemed to possess the ability to assist me was the stranger Marnoo; but would he ever return to the valley? and if he did, should I be permitted to hold any communication with him? It seemed as if I were cut off from every source of hope, and that nothing remained but passively to await whatever fate was in store for me. A thousand times I endeavored to account for the mysterious conduct of the natives. For what conceivable purpose did they thus retain me a captive? What could be their object in treating me with such apparent kindness, and did it not cover some treacherous scheme? Or, if they had no other design than to hold me a prisoner, how should I be able to pass away my days in this narrow valley, deprived of all intercourse with civilized beings, and for ever separated from friends and home? . . .

APPENDIX

The author of this volume arrived at Tahiti the very day that the iniquitous designs of the French were consummated by inducing the subordinate chiefs, during the absence of their queen, to ratify an artfully drawn treaty, by which she was virtually deposed. Both menaces and caresses were employed on this occasion, and the 32-pounders which peeped out of the portholes of the frigate were the principal arguments adduced to quiet the scruples of the more conscientious islanders.

And yet this piratical seizure of Tahiti, with all the woe and desolation which resulted from it, created not half so great a sensation, at least in America, as was caused by the proceedings of the English at the Sandwich Islands. No transaction has ever been more grossly misrepresented than the events which occurred upon the arrival of Lord George Paulet at Oahu. During a residence of four months at Honolulu, the metropolis of the group, the author was in the confidence of an Englishman who was much employed by his lordship; and great was the author's astonishment on his arrival at Boston, in the autumn of 1844, to read the distorted accounts and fabrications which had produced in the United States so violent an outbreak of indignation against the English. He deems it, therefore, a mere act of justice towards a gallant officer briefly to state the leading circumstances connected with the event in question.

It is needless to rehearse all the abuse that for some time previous to the spring of 1843 had been heaped upon the British residents, especially upon Captain Charlton, her Britannic Majesty's consul-general, by the native authorities of the Sandwich Islands. High in the favor of the imbecile king at this time was one Dr. Judd, a sanctimonious apothecary-adventurer, who, with other kindred and influential spirits, were animated by an inveterate dislike to England. The ascendancy of a junto of ignorant and designing Methodist elders in the councils of a half-civilized king, ruling with absolute sway over a nation just poised between barbarism and civilization, and exposed by the peculiarities of its relations with foreign states to unusual difficulties, was not precisely calculated to impart a healthy tone to the policy of the government.

At last matters were brought to such an extremity, through the iniquitous maladministration of affairs, that the endurance of further insults and injuries on the part of the British consul was no longer to be borne. Captain Charlton, insultingly forbidden to leave the islands, clandestinely withdrew, and arriving at Valparaiso, conferred with Rear-Admiral Thomas, the English commander-in-chief on the Pacific station. In consequence of this communication, Lord George Paulet was despatched by the admiral in the Carysfort frigate, to enquire into and correct the alleged abuses. On arriving at his destination, he sent his first-lieutenant ashore with a letter to the king, couched in terms of the utmost courtesy, and soliciting the honor of an audience. The messenger was denied access to his Majesty, and Paulet was coolly referred to Doctor Judd, and informed that the apothecary was invested with plenary powers to treat with him. Rejecting this insolent proposition, his lordship again addressed the king by letter, and renewed his previous request; but he encountered another repulse. Justly indignant at this treatment, he penned a third epistle, enumerating the grievances to be redressed, and demanding a compliance with his requisitions, under penalty of immediate hostilities.

The government was now obliged to act, and an artful stroke of policy was decided upon by the despicable counsellors of the king to entrap the sympathies and rouse the indignation of Christendom. His Majesty was made to intimate to the British captain that he could not, as the conscientious ruler of his beloved people, comply with the arbitrary demands of his lordship, and in deprecation of the horrors of war, tendered to his acceptance the "provisional cession" of the islands, subject to the result of the negotiations then pending in London. Paulet, a bluff and straight-forward sailor, took the king at his word, and after some preliminary arrangements, entered upon the administration of Hawaiian affairs, in the same firm and benignant spirit which marked the discipline of his frigate, and which had rendered him the idol of his ship's company. He soon endeared himself to nearly all orders of the islanders; but the king and the chiefs, whose feudal sway over the common people is laboriously sought to be perpetuated by their missionary advisers, regarded all his proceedings with the most vigilant animosity. Jealous of his growing popularity, and unable to counteract it, they endeavored to assail his reputation abroad by ostentatiously protesting against his acts, and appealing in Oriental phrase to the *wide universe* to witness and compassionate their *unparalleled wrongs*.

Heedless of their idle clamors, Lord George Paulet addressed himself to the task of reconciling the differences among the foreign residents, remedying their grievances, promoting their mercantile interests, and ameliorating as far as lay in his power the condition of the degraded natives. The iniquities he brought to light and instantly suppressed are too numerous to be here recorded; but one instance may be mentioned that will give some idea of the lamentable misrule to which these poor islanders are subjected.

It is well known that the laws at the Sandwich Islands are subject to the most capricious alterations, which, by confounding all idea of right and wrong in the minds of the natives, produce the most pernicious effects. In no case is this mischief more plainly discernible than in the continually shifting regulations concerning licentiousness. At one time the most innocent freedoms between the sexes are punished with fine and imprisonment; at another the revocation of the statute is followed by the most open and undisguised profligacy.

It so happened that at the period of Paulet's arrival the Connecticut blue laws had been for at least three weeks steadily enforced. In consequence of this, the fort at Honolulu was filled with a great number of young girls, who were confined there doing penance for their slips from virtue. Paulet, although at first unwilling to interfere with regulations having reference solely to the natives themselves, was eventually, by the prevalence of certain reports, induced to institute a strict inquiry into the internal administration of General Kekuanoa, governor of the island of Oahu, one of the pillars of the Hawaiian church, and captain of the fort. He soon ascertained that numbers of the young females employed during the day at work intended for the benefit of the king, were at night smuggled over the ramparts of the fort—which on one side directly overhangs the sea—and were conveyed by stealth on board such vessels as had contracted with the General to be supplied with them. Before daybreak they returned to their quarters, and their own silence with regard to these secret excursions was purchased by a small portion of those wages of iniquity which were placed in the hands of Kekuanoa.

The vigor with which the laws concerning licentiousness were at that period enforced, enabled the General to monopolize in a great measure the detestable trade in which he was engaged, and there consequently flowed into his coffers—and some say into those of the government also—considerable sums of money. It is indeed a lamentable fact, that the principal revenue of the Hawaiian government is derived from the fines levied upon, or rather the licences taken out by Vice, the prosperity of which is linked with that of the government. Were the people to become virtuous the authorities would become poor; but from present indications there is little apprehension to be entertained on that score.

Some five months after the date of the cession, the Dublin frigate, carrying the flag of Rear-Admiral Thomas, entered the harbor of Honolulu. The excitement that her sudden appearance produced on shore was prodigious. Three days after her arrival an English sailor hauled down the red cross which had been flying from the heights of the fort, and the Hawaiian colors were again displayed upon the same staff. At the same moment the long 42-pounders upon Punchbowl Hill opened their iron throats in triumphant reply to the thunders of the five men-of-war in the harbor; and King Kammahamaha III., surrounded by a splendid group of British and American officers, unfurled the royal standard to assembled thousands of his subjects, who, attracted by the imposing military display of the foreigners, had flocked to witness the formal restoration of the islands to their ancient rulers.

The Admiral, after sanctioning the proceedings of his subaltern, had brought the authorities to terms; and so removed the necessity of acting any longer under the provisional cession.

The event was made an occasion of riotous rejoicing by the king and the principal chiefs, who easily secured a display of enthusiasm from the inferior orders, by remitting for a time the accustomed severity of the laws. Royal proclamations in English and Hawaiian were placarded in the streets of Honolulu, and posted up in the more populous villages of the group, in which his Majesty announced to his loving subjects the re-establishment of his throne, and called upon them to celebrate it by breaking through all moral, legal, and religious restraint for ten consecutive days, during which time all the laws of the land were solemnly declared to be suspended.

Who that happened to be at Honolulu during those ten memorable days will ever forget them! The spectacle of universal broad-day debauchery, which was then exhibited, beggars description. The natives of the surrounding islands flocked to Honolulu by hundreds, and the crews of two frigates, opportunely let loose like so many demons to swell the heathenish uproar, gave the crowning flourish to the scene. It was a sort of Polynesian saturnalia. Deeds too atrocious to be mentioned were done at noon-day in the open street, and some of the islanders caught in the very act of stealing from the foreigners, were, on being taken to the fort by the aggrieved party, suffered immediately to go at large and to retain the stolen property—Kekuanoa informing the white men, with a sardonic grin, that the laws were "hannapa" (tied up).

The history of these ten days reveals in their true colors the character of the Sandwich islanders, and furnishes an eloquent commentary on the results which have flowed from the labors of the missionaries. Freed from the restraints of severe penal laws, the natives almost to a man had plunged voluntarily into every species of wickedness and excess, and by their utter disregard of all decency plainly showed, that although they had been schooled into a seeming submission to the new order of things, they were in reality as depraved and vicious as ever.

Such were the events which produced in America so general an outbreak of indignation against the spirited and high-minded Paulet. He is not the first man who, in the fearless discharge of his duty, has awakened the senseless clamors of those whose narrow-minded suspicions blind them to a proper appreciation of measures which unusual exigencies may have rendered necessary.

It is almost needless to add that the British cabinet never had any idea of appropriating the islands; and it furnishes a sufficient vindication of the acts of Lord George Paulet, that he not only received the unqualified approbation of his own government, but that to this hour the great body of the Hawaiian people invoke blessings on his head, and look back with gratitude to the time when his liberal and paternal sway diffused peace and happiness among them.

PART III

A PASSAGE
TO TAHITI:
Omoo
(1847)

⌗ ⌗ ⌗

INTRODUCTION

Omoo (the word, Melville explains in his Preface, means "a rover") is a proper companion volume to *Typee*. "The present narrative," he remarks, "necessarily begins where *Typee* concludes, but has no further connection with the latter work." The author had learned much about writing and publishing by the time he came to his second book, which on the whole has an improved style and a wider appeal than *Typee* to those of his readers who want authentic accounts of South Sea life by one who lived in the places described. Melville's wanderings on the sea and around the shores of Tahiti—the most romantic island on our planet—and its neighboring island of Mooréa provided him with the chance to offer many more views of the changing Polynesian scene than when he had limited his scope to one Marquesan valley. The tone of *Omoo* is more raffish, and Melville added unexpected Dickensian comedy. It is the most autobiographical of all his novels, but even here there are a number of fictional qualities and romancing inventions that reinforce his theme.

The main meaning of *Omoo* is the reverse of the *Typee* coin. The earlier book is primarily an idyllic defense of unspoiled primitivism. *Omoo* takes the offensive with a positive attack on the results of European incursion—specifically in Tahiti —more than a lifetime after one discoverer had named it the New Cytherea, the island of the love goddess herself. Three score and ten years after Samuel Wallis and Louis Antoine de Bougainville had independently come upon the lovely Society Islands, Melville viewed there the results of commercial and mission activity and found that the Occidental vices had been adopted and the virtues circumvented. "To me, so recently from a primitive valley in the Marquesas," he remarks in Chapter 49, "a comparison immeasurably to the disadvantage of these partially civilised islanders [was unavoidable]." The Noble Savage had assumed the role of a member of the Vanishing Race. So broad is Melville's indictment of those who had corrupted the pagans of the South Seas that *Omoo* at times appears to be an attack on all officials, appointed or self-appointed, and presages rebellious outbursts in later volumes.

Melville's actual adventures between his joining the *Lucy Ann* off Taipi Valley and his joining the *Charles and Henry* off Papetoi on Mooréa, as previously sketched, form the spine of *Omoo*. Recollections of these episodes enabled him to handle much of the story without research. Many magnifications are found in this book, but fewer than those in *Typee,* since Melville was anxious to allay the fears of his London publisher that the new book was not "authentic." When Melville departs from fact here, he may make his hero a bit more heroic, but usually the exaggerations elsewhere are so great that even the most humorless English reader of *Punch* would get the joke.

No manuscript of *Omoo* exists except a draft of the Round-Robin of Chapter 20. Several chapters may have been omitted because they would have been offensive to pious people who contributed to mission efforts overseas. Even so, the anti-missionary bias is strong. The paradox of *Omoo* is that much of the ammunition Melville used to attack the missionaries came from four authors who defended their activities in the South Seas. William Ellis, Charles S. Stewart, M. M. Russell, and Daniel Wheeler (a Quaker) were all clergymen.[1]

Melville in his Preface acknowledges that upon several points "collateral information has been obtained from the oldest books of South Sea voyages, and also from the 'Polynesian Researches' of Ellis." Often he transposes much material from Ellis, but since the missionary's views were the opposite of his own, he had to recast it or handle it with irony.

Characterization in *Omoo* is more developed than in *Typee*. Melville himself is again the protagonist, and again he has a comrade, but one much more fascinating than Toby. "Doctor Long Ghost," in fact, almost overshadows the narrator, for he takes the lead in every escapade from mutiny to philandering with Tahitian maidens. The adventures of this pair, who at one time assume the *noms de guerre* of Peter and Paul, make the form of this book resemble closely the picaresque, a type going back in English to Henry Fielding's *Tom Jones*. Episodes of rollicking adventure are occasionally varied by solemn commentaries on the South Sea world.

This novel also has a larger cast of characters, both native and white, since the theme shows the corruption of the former by the latter. The invaders, also, are in conflict among themselves. The sailors suffering under Captain Guy and Mate Jermin are individualized, and most of the shore officials are so clearly depicted that some of those identified might well have had cause for slander charges. Representation of the takeover of the Society Islands by the French—

Admiral Dupetit-Thouars versus Queen Pomaré—is as accurate as a lowly eye-witness could make it.

The action of this novel is again a pilgrimage, but after the mutiny is ended and the mutineers are allowed to leave the Calabooza Beretanee and rove about Tahiti, suspense dies down. The narrator becomes infected with the indolence of the South Seas; his quest for evidence of the corruption of the people slackens and is often diverted by the whims of a beachcomber—for that is what the storyteller has become. It should be noted that, as in *Typee,* the action of the book begins and ends on the deck of a whale ship.

Again the setting of the novel is its most important aspect. *Omoo* is un-doubtedly filled with the best descriptions of Tahiti in 1842 that one can find anywhere. Melville liked the native people and the places he visited. In his later long poem *Clarel* (1876), Tahiti is mentioned as the only fit place on earth for the advent of Christ. Melville's second book almost became a tourist guide to the region. "Pierre Loti," Henry Adams, Charles Warren Stoddard, Robert Louis Stevenson, and Jack London read their *Omoo* before voyaging to the Societies.

Melville produced this novel during 1846, which one American author chris-tened "the year of decision." It was not only the year of publication of *Typee* but also of the outbreak of the war with Mexico, the annexation of California, and the settling of the Oregon dispute, which opened up the trails to our Northwest. Melville had other distractions than the political scene. He visited Toby in Buffalo and sold the story of his wanderings to John Murray in Lon-don for £50. He buckled down to work on *Omoo* at Lansingburgh in the autumn, but for two months his sisters' friend Elizabeth Shaw, daughter of the chief justice of Massachusetts (to whom Herman had dedicated *Typee*), visited in the Melville home. She was to become Herman's wife and the mother of his four children.

Despite the temptations of courtship, *Omoo* somehow progressed. Melville was able to use some material left over from *Typee,* such as the description of the dance in the valley of Tamai. By the end of the year the author was offering the manuscript in New York City. Knowing that the second book was even stronger in its condemnation of the clergy, Melville may not even have shown it to Wiley & Putnam. The story that he called upon Harper & Brothers and that the book was accepted by Mr. Fletcher Harper as he stepped into his carriage on his way to a European trip may be true. That Harper served as American publisher of Melville's next five books is a fact.

Omoo, with a lengthy subtitle, was also enthusiastically added by John Murray in London to his Home and Colonial Library for the sum of £150—half again as much as he had paid for *Typee*. The British edition, published first for copyright reasons, was set from proofs of the American edition, which Melville had a chance to correct. The text is therefore closer to what he wished to put on record regarding his feelings about his Pacific adventures.

Omoo was warmly praised on both sides of the Atlantic, and has been reprinted dozens of times. Its popularity caused sales of *Typee* to pick up as well. *Omoo* was accorded more reviews than any other of Melville's books. Some were revolted by his raciness or indecencies, but as Dr. Leon Howard says: "The majority remarked on his sprightliness of spirit, on his gusto, on his sense of comedy, and on his humanity. . . . The characterization of Doctor Long Ghost was repeatedly singled out as original, lively, and skillful. Many admired Melville's power in his evocative description and 'glowing pencillings' of 'poetic,' 'dreamy,' and 'picturesque' scenes 'like cabinet pictures.' "[2] Some people—even John Murray—still rightly worried about its factuality, but later visitors to the Society Islands testified that Melville had described the region and his activities there with remarkable accuracy.

Despite this book's continuing readership, many critics of the Melville revival have had little to say about *Omoo,* except to contrast it with *Typee* or dismiss it as a sequel. Perhaps the best way to appreciate these two earliest books is to consider them as twin views of the South Seas in the early 1840s, each complementing the other. Not that *Omoo* has lacked partisans. Possibly the most enthusiastic is D. H. Lawrence, who says: "Perhaps Melville is at his best, his happiest, in *Omoo.* For once he is really reckless. For once he takes life as it comes. For once he is the gallant, rascally epicurean."[3]

❀ ❀ ❀

CHAPTER 6

Fearful of spending another night in Hytyhoo, Captain Guy caused the ship to be got under way shortly after dark. The next morning, when all supposed that we were fairly embarked for a long cruise, our course was suddenly altered for La Dominica, or Hivarhoo, an island just north of the one we had quitted. The object of this, as we learned, was to procure, if possible, several English sailors, who, according to the commander of the corvette, had recently gone ashore there from an American whaler and were desirous of shipping aboard of one of their own country vessels.

We made the land in the afternoon, coming abreast of a shady glen opening from a deep bay, and winding by green defiles far out of sight. "Hands by the weather-main-brace!" roared the mate, jumping up on the bulwarks; and in a moment the prancing Julia, suddenly arrested in her course, bridled her head like a steed reined in, while the foam flaked under her bows.

This was the place where we expected to obtain the men; so a boat was at once got in readiness to go ashore. Now it was necessary to provide a picked crew—men the least likely to abscond. After considerable deliberation on the part of the captain and mate, four of the seamen were pitched upon as the most trustworthy; or rather they were selected from a choice assortment of suspicious characters as being of an inferior order of rascality.

Armed with cutlasses all round—the natives were said to be an ugly set—they were followed over the side by the invalid captain, who, on this occasion, it seems, was determined to signalize himself. Accordingly, in addition to his cutlass, he wore an old boarding belt, in which was thrust a brace of pistols. They at once shoved off.

My friend Long Ghost had, among other things which looked somewhat strange in a ship's forecastle, a capital spy-glass, and on the present occasion we had it in use.

When the boat neared the head of the inlet, though invisible to the naked eye, it was plainly revealed by the glass; looking no bigger than an egg-shell, and the men diminished to pigmies.

At last, borne on what seemed a long flake of foam the tiny craft shot up the beach amid a shower of sparkles. Not a soul was there. Leaving one of their number by the water, the rest of the pigmies stepped ashore, looking about them very circumspectly, pausing now and then hand to ear, and peering under a dense grove which swept down within a few paces of the sea. No one came, and to all appearances every thing was as still as the grave. Presently, he with the pistols, followed by the rest flourishing their bodkins, entered the wood and were soon lost to view. They did not stay long; probably anticipating some inhospitable ambush were they to stray any distance up the glen.

In a few moments they embarked again, and were soon riding pertly over the waves of the bay. All of a sudden the captain started to his feet—the boat spun round, and again made for the shore. Some twenty or thirty natives armed with spears which through the glass looked like reeds, had just come out of the grove, and were apparently shouting to the strangers not to be in such a hurry, but return and be sociable. But they were somewhat distrusted, for the boat paused about its length from the beach, when the captain standing up in its head delivered an address in pantomime, the object of which seemed to be, that the islanders should draw near. One of them stepped forward and made answer, seemingly again urging the strangers not to be difficult, but beach their boat. The captain declined, tossing his arms about in another pantomime. In the end he said something which made them shake their spears; whereupon he fired a pistol among them, which set the whole party running; while one poor little fellow, dropping his spear and clapping his hand behind him, limped away in a manner which almost made me itch to get a shot at his assailant.

Wanton acts of cruelty like this are not unusual on the part of sea captains landing at islands comparatively unknown. Even at the Pomotu group, but a day's sail from Tahiti, the islanders coming down to the shore have several times been fired at by trading schooners passing through their narrow channels; and this too as a mere amusement on the part of the ruffians.

Indeed, it is almost incredible, the light in which many sailors regard these naked heathens. They hardly consider them human. But it is a curious fact, that the more ignorant and degraded men are, the more contemptuously they look upon those whom they deem their inferiors.

All powers of persuasion being thus lost upon these foolish savages, and no hope left of holding further intercourse, the boat returned to the ship.

CHAPTER 7

On the other side of the island was the large and populous bay of Hannamanoo, where the men sought might yet be found. But as the sun was setting by the time the boat came alongside, we got our off-shore tacks aboard and stood away for an offing. About daybreak we wore, and ran in, and by the time the sun was well up, entered the long, narrow channel dividing the islands of La Dominica and St. Christina.

On one hand was a range of steep green bluffs hundreds of feet high, the white huts of the natives here and there nestling like birdsnests in deep clefts gushing with verdure. Across the water, the land rolled away in bright hillsides, so warm and undulating, that they seemed almost to palpitate in the sun. On we swept, past bluff and grove, wooded glen and valley, and dark ravines lighted up far inland with wild falls of water. A fresh land-breeze filled our sails, the embayed waters were gentle as a lake, and every blue wave broke with a tinkle against our coppered prow.

On gaining the end of the channel we rounded a point, and came full upon the bay of Hannamanoo. This is the only harbor of any note about the island, though as far as a safe anchorage is concerned it hardly deserves the title.

Before we held any communication with the shore, an incident occurred which may convey some further idea of the character of our crew.

Having approached as near the land as we could prudently, our headway was stopped, and we awaited the arrival of a canoe which was coming out of the bay. All at once we got into a strong current, which swept us rapidly toward a rocky promontory forming one side of the harbor. The wind had died away; so two boats were at once lowered for the purpose of pulling the ship's head round. Before this could be done, the eddies were whirling upon all sides, and the rock so near, that it seemed as if one might leap upon it from the mast-head. Notwithstanding the speechless fright of the captain, and the hoarse shouts of the unappalled Jermin, the men handled the ropes as deliberately as possible, some of them chuckling at the prospect of going ashore, and others so eager for the vessel to strike, that they could hardly contain themselves. Unexpectedly a counter-current befriended us, and assisted by the boats we were soon out of danger.

What a disappointment for our crew! All their little plans for swimming ashore from the wreck, and having a fine time of it for the rest of their days, thus cruelly nipt in the bud.

Soon after, the canoe came alongside. In it were eight or ten natives, comely, vivacious-looking youths, all gesture and exclamation; the red feathers in their headbands perpetually nodding. With them also came a stranger, a renegado from Christendom and humanity—a white man, in the South Sea girdle, and tattooed in the face. A broad blue band stretched across his face from ear to ear, and on his forehead was the taper figure of a blue shark, nothing but fins from head to tail.

Some of us gazed upon this man with a feeling akin to horror, no ways abated when informed that he had voluntarily submitted to this embellishment of his countenance. What an impress! Far worse than Cain's—*his* was perhaps a wrinkle, or a freckle, which some of our modern cosmetics might have effaced; but the blue shark was a mark indelible, which all the waters of Abana and Pharpar, rivers of Damascus, could never wash out. He was an Englishman, Lem Hardy he called himself, who had deserted from a trading brig touching at the island for wood and water some ten years previous. He had gone ashore as a sovereign power, armed with a musket and a bag of ammunition, and ready, if need were, to prosecute war on his own account. The country was divided by the hostile kings of several large valleys. With one of them, from whom he first received overtures, he formed an alliance, and became what he now was, the military leader of the tribe, and war-god of the entire island.

His campaigns beat Napoleon's. In one night-attack, his invincible musket, backed by the light infantry of spears and javelins, vanquished two clans, and the next morning brought all the others at the feet of his royal ally.

Nor was the rise of his domestic fortunes at all behind the Corsican's: three days after landing, the exquisitely tattooed hand of a princess was his; receiving along with the damsel as her portion, one thousand fathoms of fine tappa, fifty double-braided mats of split grass, four hundred hogs, ten houses in different parts of her native valley, and the sacred protection of an express edict of the Taboo, declaring his person inviolable forever.

Now, this man was settled for life, perfectly satisfied with his circumstances, and feeling no desire to return to his friends. "Friends," indeed, he had none. He told me his history. Thrown upon the world a foundling, his paternal origin was as much a mystery to him as the genealogy of Odin; and, scorned by every body, he fled the parish workhouse when a boy, and lanched upon the sea. He had followed it for several years, a dog before the mast, and now he had thrown it up forever.

And for the most part, it is just this sort of men—so many of whom are found among sailors—uncared for by a single soul, without ties, reckless, and impatient of the restraints of civilization, who are occasionally found quite at home upon the savage islands of the Pacific. And, glancing at their hard lot in their own country, what marvel at their choice?

According to the renegado, there was no other white man on the island; and as the captain could have no reason to suppose that Hardy intended to deceive us, he concluded that the Frenchmen were in some way or other mistaken in what they had told us. However, when our errand was made known to the rest of our visitors, one of them, a fine, stalwart fellow, his face all eyes and expression, volunteered for a cruise. All the wages he asked, was a red shirt, a pair of trowsers, and a hat, which were to be put on there and then; beside a plug of tobacco and a pipe. The bargain was struck directly; but Wymontoo afterward came in with a codicil, to the effect that a friend of his, who had come along with him, should be given ten whole sea-biscuits, without crack or flaw, twenty perfectly new and symmetrically straight nails, and one jackknife. This being agreed to, the articles were at once handed over, the native receiving them with great avidity, and in the absence of clothing, using his mouth as a pocket to put the nails in. Two of them, however, were first made to take the place of a pair of ear-ornaments, curiously fashioned out of bits of whitened wood.

It now began breezing strongly from seaward, and no time was to be lost in getting away from the land; so after an affecting rubbing of noses between our new shipmate and his countrymen, we sailed away with him.

To our surprise, the farewell shouts from the canoe, as we dashed along under bellied royals, were heard unmoved by our islander; but it was not long thus. That very evening, when the dark blue of his native hills sunk in the horizon, the poor savage leaned over the bulwarks, dropped his head upon his chest, and gave way to irrepressible emotions. The ship was plunging hard, and Wymontoo, sad to tell, in addition to his other pangs, was terribly sea-sick.

CHAPTER 18

At early dawn of the following morning we saw the Peaks of Tahiti. In clear weather they may be seen at the distance of ninety miles.

"Hivarhoo!" shouted Wymontoo, overjoyed, and running out upon the bow-sprit when the land was first faintly descried in the distance. But when the clouds floated away, and showed the three peaks standing like obelisks against the sky; and the bold shore undulating along the horizon, the tears gushed from his eyes. Poor fellow! It was not Hivarhoo. Green Hivarhoo was many a long league off.

Tahiti is by far the most famous island in the South Seas; indeed, a variety of causes has made it almost classic. Its natural features alone distinguish it from the surrounding groups. Two round and lofty promontories, whose mountains rise nine thousand feet above the level of the ocean, are connected by a low, narrow isthmus; the whole being some one hundred miles in circuit. From the great central peaks of the larger peninsula—Orohena, Aorai, and Pirohitee—the land radiates on all sides to the sea in sloping green ridges. Between these are broad and shadowy valleys—in aspect, each a Tempe—watered with fine streams, and thickly wooded. Unlike many of the other islands, there extends nearly all round Tahiti, a belt of low, alluvial soil, teeming with the richest vegetation. Here, chiefly, the natives dwell.

Seen from the sea, the prospect is magnificent. It is one mass of shaded tints of green, from beach to mountain top; endlessly diversified with valleys, ridges, glens, and cascades. Over the ridges, here and there, the loftier peaks fling their shadows, and far down the valleys. At the head of these, the water-falls flash out into the sunlight as if pouring through vertical bowers of verdure. Such enchantment, too, breathes over the whole, that it seems a fairy world, all fresh and blooming from the hand of the Creator.

Upon a near approach, the picture loses not its attractions. It is no exaggeration to say, that to a European of any sensibility, who, for the first time, wanders back into these valleys—away from the haunts of the natives—the ineffable repose and beauty of the landscape is such, that every object strikes him like something seen in a dream; and for a time he almost refuses to believe that scenes like these should have a commonplace existence. No wonder that the French bestowed upon the island the appellation of the New Cytherea. "Often," says De Bougainville, "I thought I was walking in the Garden of Eden."

Nor, when first discovered, did the inhabitants of this charming country at all diminish the wonder and admiration of the voyager. Their physical beauty and amiable dispositions harmonized completely with the softness of their clime. In truth, every thing about them was calculated to awaken the liveliest interest. Glance at their civil and religious institutions. To their king, divine rights were paid; while for poetry, their mythology rivaled that of ancient Greece.

Of Tahiti, earlier and more full accounts were given, than of any other island in Polynesia; and this is the reason why it still retains so strong a hold on the sympathies of all readers of South Sea voyages. The journals of its first visitors, containing, as they did, such romantic descriptions of a country and people before unheard of, produced a marked sensation throughout Europe; and when the first Tahitians were carried thither, Omai in London, and Aotooroo in Paris, were caressed by nobles, scholars, and ladies.

In addition to all this, several eventful occurrences, more or less connected with Tahiti, have tended to increase its celebrity. Over two centuries ago, Quiros, the Spaniard, is supposed to have touched at the island; and at intervals, Wallis, Byron, Cook, De Bougainville, Vancouver, La Perouse, and other illustrious navigators, refitted their vessels in its harbors. Here the famous Transit of Venus was observed, in 1769. Here the memorable mutiny of the Bounty afterward had its origin. It was to the pagans of Tahiti that the first regularly constituted Protestant missionaries were sent; and from their shores also, have sailed successive missions to the neighboring islands.

These, with other events, which might be mentioned, have united in keeping up the first interest which the place awakened; and the recent proceedings of the French have more than ever called forth the sympathies of the public.

CHAPTER 30

. . . The examination over, Wilson and his friends advanced to the doorway; when the former, assuming a severe expression, pronounced our perverseness, infatuation in the extreme. Nor was there any hope left: our last chance for pardon was gone. Even were we to become contrite, and crave permission to return to duty, it would not now be permitted.

"Oh! get along with your gammon, *counselor,*" exclaimed Black Dan, absolutely indignant that his understanding should be thus insulted.

Quite enraged, Wilson bade him hold his peace; and then, summoning a fat old native to his side, addressed him in Tahitian, giving directions for leading us away to a place of safe keeping.

Hereupon, being marshaled in order, with the old man at our head, we were put in motion, with loud shouts, along a fine pathway, running far on, through wide groves of the cocoa-nut and bread-fruit.

The rest of our escort trotted on beside us in high good-humor; jabbering broken English, and in a hundred ways giving us to understand that Wilson was no favorite of theirs, and that we were prime, good fellows for holding out as we did. They seemed to know our whole history.

The scenery around was delightful. The tropical day was fast drawing to a close; and from where we were, the sun looked like a vast red fire burning in the woodlands—its rays falling aslant through the endless ranks of trees, and every leaf fringed with flame. Escaped from the confined desks of the frigate, the air breathed spices to us; streams were heard flowing; green boughs were rocking; and far inland, all sunset flushed, rose the still, steep peaks of the island.

As we proceeded, I was more and more struck by the picturesqueness of the wide, shaded road. In several places, durable bridges of wood were thrown over large water-courses; others were spanned by a single arch of stone. In any part of the road, three horsemen might have ridden abreast.

This beautiful avenue—by far the best thing which civilization has done for the island—is called by foreigners "the Broom Road," though for what reason I do not know. Originally planned for the convenience of the missionaries journeying from one station to another, it almost completely encompasses the larger peninsula; skirting for a distance of at least sixty miles along the low, fertile lands bordering the sea. But on the side next Taiarboo, or the lesser peninsula, it sweeps through a narrow, secluded valley, and thus crosses the island in that direction.

The uninhabited interior, being almost impenetrable from the densely wooded glens, frightful precipices, and sharp mountain ridges absolutely inaccessible, is but little known, even to the natives themselves; and so, instead of striking directly across from one village to another, they follow the Broom Road round and round.*

It is by no means, however, altogether traveled on foot; horses being now quite plentiful. They were introduced from Chili; and possessing all the gayety, fleetness, and docility of the Spanish breed, are admirably adapted to the tastes of the higher classes, who as equestrians have become very expert. The missionaries and chiefs never think of journeying except in the saddle; and at all hours of the day, you see the latter galloping along at full speed. Like the Sandwich Islanders, they ride like Pawnee-Loups.

For miles and miles I have traveled the Broom Road, and never wearied of the continual change of scenery. But wherever it leads you—whether through level woods, across grassy glens, or over hills waving with palms—the bright blue sea on one side, and the green mountain pinnacles on the other, are always in sight.

CHAPTER 31

About a mile from the village we came to a halt.

It was a beautiful spot. A mountain stream here flowed at the foot of a verdant slope; on one hand, it murmured along until the waters, spreading themselves upon a beach of small, sparkling shells, trickled into the sea; on the other, was a long defile, where the eye pursued a gleaming, sinuous thread, lost in shade and verdure.

The ground next the road was walled in by a low, rude parapet of stones; and, upon the summit of the slope beyond, was a large, native house, the thatch dazzling white, and, in shape, an oval.

"Calabooza! Calabooza Beretanee!" (the English Jail), cried our conductor, pointing to the building.

For a few months past, having been used by the consul as a house of confinement for his refractory sailors, it was thus styled to distinguish it from similar places in and about Papeetee.

Though extremely romantic in appearance, on a near approach it proved but

---

* Concerning the singular ignorance of the natives respecting their own country, it may be here observed, that a considerable inland lake—Whaiherea by name—is known to exist, although their accounts of it strangely vary. Some told me it had no bottom, no outlet, and no inlet; others, that it fed all the streams on the island. A sailor of my acquaintance said, that he once visited this marvelous lake, as one of an exploring party from an English sloop-of-war. It was found to be a great curiosity: very small, deep, and green; a choice well of water bottled up among the mountains, and abounding with delicious fish.

ill adapted to domestic comfort. In short, it was a mere shell, recently built, and still unfinished. It was open all round, and tufts of grass were growing here and there under the very roof. The only piece of furniture was the "stocks," a clumsy machine for keeping people in one place, which, I believe, is pretty much out of date in most countries. It is still in use, however, among the Spaniards in South America; from whom, it seems, the Tahitians have borrowed the contrivance, as well as the name by which all places of confinement are known among them.

The stocks were nothing more than two stout timbers, about twenty feet in length, and precisely alike. One was placed edgeways on the ground, and the other resting on top, left, at regular intervals along the seam, several round holes, the object of which was evident at a glance.

By this time, our guide had informed us, that he went by the name of "*Capin Bob*" (Captain Bob); and a hearty old Bob he proved. It was just the name for him. From the first, so pleased were we with the old man, that we cheerfully acquiesced in his authority.

Entering the building, he set us about fetching heaps of dry leaves to spread behind the stocks for a couch. A trunk of a small cocoa-nut tree was then placed for a bolster—rather a hard one, but the natives are used to it. For a pillow, they use a little billet of wood, scooped out, and standing on four short legs—a sort of head-stool.

These arrangements completed, Captain Bob proceeded to "hannapar," or secure us, for the night. The upper timber of the machine being lifted at one end, and our ankles placed in the semicircular spaces of the lower one, the other beam was then dropped; both being finally secured together by an old iron hoop at either extremity. This initiation was performed to the boisterous mirth of the natives, and diverted ourselves not a little.

Captain Bob now bustled about, like an old woman seeing the children to bed. A basket of baked "taro," or Indian turnip, was brought in, and we were given a piece all round. Then a great counterpane, of coarse, brown "tappa," was stretched over the whole party; and, after sundry injunctions to "moee-moee," and be "maitai"—in other words, to go to sleep, and be good boys—we were left to ourselves, fairly put to bed and tucked in.

Much talk was now had concerning our prospects in life; but the doctor and I, who lay side by side, thinking the occasion better adapted to meditation, kept pretty silent; and, before long, the rest ceased conversing, and, wearied with loss of rest on board the frigate, were soon sound asleep.

After sliding from one revery into another, I started, and gave the doctor a pinch. He was dreaming, however; and, resolved to follow his example, I troubled him no more.

How the rest managed, I know not; but, for my own part, I found it very hard to get asleep. The consciousness of having one's foot *pinned;* and the impossibility of getting it anywhere else than just where it was, was most distressing.

But this was not all: there was no way of lying but straight on your back; unless, to be sure, one's limb went round and round in the ankle, like a swivel. Upon getting into a sort of doze, it was no wonder this uneasy posture gave me the nightmare. Under the delusion that I was about some gymnastics or other, I gave my unfortunate member such a twitch, that I started up with the idea that some one was dragging the stocks away.

Captain Bob and his friends lived in a little hamlet hard by; and when morning showed in the East, the old gentleman came forth from that direction likewise, emerging from a grove, and saluting us loudly as he approached.

Finding every body awake, he set us at liberty; and, leading us down to the stream, ordered every man to strip and bathe.

"All han's, my boy, hanna-hanna, wash!" he cried. Bob was a linguist, and had been to sea in his day, as he many a time afterward told us.

At this moment, we were all alone with him; and it would have been the easiest thing in the world to have given him the slip; but he seemed to have no idea of such a thing; treating us so frankly and cordially, indeed, that even had we thought of running, we would have been ashamed of attempting it. He very well knew, nevertheless (as we ourselves were not slow in finding out), that, for various reasons, any attempt of the kind, without some previously arranged plan for leaving the island, would be certain to fail.

As Bob was a rare one every way, I must give some account of him. There was a good deal of "personal appearance" about him; in short, he was a corpulent giant, over six feet in height, and literally as big round as a hogshead. The enormous bulk of some of the Tahitians has been frequently spoken of by voyagers.

Beside being the English consul's jailer, as it were, he carried on a little Tahitian farming; that is to say, he owned several groves of the bread-fruit and palm, and never hindered their growing. Close by was a "taro" patch of his, which he occasionally visited.

Bob seldom disposed of the produce of his lands; it was all needed for domestic consumption. Indeed, for gormandizing, I would have matched him against any three common-council men at a civic feast.

A friend of Bob's told me, that, owing to his voraciousness, his visits to other parts of the island were much dreaded; for, according to Tahitian customs, hospitality without charge is enjoined upon every one; and though it is reciprocal in most cases, in Bob's it was almost out of the question. The damage done to a native larder in one of his morning calls, was more than could be made good by his entertainer's spending the holydays with him.

The old man, as I have hinted, had, once upon a time, been a cruise or two in a whaling-vessel; and, therefore, he prided himself upon his English. Having acquired what he knew of it in the forecastle, he talked little else than sailor phrases, which sounded whimsically enough.

I asked him one day how old he was. "Olee?" he exclaimed, looking very profound in consequence of thoroughly understanding so subtile a question— "Oh! very olee—'tousand 'ear—more—big man when Capin Tootee (Captain Cook) heavey in sight." (In sea parlance, came into view.)

This was a thing impossible; but adapting my discourse to the man, I rejoined—"Ah! you see Capin Tootee—well, how you like him?"

"Oh! he maitai (good) friend of me, and know my wife."

On my assuring him strongly, that he could not have been born at the time, he explained himself by saying, that he was speaking of his father, all the while. This, indeed, might very well have been.

It is a curious fact, that all these people, young and old, will tell you that they have enjoyed the honor of a personal acquaintance with the great navigator; and if you listen to them, they will go on and tell anecdotes without end. This springs from nothing but their great desire to please; well knowing that a more agreeable topic for a white man could not be selected. As for the anachronism of the thing, they seem to have no idea of it: days and years are all the same to them.

After our sunrise bath, Bob once more placed us in the stocks, almost moved to tears at subjecting us to so great a hardship; but he could not treat us otherwise, he said, on pain of the consul's displeasure. How long we were to be confined, he did not know; nor what was to be done with us in the end.

As noon advanced, and no signs of a meal were visible, some one inquired whether we were to be boarded, as well as lodged, at the Hotel de Calabooza?

"Vast heavey" (avast heaving, or wait a bit)—said Bob—"kow-kow" (food) "come ship by by."

And, sure enough, along comes Rope Yarn with a wooden bucket of the Julia's villainous biscuit. With a grin, he said it was a present from Wilson; it was all we were to get that day. A great cry was now raised; and well was it for the land-lubber, that he had a pair of legs, and the men could not use theirs. One and all, we resolved not to touch the bread, come what come might; and so we told the natives.

Being extravagantly fond of ship-biscuit—the harder the better—they were quite overjoyed; and offered to give us every day, a small quantity of baked bread-fruit and Indian turnip in exchange for the bread. This we agreed to; and every morning afterward, when the bucket came, its contents were at once handed over to Bob and his friends, who never ceased munching until nightfall.

Our exceedingly frugal meal of bread-fruit over, Captain Bob waddled up to us with a couple of long poles hooked at one end, and several large baskets of woven cocoa-nut branches.

Not far off was an extensive grove of orange-trees in full bearing; and myself and another were selected to go with him, and gather a supply for the party. When we went in among the trees, the sumptuousness of the orchard was unlike any thing I had ever seen; while the fragrance shaken from the gently waving boughs, regaled our senses most delightfully.

In many places the trees formed a dense shade, spreading overhead a dark, rustling vault, groined with boughs, and studded here and there with the ripened spheres, like gilded balls. In several places, the overladen branches were borne to the earth, hiding the trunk in a tent of foliage. Once fairly in the grove, we could see nothing else; it was oranges all round.

To preserve the fruit from bruising, Bob, hooking the twigs with his pole, let them fall into his basket. But this would not do for us. Seizing hold of a bough, we brought such a shower to the ground, that our old friend was fain to run from under. Heedless of remonstrance, we then reclined in the shade, and feasted to our heart's content. Heaping up the baskets afterward, we returned to our comrades, by whom our arrival was hailed with loud plaudits; and in a marvelously short time, nothing was left of the oranges we brought, but the rinds.

While inmates of the Calabooza, we had as much of the fruit as we wanted; and to this cause, and others that might be mentioned, may be ascribed the speedy restoration of our sick to comparative health.

The orange of Tahiti is delicious—small and sweet, with a thin, dry rind. Though now abounding, it was unknown before Cook's time, to whom the natives are indebted for so great a blessing. He likewise introduced several other kinds of fruit; among these were the fig, pine-apple, and lemon, now seldom met with. The lime still grows, and some of the poorer natives express the juice to sell to the shipping. It is highly valued as an anti-scorbutic. Nor was the variety of foreign fruits and vegetables which were introduced, the only benefit conferred by the first visitors to the Society group. Cattle and sheep were left at various places. More of them anon.

Thus, after all that of late years has been done for these islanders, Cook and Vancouver may, in one sense at least, be considered their greatest benefactors.

CHAPTER 33

Our place of confinement being open all round, and so near the Broom Road, of course we were in plain sight of every body passing; and, therefore, we had no lack of visitors among such an idle, inquisitive set, as the Tahitians. For a few days, they were coming and going continually; while thus ignobly fast by the foot, we were fain to give passive audience.

During this period, we were the lions of the neighborhood; and, no doubt, strangers from the distant villages were taken to see the "Karhowrees" (white men), in the same way that countrymen, in a city, are gallanted to the Zoological Gardens.

All this gave us a fine opportunity of making observations. I was painfully struck by the considerable number of sickly or deformed persons; undoubtedly made so by a virulent complaint, which, under native treatment, almost invariably affects, in the end, the muscles and bones of the body. In particular, there is a distortion of the back, most unsightly to behold, originating in a horrible form of the malady.

Although this, and other bodily afflictions, were unknown before the discovery of the islands by the whites, there are several cases found of the Fa-Fa, or Elephantiasis—a native disease, which seems to have prevailed among them from the earliest antiquity. Affecting the legs and feet alone, it swells them, in some instances, to the girth of a man's body, covering the skin with scales. It might be supposed, that one, thus afflicted, would be incapable of walking; but, to all appearance, they seem to be nearly as active as any body; apparently, suffering no pain, and bearing the calamity with a degree of cheerfulness truly marvelous.

The Fa-Fa is very gradual in its approaches, and years elapse before the limb is fully swollen. Its origin is ascribed by the natives to various causes; but the general impression seems to be, that it arises, in most cases, from the eating of unripe bread-fruit and Indian turnip. So far as I could find out, it is not hereditary. In no stage do they attempt a cure; the complaint being held incurable.

Speaking of the Fa-Fa, reminds me of a poor fellow, a sailor, whom I afterward saw at Roorootoo, a lone island, some two days' sail from Tahiti.

The island is very small, and its inhabitants nearly extinct. We sent a boat off to see whether any yams were to be had, as formerly, the yams of Roorootoo were as famous among the islands round about, as Sicily oranges in the Mediterranean. Going ashore, to my surprise, I was accosted, near a little shanty of a church, by a white man, who limped forth from a wretched hut. His hair and beard were unshorn, his face deadly pale and haggard, and one limb swelled with the Fa-Fa to an incredible bigness. This was the first instance of a foreigner suffering from it, that I had ever seen, or heard of; and the spectacle shocked me accordingly.

He had been there for years. From the first symptoms, he could not believe his complaint to be what it really was, and trusted it would soon disappear. But when it became plain, that his only chance for recovery was a speedy change of climate, no ship would receive him as a sailor: to think of being taken as a passenger, was idle. This speaks little for the humanity of sea captains; but the truth is, that those in the Pacific have little enough of the virtue; and, nowadays, when so many charitable appeals are made to them, they have become callous.

I pitied the poor fellow from the bottom of my heart; but nothing could I do, as our captain was inexorable. "Why," said he, "here we are—started on a six months' cruise—I can't put back; and he is better off on the island than at sea. So on Roorootoo he must die." And probably he did.

I afterward heard of this melancholy object, from two seamen. His attempts to leave were still unavailing, and his hard fate was fast closing in.

Notwithstanding the physical degeneracy of the Tahitians as a people, among the chiefs, individuals of personable figures are still frequently met with; and, occasionally, majestic-looking men, and diminutive women as lovely as the nymphs who, nearly a century ago, swam round the ships of Wallis. In these instances, Tahitian beauty is quite as seducing as it proved to the crew of the Bounty; the young girls being just such creatures as a poet would picture in the tropics—soft, plump, and dreamy-eyed.

The natural complexion of both sexes is quite light; but the males appear much darker, from their exposure to the sun. A dark complexion, however, in a man, is highly esteemed, as indicating strength of both body and soul. Hence there is a saying, of great antiquity among them,

> "If dark the cheek of the mother,
>   The son will sound the war-conch;
> If strong her frame, he will give laws."

With this idea of manliness, no wonder the Tahitians regard all pale and tepid-looking Europeans, as weak and feminine; whereas, a sailor, with a cheek like the breast of a roast turkey, is held a lad of brawn: to use their own phrase, a "taata tona," or man of bones.

Speaking of bones, recalls an ugly custom of theirs, now obsolete—that of making fish-hooks and gimblets out of those of their enemies. This beats the Scandinavians turning people's skulls into cups and saucers.

But to return to the Calabooza Beretanee. Immense was the interest we excited among the throngs that called there; they would stand talking about us by the hour, growing most unnecessarily excited too, and dancing up and down with all the vivacity of their race. They invariably sided with us; flying out against the consul, and denouncing him as "Ita maitai nuee," or very bad exceedingly. They must have borne him some grudge or other.

Nor were the women, sweet souls, at all backward in visiting. Indeed, they manifested even more interest than the men; gazing at us with eyes full of a thousand meanings, and conversing with marvelous rapidity. But, alas! inquisitive though they were, and, doubtless, taking some passing compassion on us, there was little real feeling in them after all, and still less sentimental sympathy. Many of them laughed outright at us, noting only what was ridiculous in our plight.

I think it was the second day of our confinement, that a wild, beautiful girl burst into the Calabooza, and, throwing herself into an arch attitude, stood afar off, and gazed at us. She was a heartless one:—tickled to death with Black Dan's nursing his chafed ankle, and indulging in certain moral reflections on the consul and Captain Guy. After laughing her fill at him, she condescended to notice the rest; glancing from one to another, in the most methodical and provoking manner imaginable. Whenever any thing struck her comically, you saw it like a flash—her finger leveled instantaneously, and, flinging herself back, she gave loose to strange, hollow little notes of laughter, that sounded like the bass of a music-box, playing a lively air with the lid down.

Now, I knew not, that there was any thing in my own appearance calculated to disarm ridicule; and, indeed, to have looked at all heroic, under the circumstances, would have been rather difficult. Still, I could not but feel exceedingly annoyed at the prospect of being screamed at in turn, by this mischievous young witch, even though she were but an islander. And, to tell a secret, her beauty had something to do with this sort of feeling; and, pinioned as I was, to a log, and clad most unbecomingly, I began to grow sentimental.

Ere her glance fell upon me, I had, unconsciously, thrown myself into the most graceful attitude I could assume, leaned my head upon my hand, and summoned up as abstracted an expression as possible. Though my face was averted, I soon felt it flush, and knew that the glance was on me: deeper and deeper grew the flush, and not a sound of laughter.

Delicious thought! she was moved at the sight of me. I could stand it no longer, but started up. Lo! there she was; her great hazel eyes rounding and rounding in her head, like two stars, her whole frame in a merry quiver, and an expression about the mouth that was sudden and violent death to any thing like sentiment.

The next moment she spun round, and, bursting from peal to peal of laughter, went racing out of the Calabooza; and, in mercy to me, never returned.

CHAPTER 34

A few days passed; and, at last, our docility was rewarded by some indulgence on the part of Captain Bob.

He allowed the entire party to be at large during the day; only enjoining upon us always to keep within hail. This, to be sure, was in positive disobedience to

Wilson's orders; and so, care had to be taken that he should not hear of it. There was little fear of the natives telling him; but strangers traveling the Broom Road might. By way of precaution, boys were stationed as scouts along the road. At sight of a white man, they sounded the alarm; when we all made for our respective holes (the stocks being purposely left open): the beam then descended, and we were prisoners. As soon as the traveler was out of sight, of course, we were liberated.

Notwithstanding the regular supply of food which we obtained from Captain Bob and his friends, it was so small, that we often felt most intolerably hungry. We could not blame them for not bringing us more, for we soon became aware that they had to pinch themselves, in order to give us what they did; beside, they received nothing for their kindness but the daily bucket of bread.

Among a people, like the Tahitians, what we call "hard times," can only be experienced in a scarcity of edibles; yet, so destitute are many of the common people, that this most distressing consequence of civilization may be said, with them, to be ever present. To be sure, the natives about the Calabooza, had abundance of limes and oranges; but what were *these* good for, except to impart a still keener edge to appetites which there was so little else to gratify? During the height of the bread-fruit season, they fare better; but, at other times, the demands of the shipping exhaust the uncultivated resources of the island; and the lands being mostly owned by the chiefs, the inferior orders have to suffer for their cupidity. Deprived of their nets, many of them would starve.

As Captain Bob insensibly remitted his watchfulness, and we began to stroll farther and farther from the Calabooza, we managed, by a systematic foraging upon the country round about, to make up for some of our deficiencies. And fortunate it was, that the houses of the wealthier natives were just as open to us as those of the most destitute; we were treated as kindly in one as the other.

Once in a while, we came in at the death of a chief's pig; the noise of whose slaughtering was generally to be heard at a great distance. An occasion like this gathers the neighbors together, and they have a bit of a feast, where a stranger is always welcome. A good loud squeal, therefore, was music in our ears. It showed something going on in that direction.

Breaking in upon the party tumultuously, as we did, we always created a sensation. Sometimes, we found the animal still alive and struggling; in which case, it was generally dropped at our approach. To provide for these emergencies, Flash Jack generally repaired to the scene of operations with a sheath knife between his teeth, and a club in his hand. Others were exceedingly officious in singeing off the bristles, and disemboweling. Doctor Long Ghost and myself, however, never meddled with these preliminaries, but came to the feast itself, with unimpaired energies.

Like all lank men, my long friend had an appetite of his own. Others occasionally went about seeking what they might devour, but *he* was always on the alert.

He had an ingenious way of obviating an inconvenience which we all experienced at times. The islanders seldom use salt with their food; so he begged Rope Yarn to bring him some from the ship; also a little pepper, if he could; which, accordingly, was done. This he placed in a small leather wallet—a "monkey bag" (so called by sailors)—usually worn as a purse about the neck.

"In my poor opinion," said Long Ghost, as he tucked the wallet out of sight, "it behooves a stranger, in Tahiti, to have his knife in readiness, and his caster slung."

CHAPTER 39

The ship out of the way, we were quite anxious to know what was going to be done with us. On this head, Captain Bob could tell us nothing; no further at least, than that he still considered himself responsible for our safe-keeping. However, he never put us to bed any more; and we had every thing our own way.

The day after the Julia left, the old man came up to us in great tribulation, saying that the bucket of bread was no longer forthcoming, and that Wilson had refused to send any thing in its place. One and all, we took this for a hint to disperse quietly, and go about our business. Nevertheless, we were not to be shaken off so easily; and taking a malicious pleasure in annoying our old enemy, we resolved, for the present, to stay where we were. For the part he had been acting, we learned that the consul was the laughing-stock of all the foreigners ashore, who frequently twitted him upon his hopeful protegées of the Calabooza Beretanee.

As we were wholly without resources, so long as we remained on the island no better place than Captain Bob's could be selected for an abiding-place. Beside, we heartily loved the old gentleman, and could not think of leaving him; so, telling him to give no thought as to wherewithal we should be clothed and fed, we resolved, by extending and systematizing our foraging operations, to provide for ourselves.

We were greatly assisted by a parting legacy of Jermin's. To him we were indebted for having all our chests sent ashore, and every thing left therein. They were placed in the custody of a petty chief living near by, who was instructed by the consul not to allow them to be taken away; but we might call and make our toilets whenever we pleased.

We went to see Mahinee, the old chief; Captain Bob going along, and stoutly insisting upon having the chattels delivered up. At last this was done;

and in solemn procession the chests were borne by the natives to the Calabooza. Here, we disposed them about quite tastefully; and made such a figure, that in the eyes of old Bob and his friends, the Calabooza Beretanee was by far the most sumptuously furnished saloon in Tahiti.

Indeed, so long as it remained thus furnished, the native courts of the district were held there; the judge, Mahinee, and his associates, sitting upon one of the chests, and the culprits and spectators thrown at full length upon the ground, both inside of the building, and under the shade of the trees without; while, leaning over the stocks as from a gallery, the worshipful crew of the Julia looked on, and canvassed the proceedings.

I should have mentioned before, that previous to the vessel's departure, the men had bartered away all the clothing they could possibly spare; but now, it was resolved to be more provident.

The contents of the chests were of the most miscellaneous description:—sewing utensils, marling-spikes, strips of calico, bits of rope, jackknives; nearly every thing, in short, that a seaman could think of. But of wearing apparel, there was little but old frocks, remnants of jackets, and legs of trowsers, with now and then the foot of a stocking. These, however, were far from being valueless; for, among the poorer Tahitians, every thing European is highly esteemed. They come from "Beretanee, Fenooa Pararee" (Britain, Land of Wonders), and that is enough.

The chests themselves were deemed exceedingly precious, especially those with unfractured locks, which would absolutely click, and enable the owner to walk off with the key. Scars, however, and bruises, were considered great blemishes. One old fellow, smitten with the doctor's large mahogany chest (a well filled one, by the by), and finding infinite satisfaction in merely sitting thereon, was detected in the act of applying a healing ointment to a shocking scratch which impaired the beauty of the lid.

There is no telling the love of a Tahitian for a sailor's trunk. So ornamental is it held as an article of furniture in his hut, that the women are incessantly tormenting their husbands to bestir themselves, and make them a present of one. When obtained, no pier-table just placed in a drawing-room, is regarded with half the delight. For these reasons, then, our coming into possession of our estate at this time, was an important event.

The islanders are much like the rest of the world; and the news of our good fortune brought us troops of "tayos" or friends, eager to form an alliance after the national custom, and do our slightest bidding.

The really curious way in which all the Polynesians are in the habit of making bosom friends at the shortest possible notice, is deserving of remark. Although, among a people like the Tahitians, vitiated as they are by sophisticating influences, this custom has in most cases degenerated into a mere mercenary relation, it nevertheless had its origin in a fine, and in some instances, heroic sentiment, formerly entertained by their fathers.

In the annals of the island are examples of extravagant friendships, unsurpassed by the story of Damon and Pythias: in truth, much more wonderful; for, notwithstanding the devotion—even of life in some cases—to which they led, they were frequently entertained at first sight for some stranger from another island.

Filled with love and admiration for the first whites who came among them, the Polynesians could not testify the warmth of their emotions more strongly, than by instantaneously making their abrupt proffer of friendship. Hence, in old voyages we read of chiefs coming off from the shore in their canoes, and going through with strange antics, expressive of this desire. In the same way, their inferiors accosted the seamen; and thus the practice has continued in some islands down to the present day.

There is a small place, not many days' sail from Tahiti, and seldom visited by shipping, where the vessel touched to which I then happened to belong.

Of course, among the simple-hearted natives, we had a friend all round. Mine was Poky, a handsome youth, who never could do enough for me. Every morning at sunrise, his canoe came alongside loaded with fruits of all kinds; upon being emptied, it was secured by a line to the bowsprit, under which it lay all day long, ready at any time to carry its owner ashore on an errand.

Seeing him so indefatigable, I told Poky one day, that I was a virtuoso in shells and curiosities of all kinds. That was enough; away he paddled for the head of the bay, and I never saw him again for twenty-four hours. The next morning, his canoe came gliding slowly along the shore, with the full-leaved bough of a tree for a sail. For the purpose of keeping the things dry, he had also built a sort of platform just behind the prow, railed in with green wicker-work; and here was a heap of yellow bananas and cowree shells; young cocoanuts and antlers of red coral; two or three pieces of carved wood; a little pocket-idol, black as jet, and rolls of printed tappa.

We were given a holyday; and upon going ashore, Poky, of course, was my companion and guide. For this, no mortal could be better qualified; his native country was not large, and he knew every inch of it. Gallanting me about, every one was stopped and ceremoniously introduced to Poky's "tayo karhowree nuee" or his particular white friend.

He showed me all the lions; but more than all, he took me to see a charming lioness—a young damsel—the daughter of a chief—the reputation of whose charms had spread to the neighboring islands, and even brought suitors therefrom. Among these was Tooboi, the heir of Tamatoy, King of Raiatair, one of the Society Isles. The girl was certainly fair to look upon. Many heavens were in her sunny eyes; and the outline of that arm of hers, peeping forth from a capricious tappa robe, was the very curve of beauty.

Though there was no end to Poky's attentions, not a syllable did he ever breathe of reward; but sometimes he looked very knowing. At last the day came for sailing, and with it, also, his canoe, loaded down to the gunwale with a sea stock of fruits. Giving him all I could spare from my chest, I went on deck to take my place at the windlass; for the anchor was weighing. Poky followed, and heaved with me at the same handspike.

The anchor was soon up; and away we went out of the bay with more than twenty shallops towing astern. At last they left us; but long as I could see him at all, there was Poky, standing alone and motionless in the bow of his canoe.

CHAPTER 44

On Sundays I always attended the principal native church on the outskirts of the village of Papeetee, and not far from the Calabooza Beretanee. It was esteemed the best specimen of architecture in Tahiti.

Of late, they have built their places of worship with more reference to durability than formerly. At one time, there were no less than thirty-six on the island— mere barns, tied together with thongs, which went to destruction in a very few years.

One, built many years ago in this style, was a most remarkable structure. It was erected by Pomaree II., who, on this occasion, showed all the zeal of a royal proselyte. The building was over seven hundred feet in length, and of a proportionate width; the vast ridge-pole was at intervals supported by a row of thirty-six cylindrical trunks of the bread-fruit tree; and, all round, the wall-plates rested on shafts of the palm. The roof—steeply inclining to within a man's height of the ground—was thatched with leaves, and the sides of the edifice were open. Thus spacious was the Royal Mission Chapel of Papoar.

At its dedication, three distinct sermons were, from different pulpits, preached to an immense concourse gathered from all parts of the island.

As the chapel was built by the king's command, nearly as great a multitude was employed in its construction, as swarmed over the scaffolding of the great temple of the Jews. Much less time, however, was expended. In less than three weeks from planting the first post, the last tier of palmetto-leaves drooped from the eaves, and the work was done.

Apportioned to the several chiefs and their dependents, the labor, though immense, was greatly facilitated by every one's bringing his post, or his rafter, or his pole strung with thatching, ready for instant use. The materials thus prepared being afterward secured together by thongs, there was literally "neither hammer, nor axe, nor any tool of iron head in the house while it was building."

But the most singular circumstance connected with this South Sea cathedral, remains to be related. As well for the beauty, as the advantages of such a site, the islanders love to dwell near the mountain streams; and so, a considerable brook, after descending from the hills and watering the valley, was bridged over in three places, and swept clean through the chapel.

Flowing waters! what an accompaniment to the songs of the sanctuary; mingling with them, the praises and thanksgivings of the green solitudes inland.

But the chapel of the Polynesian Solomon has long since been deserted. Its thousand rafters of habiscus have decayed, and fallen to the ground; and now, the stream murmurs over them in its bed.

The present metropolitan church of Tahiti is very unlike the one just described. It is of moderate dimensions, boarded over, and painted white. It is furnished also with blinds, but no sashes; indeed, were it not for the rustic thatch, it would remind one of a plain chapel at home.

The wood-work was all done by foreign carpenters, of whom there are always several about Papeetee.

Within, its aspect is unique, and can not fail to interest a stranger. The rafters overhead are bound round with fine matting of variegated dyes; and all along the ridge-pole, these trappings hang pendent, in alternate bunches of tassels and deep fringes of stained grass. The floor is composed of rude planks. Regular aisles run between ranges of native settees, bottomed with crossed braids of the cocoa-nut fibre, and furnished with backs.

But the pulpit, made of a dark, lustrous wood, and standing at one end, is by far the most striking object. It is preposterously lofty; indeed, a capital bird's-eye view of the congregation ought to be had from its summit.

Nor does the church lack a gallery, which runs round on three sides, and is supported by columns of the cocoa-nut tree.

Its facings are here and there daubed over with a tawdry blue; and in other places (without the slightest regard to uniformity), patches of the same color may be seen. In their ardor to decorate the sanctuary, the converts must have borrowed each a brush full of paint, and zealously daubed away at the first surface that offered.

As hinted, the general impression is extremely curious. Little light being admitted, and every thing being of a dark color, there is an indefinable Indian aspect of duskiness, throughout. A strange, woody smell, also—more or less pervading every considerable edifice in Polynesia—is at once perceptible. It suggests the idea of worm-eaten idols packed away in some old lumber-room at hand.

For the most part, the congregation attending this church is composed of the better and wealthier orders—the chiefs and their retainers; in short, the rank and fashion of the island. This class is infinitely superior in personal beauty and general healthfulness to the "marenhoar," or common people; the latter having been more exposed to the worst and most debasing evils of foreign intercourse. On Sundays, the former are invariably arrayed in their finery; and thus appear to the best advantage. Nor are they driven to the chapel, as some of their inferiors are to other places of worship; on the contrary, capable of maintaining a handsome exterior and possessing greater intelligence, they go voluntarily.

In respect of the woodland colonnade supporting its galleries, I called this chapel the Church of the Cocoa-nuts.

It was the first place for Christian worship in Polynesia that I had seen; and the impression upon entering during service was all the stronger. Majestic-looking chiefs, whose fathers had hurled the battle-club, and old men who had seen sacrifices smoking upon the altars of Oro, were there. And hark! hanging from the boughs of a bread-fruit tree without, a bell is being struck with a bar of iron by a native lad. In the same spot, the blast of the war-conch had often resounded. But to the proceedings within.

The place is well filled. Everywhere meets the eye the gay calico draperies worn on great occasions by the higher classes, and forming a strange contrast of patterns and colors. In some instances, these are so fashioned as to resemble as much as possible, European garments. This is in excessively bad taste. Coats and pantaloons, too, are here and there seen; but they look awkwardly enough, and take away from the general effect.

But it is the array of countenances that most strikes you. Each is suffused with the peculiar animation of the Polynesians, when thus collected in large numbers. Every robe is rustling, every limb in motion, and an incessant buzzing going on throughout the assembly. The tumult is so great, that the voice of the placid old missionary, who now rises, is almost inaudible. Some degree of silence is at length obtained through the exertions of half-a-dozen strapping fellows, in white shirts and no pantaloons. Running in among the settees, they are at great pains to inculcate the impropriety of making a noise, by creating a most unnecessary racket themselves. This part of the service was quite comical.

There is a most interesting Sabbath School connected with the church; and the scholars, a vivacious, mischievous set, were in one part of the gallery. I was amused by a party in a corner. The teacher sat at one end of the bench, with a meek little fellow by his side. When the others were disorderly, this young martyr received a rap; intended, probably, as a sample of what the rest might expect, if they didn't amend.

Standing in the body of the church, and leaning against a pillar, was an old man, in appearance very different from others of his countrymen. He wore nothing but a coarse, scant mantle, of faded tappa; and from his staring, bewildered manner, I set him down as an aged bumpkin from the interior, unaccustomed to the strange sights and sounds of the metropolis. This old worthy was sharply reprimanded for standing up, and thus intercepting the view of those behind; but not comprehending exactly what was said to him, one of the white liveried gentry made no ceremony of grasping him by the shoulders, and fairly crushing him down into a seat.

During all this, the old missionary in the pulpit—as well as his associates beneath, never ventured to interfere—leaving every thing to native management. With South Sea islanders, assembled in any numbers, there is no other way of getting along.

CHAPTER 46

A worthy young man, formerly a friend of mine (I speak of Kooloo with all possible courtesy, since after our intimacy there would be an impropriety in doing otherwise)—this worthy youth, having some genteel notions of retirement, dwelt in a "maroo boro," or bread-fruit shade, a pretty nook in a wood, mid-way between the Calabooza Beretanee and the Church of Cocoa-nuts. Hence, at the latter place, he was one of the most regular worshipers.

Kooloo was a blade. Standing up in the congregation in all the bravery of a striped calico shirt, with the skirts rakishly adjusted over a pair of white sailor trousers, and hair well anointed with cocoa-nut oil, he ogled the ladies with an air of supreme satisfaction. Nor were his glances unreturned.

But such looks as the Tahitian belles cast at each other: frequently turning up their noses at the advent of a new cotton mantle recently imported in the chest of some amorous sailor. Upon one occasion, I observed a group of young girls, in tunics of coarse, soiled sheeting, disdainfully pointing at a damsel in a flaming red one. "Oee tootai owree!" said they with ineffable scorn, "itai maitai!" (you are a good-for-nothing huzzy, no better than you should be).

Now, Kooloo communed with the church; so did all these censorious young ladies. Yet after eating bread-fruit at the Eucharist, I knew several of them, the same night, to be guilty of some sad derelictions.

Puzzled by these things, I resolved to find out, if possible, what ideas, if any, they entertained of religion; but as one's spiritual concerns are rather delicate for a stranger to meddle with, I went to work as adroitly as I could.

Farnow, an old native who had recently retired from active pursuits, having thrown up the business of being a sort of running footman to the queen, had settled down in a snug little retreat, not fifty rods from Captain Bob's. His selecting our vicinity for his residence, may have been with some view to the advantages it afforded for introducing his three daughters into polite circles. At any rate, not averse to receiving the attentions of so devoted a gallant as the doctor, the sisters (communicants, be it remembered) kindly extended to him, free permission to visit them sociably, whenever he pleased.

We dropped in one evening, and found the ladies at home. My long friend engaged his favorites, the two younger girls, at the game of "Now," or hunting a stone under three piles of tappa. For myself, I lounged on a mat with Ideea the eldest, dallying with her grass fan, and improving my knowledge of Tahitian.

The occasion was well adapted to my purpose, and I began.

"Ah, Ideea, mickonaree oee?" the same as drawling out—"By the by, Miss Ideea, do you belong to the church?"

"Yes, me mickonaree," was the reply.

But the assertion was at once qualified by certain reservations; so curious, that I can not forbear their relation.

"Mickonaree *ena*" (church member *here*), exclaimed she, laying her hand upon her mouth, and a strong emphasis on the adverb. In the same way, and with similar exclamations, she touched her eyes and hands. This done, her whole air changed in an instant; and she gave me to understand, by unmistakable gestures, that in certain other respects she was not exactly a "mickonaree." In short, Ideea was

> "A sad good Christian at the heart—
> A very heathen in the carnal part."*

The exclamation terminated in a burst of laughter, in which all three sisters joined; and for fear of looking silly, the doctor and myself. As soon as good-breeding would permit, we took leave.

The hypocrisy in matters of religion, so apparent in all Polynesian converts, is most injudiciously nourished in Tahiti, by a zealous, and in many cases, a coercive superintendence over their spiritual well-being. But it is only manifested with respect to the common people, their superiors being exempted.

On Sunday mornings, when the prospect is rather small for a full house in the minor churches, a parcel of fellows are actually sent out with ratans into the highways and byways as whippers-in of the congregation. This is a sober fact.**

These worthies constitute a religious police; and you always know them by the great white diapers they wear. On week days, they are quite as busy as on Sundays; to the great terror of the inhabitants, going all over the island, and spying out the wickedness thereof.

Moreover, they are the collectors of fines—levied generally in grass mats—for obstinate non-attendance upon divine worship, and other offenses amenable to the ecclesiastical judicature of the missionaries.

Old Bob called these fellows "kannakippers," a corruption, I fancy, of our word constable.

* Pope. (Epistle to a lady.)
**With abhorrence and disgust the custom is alluded to by a late benevolent visitor at the island. See page 763 of the "Memoirs of the Life and Gospel Labors of the late Daniel Wheeler." A work hereafter to be more particularly alluded to.

He bore them a bitter grudge; and one day, drawing near home, and learning that two of them were just then making a domiciliary visit at his house, he ran behind a bush; and as they came forth, two green bread-fruit from a hand unseen, took them each between the shoulders. The sailors in the Calabooza were witnesses to this, as well as several natives; who, when the intruders were out of sight, applauded Captain Bob's spirit in no measured terms; the ladies present vehemently joining in. Indeed, the kannakippers have no greater enemies than the latter. And no wonder: the impertinent varlets, popping into their houses at all hours, are forever prying into their peccadilloes.

Kooloo, who at times was patriotic and pensive, and mourned the evils under which his country was groaning, frequently inveighed against the statute, which thus authorized an utter stranger to interfere with domestic arrangements. He himself—quite a ladies' man—had often been annoyed thereby. He considered the kannakippers a bore.

Besides their confounded inquisitiveness, they add insult to injury, by making a point of dining out every day at some hut within the limits of their jurisdiction. As for the gentleman of the house, his meek endurance of these things is amazing. But "good easy man," there is nothing for him but to be as hospitable as possible.

These gentry are indefatigable. At the dead of night prowling round the houses, and in the daytime hunting amorous couples in the groves. Yet in one instance, the chase completely baffled them.

It was thus.

Several weeks previous to our arrival at the island, some one's husband and another person's wife, having taken a mutual fancy for each other, went out for a walk. The alarm was raised, and with hue and cry they were pursued; but nothing was seen of them again until the lapse of some ninety days; when we were called out from the Calabooza to behold a great mob inclosing the lovers, and escorting them for trial to the village.

Their appearance was most singular. The girdle excepted, they were quite naked; their hair was long, burned yellow at the ends, and entangled with burs; and their bodies scratched and scarred in all directions. It seems, that acting upon the "love in a cottage" principle, they had gone right into the interior; and throwing up a hut in an uninhabited valley, had lived there, until in an unlucky stroll, they were observed and captured.

They were subsequently condemned to make one hundred fathoms of Broom Road—a six months' work, if not more.

Often, when seated in a house, conversing quietly with its inmates, I have known them betray the greatest confusion at the sudden announcement of a kannakipper's being in sight. To be reported by one of these officials as a "Tootai Owree" (in general, signifying a bad person or disbeliever in Christianity), is as much dreaded as the forefinger of Titus Oates was, leveled at an alleged papist.

But the islanders take a sly revenge upon them. Upon entering a dwelling, the kannakippers oftentimes volunteer a pharisaical prayer-meeting: hence, they go in secret by the name of "Boora-Artuas," literally, "Pray-to-Gods."

CHAPTER 47

Except where the employment of making "tappa" is inflicted as a punishment, the echoes of the cloth-mallet have long since died away in the listless valleys of Tahiti. Formerly, the girls spent their mornings like ladies at their tambour frames; *now,* they are lounged away in almost utter indolence. True, most of them make their own garments; but this comprises but a stitch or two; the ladies of the mission, by the by, being entitled to the credit of teaching them to sew.

The "kihee whihenee," or petticoat, is a mere breadth of white cotton, or calico; loosely enveloping the person, from the waist to the feet. Fastened simply, by a single tuck, or by twisting the upper corners together, this garment frequently becomes disordered; thus affording an opportunity of being coquettishly adjusted. Over the "kihee," they wear a sort of gown, open in front, very loose, and as negligent as you please. The ladies here, never dress for dinner.

But what shall be said of those horrid hats! Fancy a bunch of straw, plaited into the shape of a coal-scuttle, and stuck, bolt upright, on the crown; with a yard or two of red ribbon, flying about like kite-strings. Milliners of Paris, what would ye say to them! Though made by the natives, they are said to have been first contrived and recommended by the missionaries' wives; a report, which, I really trust, is nothing but scandal.

Curious to relate, these things for the head, are esteemed exceedingly becoming. The braiding of the straw is one of the few employments of the higher classes; all of which, but minister to the silliest vanity. The young girls, however, wholly eschew the hats; leaving those dowdy old souls, their mothers, to make frights of themselves.

As for the men, those who aspire to European garments, seem to have no perception of the relation subsisting between the various parts of a gentleman's costume. To the wearer of a coat, for instance, pantaloons are by no means indispensable; and, a bell-crowned hat and a girdle, are full dress. The young sailor, for whom Kooloo deserted me, presented him with a shaggy old pea-jacket; and, with this buttoned up to his chin, under a tropical sun, he promenaded the Broom Road, quite elated. Doctor Long Ghost, who saw him thus, ran away with the idea, that he was under medical treatment at the time—in the act of taking, what the quacks call, a "sweat."

A bachelor friend of Captain Bob rejoiced in the possession of a full European suit; in which he often stormed the ladies' hearts. Having a military leaning, he ornamented the coat with a great scarlet patch on the breast; and mounted it also, here and there, with several regimental buttons, slyly cut from the uniform of a parcel of drunken marines, sent ashore on a holyday from a man-of-war. But, in spite of the ornaments, the dress was not exactly the thing. From the tightness of the cloth across the shoulders, his elbows projected from his sides, like an ungainly rider's; and his ponderous legs were jammed so hard into his slim, nether garments, that the threads of every seam showed; and, at every step, you looked for a catastrophe.

In general, there seems to be no settled style of dressing among the males: they wear any thing they can get; in some cases, awkwardly modifying the fashions of their fathers, so as to accord with their own altered views of what is becoming.

But ridiculous as many of them now appear, in foreign habiliments, the Tahitians presented a far different appearance in the original national costume; which was graceful in the extreme, modest to all but the prudish, and peculiarly adapted to the climate. But the short kilts of dyed tappa, the tasseled maroes, and other articles formerly worn, are, at the present day, prohibited by law, as indecorous. For what reason necklaces and garlands of flowers, among the women, are also forbidden, I never could learn; but, it is said, that they were associated, in some way, with a forgotten heathen observance.

Many pleasant, and, seemingly, innocent sports and pastimes, are likewise interdicted. In old times, there were several athletic games practiced; such as wrestling, foot-racing, throwing the javelin, and archery. In all these they greatly excelled; and, for some, splendid festivals were instituted. Among their everyday amusements, were dancing, tossing the football, kite-flying, flute-playing, and singing traditional ballads; *now,* all punishable offenses; though most of them have been so long in disuse, that they are nearly forgotten.

In the same way, the "Opio," or festive harvest-home of the bread-fruit, has been suppressed; though, as described to me, by Captain Bob, it seemed wholly free from any immoral tendency. Against tattooing, of any kind, there is a severe law.

That this abolition of their national amusements and customs, was not willingly acquiesced in, is shown in the frequent violation of many of the statutes inhibiting them; and, especially, in the frequency with which their "hevars," or dances, are practiced in secret.

Doubtless, in thus denationalizing the Tahitians, as it were, the missionaries were prompted by a sincere desire for good; but the effect has been lamentable.

Supplied with no amusements, in place of those forbidden, the Tahitians, who require more recreation than other people, have sunk into a listlessness, or indulge in sensualities, a hundred times more pernicious, than all the games ever celebrated in the Temple of Tanee.

CHAPTER 52

We went up through groves to an open space, where we heard voices, and a light was glimmering from out a bamboo dwelling. It was the planters' retreat; and in their absence, several girls were keeping house, assisted by an old native, who, wrapped up in tappa, lay in the corner, smoking.

A hasty meal was prepared, and after it we essayed a nap; but, alas! a plague, little anticipated, prevented. Unknown in Tahiti, the musquitoes here fairly eddied round us. But more of them anon.

We were up betimes, and strolled out to view the country. We were in the valley of Martair; shut in, on both sides, by lofty hills. Here and there, were cliffs, gay with flowering shrubs, or hung with pendulous vines, swinging blossoms in the air. Of considerable width at the sea, the vale contracts as it runs inland; terminating, at the distance of several miles, in a range of the most grotesque elevations, which seem embattled with turrets and towers, grown over with verdure, and waving with trees. The valley itself, is a wilderness of woodland; with links of streams flashing through, and narrow pathways, fairly tunneled through masses of foliage.

All alone, in this wild place, was the abode of the planters; the only one back from the beach—their sole neighbors, the few fishermen and their families, dwelling in a small grove of cocoa-nut trees, whose roots were washed by the sea.

The cleared tract which they occupied, comprised some thirty acres, level as a prairie, part of which was under cultivation; the whole being fenced in, by a stout palisade of trunks and boughs of trees, staked firmly in the ground. This was necessary, as a defense against the wild cattle and hogs overrunning the island.

Thus far, Tombez potatoes* were the principal crop raised; a ready sale for them being obtained among the shipping touching at Papeetee. There was a small patch of the *taro,* or Indian turnip, also; another of yams; and, in one corner, a thrifty growth of the sugar-cane, just ripening.

On the side of the inclosure, next the sea, was the house; newly built of bamboos, in the native style. The furniture consisted of a couple of sea-chests,

* Perhaps the finest sweet potato in the world. It derives its name from a district of Peru, near Cape Blanco, very favorable to its growth; where, also, it is extensively cultivated: the root is very large; sometimes as big as a good-sized melon.

an old box, a few cooking utensils, and agricultural tools; together with three fowling-pieces, hanging from a rafter; and two enormous hammocks, swinging in opposite corners, and composed of dried bullocks' hides, stretched out with poles.

The whole plantation was shut in by a dense forest; and, close by the house, a dwarfed "Aoa," or species of banian-tree, had purposely been left twisting over the palisade, in the most grotesque manner, and thus made a pleasant shade. The branches of this curious tree afforded low perches, upon which the natives frequently squatted, after the fashion of their race, and smoked and gossiped by the hour.

We had a good breakfast of fish—speared by the natives, before sunrise, on the reef—pudding of Indian turnip, fried bananas, and roasted bread-fruit.

During the repast, our new friends were quite sociable and communicative. It seems that, like nearly all uneducated foreigners, residing in Polynesia, they had, some time previous, deserted from a ship; and, having heard a good deal about the money to be made by raising supplies for whaling-vessels, they determined upon embarking in the business. Strolling about, with this intention, they, at last, came to Martair; and thinking the soil would suit, set themselves to work. They began, by finding out the owner of the particular spot coveted, and then making a "tayo" of him.

He turned out to be Tonoi, the chief of the fishermen; who, one day, when exhilarated with brandy, tore his meager tappa from his loins, and gave me to know, that he was allied by blood with Pomaree herself; and that his mother came from the illustrious race of pontiffs, who, in old times, swayed their bamboo crosier over all the pagans of Imeeo. A regal, and right reverend lineage! But, at the time I speak of, the dusky noble was in decayed circumstances, and therefore, by no means unwilling to alienate a few useless acres. As an equivalent, he received from the strangers two or three rheumatic old muskets, several red woolen shirts, and a promise to be provided for in his old age: he was always to find a home with the planters.

Desirous of living on the cozy footing of a father-in-law, he frankly offered his two daughters for wives; but as such, they were politely declined; the adventurers, though not averse to courting, being unwilling to entangle themselves in a matrimonial alliance, however splendid in point of family.

Tonoi's men, the fishermen of the grove, were a sad set. Secluded, in a great measure, from the ministrations of the missionaries, they gave themselves up to all manner of lazy wickedness. Strolling among the trees of a morning, you came upon them napping on the shady side of a canoe hauled up among the bushes; lying under a tree smoking; or, more frequently still, gambling with pebbles; though, a little tobacco excepted, what they gambled for at their outlandish games, it would be hard to tell. Other idle diversions they had also, in which they seemed to take great delight. As for fishing, it employed but a small part of their time. Upon the whole, they were a merry, indigent, godless race.

Tonoi, the old sinner, leaning against the fallen trunk of a cocoa-nut tree, invariably squandered his mornings at pebbles; a gray-headed rook of a native regularly plucking him of every other stick of tobacco obtained from his friends, the planters. Toward afternoon, he strolled back to their abode; where he tarried till the next morning, smoking and snoozing, and, at times, prating about the hapless fortunes of the House of Tonoi. But like any other easy-going old dotard, he seemed for the most part perfectly content with cheerful board and lodging.

On the whole, the valley of Martair was the quietest place imaginable. Could the musquitoes be induced to emigrate, one might spend the month of August there quite pleasantly. But this was not the case with the luckless Long Ghost and myself; as will presently be seen.

CHAPTER 56

The night following the hunting trip. Long Ghost and myself, after a valiant defense, had to fly the house on account of the musquitoes.

And here I can not avoid relating a story, rife among the natives, concerning the manner in which these insects were introduced upon the island.

Some years previous, a whaling captain, touching at an adjoining bay, got into difficulty with its inhabitants, and at last carried his complaint before one of the native tribunals; but receiving no satisfaction, and deeming himself aggrieved, he resolved upon taking signal revenge. One night, he towed a rotten old water-cask ashore, and left it in a neglected *Taro* patch, where the ground was warm and moist. Hence the musquitoes.

I tried my best to learn the name of this man: and hereby do what I can to hand it down to posterity. It was Coleman—Nathan Coleman. The ship belonged to Nantucket.

When tormented by the musquitoes, I found much relief in coupling the word "Coleman" with another of one syllable, and pronouncing them together energetically.

The doctor suggested a walk to the beach, where there was a long, low shed tumbling to pieces, but open lengthwise to a current of air which he thought might keep off the musquitoes. So thither we went.

The ruin partially sheltered a relic of times gone by, which, a few days after, we examined with much curiosity. It was an old war-canoe, crumbling to dust. Being supported by the same rude blocks upon which, apparently, it had years before been hollowed out, in all probability it had never been afloat.

Outside, it seemed originally stained of a green color, which, here and there, was now changed into a dingy purple. The prow terminated in a high, blunt beak; both sides were covered with carving; and upon the stern was something which Long Ghost maintained to be the arms of the royal House of Pomaree. The device had an heraldic look, certainly—being two sharks with the talons of hawks clawing a knot left projecting from the wood.

The canoe was at least forty feet long, about two wide, and four deep. The upper part—consisting of narrow planks laced together with cords of sinnate—had in many places fallen off, and lay decaying upon the ground. Still, there were ample accommodations left for sleeping; and in we sprang—the doctor into the bow, and I, into the stern. I soon fell asleep; but waking suddenly, cramped in every joint from my constrained posture, I thought, for an instant, that I must have been prematurely screwed down in my coffin.

Presenting my compliments to Long Ghost, I asked how it fared with *him*.

"Bad enough," he replied, as he tossed about in the outlandish rubbish lying in the bottom of our couch. "Pah! how these old mats smell!"

As he continued talking in this exciting strain for some time, I at last made no reply, having resumed certain mathematical reveries to induce repose. But finding the multiplication-table of no avail, I summoned up a grayish image of chaos in a sort of sliding fluidity, and was just falling into a nap on the strength of it, when I heard a solitary and distinct buzz. The hour of my calamity was at hand. One blended hum, the creature darted into the canoe like a small sword-fish; and I out of it.

Upon getting into the open air, to my surprise, there was Long Ghost, fanning himself wildly with an old paddle. He had just made a noiseless escape from a swarm, which had attacked his own end of the canoe.

It was now proposed to try the water; so a small fishing canoe, hauled up near by, was quickly lanched; and paddling a good distance off, we dropped overboard the native contrivance for an anchor—a heavy stone, attached to a cable of braided bark. At this part of the island, the encircling reef was close to the shore, leaving the water within smooth, and extremely shallow.

It was a blessed thought! We knew nothing till sunrise, when the motion of our aquatic cot awakened us. I looked up, and beheld Zeke wading toward the shore, and towing us after him by the bark cable. Pointing to the reef, he told us we had had a narrow escape.

It was true enough; the water-sprites had rolled our stone out of its noose, and we had floated away.

CHAPTER 57

Fair dawned, over the hills of Martair, the jocund morning of our hunt.

Every thing had been prepared for it overnight; and, when we arrived at the house, a good breakfast was spread by Shorty: and old Tonoi was bustling about like an innkeeper. Several of his men, also, were in attendance, to accompany us with calabashes of food; and, in case we met with any success, to officiate as bearers of burdens, on our return.

Apprised, the evening previous, of the meditated sport, the doctor had announced his willingness to take part therein.

Now, subsequent events made us regard this expedition as a shrewd device of the Yankee's. Once get us off on a pleasure trip, and with what face could we afterward refuse to work? Beside, he enjoyed all the credit of giving us a holyday. Nor did he omit assuring us, that, work or play, our wages were all the while running on.

A dilapidated old musket of Tonoi's, was borrowed for the doctor. It was exceedingly short and heavy, with a clumsy lock, which required a strong finger to pull the trigger. On trying the piece, by firing at a mark, Long Ghost was satisfied that it could not fail of doing execution: the charge went one way, and he the other.

Upon this, he endeavored to negotiate an exchange of muskets with Shorty; but the Cockney was proof against his blandishments; at last he intrusted his weapon to one of the natives to carry for him.

Marshaling our forces, we started for the head of the valley; near which, a path ascended to a range of high land, said to be a favorite resort of the cattle.

Shortly after gaining the heights, a small herd, some way off, was perceived entering a wood. We hurried on; and, dividing our party, went in after them, at four different points; each white man followed by several natives.

I soon found myself in a dense covert; and, after looking round, was just emerging into a clear space, when I heard a report, and a bullet knocked the bark from a tree near by. The same instant, there was a trampling and crashing; and five bullocks, nearly abreast, broke into view across the opening, and plunged right toward the spot where myself and three of the islanders were standing.

They were small, black, vicious-looking creatures; with short, sharp horns, red nostrils, and eyes like coals of fire. On they came—their dark woolly heads hanging down.

By this time, my island backers were roosting among the trees. Glancing round, for an instant, to discover a retreat in case of emergency, I raised my piece, when a voice cried out, from the wood, "Right between the 'orns, Paul! right between the 'orns!" Down went my barrel, in range with a small white tuft on the forehead of the headmost one; and, letting him have it, I darted to one side. As I turned again, the five bullocks shot by like a blast, making the air eddy in their wake.

The Yankee now burst into view, and saluted them in flank. Whereupon, the fierce little bull with the tufted forehead, flirted his long tail over his buttocks; kicked out, with his hind feet, and shot forward a full length. It was nothing but a graze; and, in an instant, they were out of sight, the thicket into which they broke rocking overhead, and marking their progress.

The action over, the heavy artillery came up, in the person of the Long Doctor, with his blunderbuss.

"Where are they?" he cried, out of breath.

"A mile or two h'off, by this time," replied the Cockney. "Lord, Paul! you ought to've sent an 'ail stone into that little black 'un."

While excusing my want of skill, as well as I could, Zeke, rushing forward, suddenly exclaimed, "Creation! what are you 'bout there, Peter?"

Peter, incensed at our ill luck, and ignorantly imputing it to the cowardice of our native auxiliaries, was bringing his piece to bear upon his trembling squire —the musket carrier—now descending a tree.

Pulling trigger, the bullet went high over his head; and, hopping to the ground, bellowing like a calf, the fellow ran away as fast as his heels could carry him. The rest followed us, after this, with fear and trembling.

After forming our line of march anew, we went on for several hours, without catching a glimpse of the game; the reports of the muskets having been heard at a great distance. At last, we mounted a craggy height, to obtain a wide view of the country. From this place, we beheld three cattle, quietly browsing in a green opening of a wood below; the trees shutting them in all round.

A general reëxamination of the muskets now took place, followed by a hasty lunch from the calabashes: we then started. As we descended the mountain-side, the cattle were in plain sight, until we entered the forest, when we lost sight of them for a moment; but only to see them again, as we crept close up to the spot where they grazed.

They were a bull, a cow, and a calf. The cow was lying down in the shade, by the edge of the wood; the calf, sprawling out before her in the grass, licking her lips; while old Taurus himself stood close by, casting a paternal glance at this domestic little scene, and conjugally elevating his nose in the air.

"Now then," said Zeke, in a whisper, "let's take the poor creeturs, while they are huddled together. Crawl along, b'ys; crawl along. Fire together, mind; and not 'til I say the word."

We crept up to the very edge of the open ground, and knelt behind a clump

of bushes; resting our leveled barrels among the branches. The slight rustling
was heard. Taurus turned round, dropped his head to the ground, and sent
forth a low, sullen bellow; then snuffed the air. The cow rose on her fore
knees, pitched forward alarmedly, and stood upon her legs; while the calf, with
ears pricked, got right underneath her. All three were now grouped, and, in
an instant would be off.

"I take the bull," cried our leader; "fire!"

The calf fell like a clod; its dam uttered a cry, and thrust her head into the
thicket; but she turned, and came moaning up to the lifeless calf, going round
and round it, snuffing fiercely with her bleeding nostrils. A crashing in the wood,
and a loud roar, announced the flying bull.

Soon, another shot was fired, and the cow fell. Leaving some of the natives
to look after the dead cattle, the rest of us hurried on after the bull; his dreadful
bellowings guiding us to the spot where he lay. Wounded in the shoulder, in
his fright and agony he had bounded into the wood; but when we came up to
him, he had sunk to the earth in a green hollow, thrusting his black muzzle
into a pool of his own blood, and tossing it over his hide in clots.

The Yankee brought his piece to a rest; and, the next instant, the wild brute
sprang into the air, and with his fore legs crouching under him, fell dead.

Our island friends were now in high spirits; all courage and alacrity. Old
Tonoi thought nothing of taking poor Taurus himself by the horns, and peering
into his glazed eyes.

Our ship knives were at once in request; and, skinning the cattle, we hung
them high up by cords of bark from the boughs of a tree. Withdrawing into a
covert, we there waited for the wild hogs; which, according to Zeke, would
soon make their appearance, lured by the smell of blood. Presently, we heard
them coming, in two or three different directions; and, in a moment, they were
tearing the offal to pieces.

As only one shot at these creatures could be relied on, we intended firing
simultaneously; but, somehow or other, the doctor's piece went off by itself, and
one of the hogs dropped. The others then breaking into the thicket, the rest of
us sprang after them; resolved to have another shot at all hazards.

The Cockney darted among some bushes; and, a few moments after, we
heard the report of his musket, followed by a quick cry. On running up, we
saw our comrade doing battle with a young devil of a boar, as black as night,
whose snout had been partly torn away. Firing when the game was in full
career, and coming directly toward him, Shorty had been assailed by the enraged brute; it was now crunching the breech of the musket, with which he
had tried to club it; Shorty holding fast to the barrel, and fingering his waist
for a knife. Being in advance of the others, I clapped my gun to the boar's
head, and so put an end to the contest.

Evening now coming on, we set to work loading our carriers. The cattle were so small, that a stout native could walk off with an entire quarter; brushing through thickets, and descending rocks without an apparent effort: though, to tell the truth, no white man present could have done the thing with any ease. As for the wild hogs, none of the islanders could be induced to carry Shorty's; some invincible superstition being connected with its black color. We were, therefore, obliged to leave it. The other, a spotted one, being slung by green thongs to a pole, was marched off with by two young natives.

With our bearers of burdens ahead, we then commenced our return down the valley. Half-way home, darkness overtook us in the woods; and torches became necessary. We stopped, and made them of dry palm branches; and then, sending two lads on in advance, for the purpose of gathering fuel to feed the flambeaux, we continued our journey.

It was a wild sight. The torches, waved aloft, flashed through the forest; and, where the ground admitted, the islanders went along on a brisk trot, notwithstanding they bent forward under their loads. Their naked backs were stained with blood; and occasionally, running by each other, they raised wild cries, which startled the hillsides.

CHAPTER 62

Long before sunrise, the next morning, my sandals were laced on, and the doctor had vaulted into Zeke's boots.

Expecting to see us again before we went to Taloo, the planters wished us a pleasant journey; and, on parting, very generously presented us with a pound or two of what sailors call "plug" tobacco; telling us to cut it up into small change; the Virginian weed being the principal circulating medium on the island.

Tamai, we were told, was not more than three or four leagues distant; so making allowances for a wild road, a few hours to rest at noon, and our determination to take the journey leisurely, we counted upon reaching the shores of the lake some time in the flush of the evening.

For several hours we went on slowly through wood and ravine, and over hill and precipice, seeing nothing but occasional herds of wild cattle, and often resting; until we found ourselves, about noon, in the very heart of the island.

It was a green, cool hollow among the mountains, into which we at last descended with a bound. The place was gushing with a hundred springs, and shaded over with great solemn trees, on whose mossy boles the moisture stood in beads. Strange to say, no traces of the bullocks ever having been here were revealed. Nor was there a sound to be heard, nor a bird to be seen, nor any breath of wind stirring the leaves. The utter solitude and silence were oppressive;

and after peering about under the shades, and seeing nothing but ranks of dark, motionless trunks, we hurried across the hollow, and ascended a steep mountain opposite.

Midway up, we rested where the earth had gathered about the roots of three palms, and thus formed a pleasant lounge, from which we looked down upon the hollow, now one dark-green tuft of woodland at our feet. Here we brought forth a small calabash of *"poee,"* a parting present from Tonoi. After eating heartily, we obtained fire by two sticks, and throwing ourselves back, puffed forth our fatigue in wreaths of smoke. At last we fell asleep; nor did we waken till the sun had sunk so low, that its rays darted in upon us under the foliage.

Starting up, we then continued our journey; and as we gained the mountain top—there, to our surprise, lay the lake and village of Tamai. We had thought it a good league off. Where we stood, the yellow sunset was still lingering; but over the valley below, long shadows were stealing—the rippling green lake reflecting the houses and trees, just as they stood along its banks. Several small canoes, moored here and there to posts in the water, were dancing upon the waves; and one solitary fisherman was paddling over to a grassy point. In front of the houses, groups of natives were seen; some thrown at full length upon the ground, and others indolently leaning against the bamboos.

With whoop and halloo, we ran down the hills, the villagers soon hurrying forth to see who were coming. As we drew near, they gathered round, all curiosity to know what brought the "karhowries" into their quiet country. The doctor contriving to make them understand the purely social object of our visit, they gave us a true Tahitian welcome; pointing into their dwellings, and saying they were ours as long as we chose to remain.

We were struck by the appearance of these people, both men and women; so much more healthful than the inhabitants of the bays. As for the young girls, they were more retiring and modest, more tidy in their dress, and far fresher and more beautiful than the damsels of the coast. A thousand pities, thought I, that they should bury their charms in this nook of a valley.

That night we abode in the house of Rartoo, a hospitable old chief. It was right on the shore of the lake; and at supper, we looked out through a rustling screen of foliage upon the surface of the starlit water.

The next day we rambled about, and found a happy little community, comparatively free from many deplorable evils to which the rest of their countrymen are subject. Their time, too, was more occupied. To my surprise, the manufacture of tappa was going on in several buildings. European calicoes were seldom seen, and not many articles of foreign origin of any description.

The people of Tamai were nominally Christians; but being so remote from ecclesiastical jurisdiction, their religion sat lightly upon them. We had been told, even, that many heathenish games and dances still secretly lingered in their valley.

Now the prospect of seeing an old-fashioned "hevar," or Tahitian reel, was one of the inducements which brought us here; and so, finding Rartoo rather liberal in his religious ideas, we disclosed our desire. At first, he demurred; and shrugging his shoulders like a Frenchman, declared it could not be brought about—was a dangerous matter to attempt, and might bring all concerned into trouble. But we overcame all this, convinced him that the thing could be done, and a "hevar," a genuine pagan fandango, was arranged for that very night.

CHAPTER 63

There were some ill-natured people—tell-tales—it seemed, in Tamai; and hence there was a deal of mystery about getting up the dance.

An hour or two before midnight, Rartoo entered the house, and, throwing robes of tappa over us, bade us follow at a distance behind him; and, until out of the village, hood our faces. Keenly alive to the adventure, we obeyed. At last, after taking a wide circuit, we came out upon the farthest shore of the lake. It was a wide, dewy space; lighted up by a full moon, and carpeted with a minute species of fern, growing closely together. It swept right down to the water, showing the village opposite, glistening among the groves.

Near the trees, on one side of the clear space, was a ruinous pile of stones, many rods in extent; upon which had formerly stood a temple of Oro. At present, there was nothing but a rude hut, planted on the lowermost terrace. It seemed to have been used as a "*tappa herree;*" or house for making the native cloth.

Here, we saw lights gleaming from between the bamboos, and casting long, rod-like shadows upon the ground without. Voices also were heard. We went up, and had a peep at the dancers; who were getting ready for the ballet. They were some twenty in number; waited upon by hideous old crones, who might have been duennas. Long Ghost proposed to send the latter packing; but Rartoo said it would never do, and so they were permitted to remain.

We tried to effect an entrance at the door, which was fastened; but, after a noisy discussion with one of the old witches within, our guide became fidgety, and, at last, told us to desist, or we would spoil all. He then led us off to a distance, to await the performance; as the girls, he said, did not wish to be recognized. He, furthermore, made us promise to remain where we were, until all was over, and the dancers had retired.

We waited impatiently; and, at last, they came forth. They were arrayed in short tunics of white tappa; with garlands of flowers on their heads. Following them, were the duennas, who remained clustering about the house, while the girls advanced a few paces; and, in an instant, two of them, taller than their companions, were standing, side by side, in the middle of a ring, formed by the clasped hands of the rest. This movement was made in perfect silence.

Presently, the two girls join hands overhead; and, crying out, "Ahloo! ahloo!" wave them to and fro. Upon which, the ring begins to circle slowly; the dancers moving sideways, with their arms a little drooping. Soon they quicken their pace; and, at last, fly round and round: bosoms heaving, hair streaming, flowers dropping, and every sparkling eye circling in what seemed a line of light.

Meanwhile, the pair within are passing and repassing each other incessantly. Inclining sideways, so that their long hair falls far over, they glide this way and that; one foot continually in the air, and their fingers thrown forth, and twirling in the moonbeams.

"Ahloo! ahloo!" again cry the dance queens; and, coming together in the middle of the ring, they once more lift up the arch, and stand motionless.

"Ahloo! ahloo!" Every link of the circle is broken; and the girls, deeply breathing, stand perfectly still. They pant hard and fast, a moment or two; and then, just as the deep flush is dying away from their faces, slowly recede, all round; thus enlarging the ring.

Again the two leaders wave their hands, when the rest pause; and now, far apart, stand in the still moonlight, like a circle of fairies. Presently, raising a strange chant, they softly sway themselves, gradually quickening the movement, until, at length, for a few passionate moments, with throbbing bosoms and glowing cheeks, they abandon themselves to all the spirit of the dance, apparently lost to every thing around. But soon subsiding again into the same languid measure, as before, they become motionless; and then, reeling forward on all sides, their eyes swimming in their heads, join in one wild chorus, and sink into each other's arms.

Such is the Lory-Lory, I think they call it; the dance of the backsliding girls of Tamai.

While it was going on, we had as much as we could do, to keep the doctor from rushing forward and seizing a partner.

They would give us no more "hevars" that night; and Rartoo fairly dragged us away to a canoe, hauled up on the lake shore; when we reluctantly embarked, and, paddling over to the village, arrived there in time for a good nap before sunrise.

The next day, the doctor went about, trying to hunt up the overnight dancers. He thought to detect them by their late rising; but never was a man more mistaken; for, on first sallying out, the whole village was asleep, waking up in concert about an hour after. But, in the course of the day, he came across several, whom he at once charged with taking part in the "hevar." There were some prim-looking fellows standing by (visiting elders from Afrehitoo, perhaps), and the girls looked embarrassed; but parried the charge most skillfully.

Though soft as doves, in general, the ladies of Tamai are, nevertheless, flavored with a slight tincture of what we queerly enough call the "*devil;*" and they showed it on the present occasion. For when the doctor pressed one rather hard, she all at once turned round upon him, and, giving him a box on the ear, told him to "harree perrar!" (be off with himself.)

CHAPTER 81

It was about the middle of the second month of the Hegira, and therefore some five weeks after our arrival in Partoowye, that we at last obtained admittance to the residence of the queen.

It happened thus. There was a Marquesan in the train of Pomaree, who officiated as nurse to her children. According to the Tahitian custom, the royal youngsters are carried about until it requires no small degree of strength to stand up under them. But Marbonna was just the man for this—large and muscular, well made as a statue, and with an arm like a degenerate Tahitian's thigh.

Embarking at his native island, as a sailor, on board of a French whaler, he afterward ran away from the ship at Tahiti; where, being seen and admired by Pomaree, he had been prevailed upon to enlist in her service.

Often, when visiting the grounds, we saw him walking about in the shade, carrying two handsome boys, who encircled his neck with their arms. Marbonna's face, tattooed as it was in the ornate style of his tribe, was as good as a picture-book to these young Pomarees. They delighted to trace with their fingers, the outlines of the strange shapes there delineated.

The first time my eyes lighted upon the Marquesan, I knew his country in a moment; and hailing him in his own language, he turned round, surprised that a person so speaking should be a stranger. He proved to be a native of Tior, a glen of Nukuheva. I had visited the place more than once; and so, on the island of Imeeo, we met like old friends.

In my frequent conversations with him over the bamboo picket, I found this islander a philosopher of nature—a wild heathen, moralizing upon the vices and follies of the Christian court of Tahiti—a savage, scorning the degeneracy of the people among whom fortune had thrown him.

I was amazed at the national feelings of the man. No European, when abroad, could speak of his country with more pride than Marbonna. He assured me, again and again, that so soon as he had obtained sufficient money to purchase twenty muskets, and as many bags of powder, he was going to return to a place, with which Imeeo was not worthy to be compared.

It was Marbonna, who, after one or two unsuccessful attempts, at last brought about our admission into the queen's grounds. Through a considerable crowd, he conducted us along the pier to where an old man was sitting; to whom he introduced us as a couple of "karhowrees" of his acquaintance, anxious to see the sights of the palace. The venerable chamberlain stared at us, and shook his head: the doctor, thinking he wanted a fee, placed a plug of tobacco in his hand. This was ingratiating, and we were permitted to pass on. Upon the point of entering one of the houses, Marbonna's name was shouted in half-a-dozen different directions, and he was obliged to withdraw.

Thus left at the very threshold to shift for ourselves, my companion's assurance stood us in good stead. He stalked right in, and I followed. The place was full of women, who, instead of exhibiting the surprise we expected, accosted us as cordially as if we had called to take our Souchong with them, by express invitation. In the first place, nothing would do but we must each devour a calabash of "poee," and several roasted bananas. Pipes were then lighted, and a brisk conversation ensued.

These ladies of the court, if not very polished, were surprisingly free and easy in their manners; quite as much so as King Charles's Beauties. There was one of them—an arch little miss, who could converse with us pretty fluently—to whom we strove to make ourselves particularly agreeable, with the view of engaging her services as cicerone.

As such, she turned out to be every thing we could desire. No one disputing her will, every place was entered without ceremony, curtains brushed aside, mats lifted, and each nook and corner explored. Whether the little damsel carried her mistress' signet, that every thing opened to her thus, I know not; but Marbonna himself, the bearer of infants, could not have been half so serviceable.

Among other houses which we visited, was one of large size and fine exterior; the special residence of a European—formerly the mate of a merchant vessel,—who had done himself the honor of marrying into the Pomaree family. The lady he wedded being a near kinswoman of the queen, he became a permanent member of her majesty's household. This adventurer rose late, dressed theatrically in calico and trinkets, assumed a dictatorial tone in conversation, and was evidently upon excellent terms with himself.

We found him reclining on a mat, smoking a reed-pipe of tobacco, in the midst of an admiring circle of chiefs and ladies. He must have noticed our approach; but instead of rising and offering civilities, he went on talking and smoking, without even condescending to look at us.

"His Highness feels his 'poee,' " carelessly observed the doctor. The rest of the company gave us the ordinary salutation, our guide announcing us before-hand.

In answer to our earnest requests to see the queen, we were now conducted to an edifice, by far the most spacious, in the inclosure. It was at least one hundred and fifty feet in length, very wide, with low eaves, and an exceedingly steep roof of pandanus leaves. There were neither doors nor windows—nothing along the sides but the slight posts supporting the rafters. Between these posts, curtains of fine matting and tappa were rustling, all round; some of them were festooned, or partly withdrawn, so as to admit light and air, and afford a glimpse now and then of what was going on within.

Pushing aside one of the screens, we entered. The apartment was one im-mense hall; the long and lofty ridge-pole fluttering with fringed matting and tassels, full forty feet from the ground. Lounges of mats, piled one upon another, extended on either side; while here and there were slight screens, forming as many recesses, where groups of natives—all females—were reclining at their eve-ning meal.

As we advanced, these various parties ceased their buzzing, and in explanation of our appearance among them, listened to a few cabalistic words from our guide.

The whole scene was a strange one; but what most excited our surprise, was the incongruous assemblage of the most costly objects from all quarters of the globe. Cheek by jowl, they lay beside the rudest native articles, without the slightest attempt at order. Superb writing-desks of rose-wood, inlaid with silver and mother-of-pearl; decanters and goblets of cut glass; embossed volumes of plates; gilded candelabras; sets of globes and mathematical instruments; the finest porcelain; richly mounted sabres and fowling-pieces; laced hats and sumptuous garments of all sorts, with numerous other matters of European manufacture, were strewn about among greasy calabashes half-filled with "*poee*," rolls of old tappa and matting, paddles and fish-spears, and the ordinary furni-ture of a Tahitian dwelling.

All the articles first mentioned, were, doubtless, presents from foreign powers. They were more or less injured: the fowling-pieces and swords were rusted; the finest woods were scratched; and a folio volume of Hogarth lay open, with a cocoa-nut shell of some musty preparation capsized among the miscellaneous furniture of the Rake's apartment, where that inconsiderate young gentleman is being measured for a coat.

While we were amusing ourselves in this museum of curiosities, our con-ductor plucked us by the sleeve, and whispered, "Pomaree! Pomaree! aramai kow kow."

"She is coming to sup, then," said the doctor, staring in the direction indicated. "What say you, Paul, suppose we step up?" Just then a curtain near by, lifted;

and from a private building a few yards distant, the queen entered, unattended.

She wore a loose gown of blue silk, with two rich shawls, one red and the other yellow, tied about her neck. Her royal majesty was barefooted.

She was about the ordinary size, rather matronly; her features not very handsome; her mouth, voluptuous; but there was a care-worn expression in her face, probably attributable to her late misfortunes. From her appearance, one would judge her about forty; but she is not so old.

As the queen approached one of the recesses, her attendants hurried up, escorted her in, and smoothed the mats on which she at last reclined. Two girls soon appeared, carrying their mistress' repast; and then, surrounded by cut-glass and porcelain, and jars of sweetmeats and confections, Pomaree Vahinee I., the titular Queen of Tahiti, ate fish and poee out of her native calabashes, disdaining either knife or spoon.

"Come on," whispered Long Ghost, "let's have an audience at once;" and he was on the point of introducing himself, when our guide, quite alarmed, held him back, and implored silence. The other natives also interfered; and as he was pressing forward, raised such an outcry, that Pomaree lifted her eyes, and saw us for the first.

She seemed surprised, and offended; and issuing an order in a commanding tone to several of her women, waved us out of the house. Summary as the dismissal was, court etiquet, no doubt, required our compliance. We withdrew; making a profound inclination as we disappeared behind the tappa arras.

We departed the grounds without seeing Marbonna; and previous to vaulting over the picket, feed our pretty guide, after a fashion of our own. Looking round a few moments after, we saw the damsel escorted back by two men, who seemed to have been sent after her. I trust she received nothing more than a reprimand.

The next day Po-Po informed us that strict orders had been issued, to admit no strangers within the palace precincts.

Portrait of Herman Melville by Asa W. Twitchell, of Albany, New York, done about 1847, the year that saw the publication of *Omoo* (Reprinted by permission of The Berkshire Athenaeum)

The *Acushnet* under way: a drawing by the first mate of another vessel

The *Acushnet* leaving Gay Head on her second voyage: a watercolor by Boatsteerer Henry M. Johnson (Peabody Museum, Salem, Mass.)

The boats of the *Acushnet* killing a sperm whale (Peabody Museum)

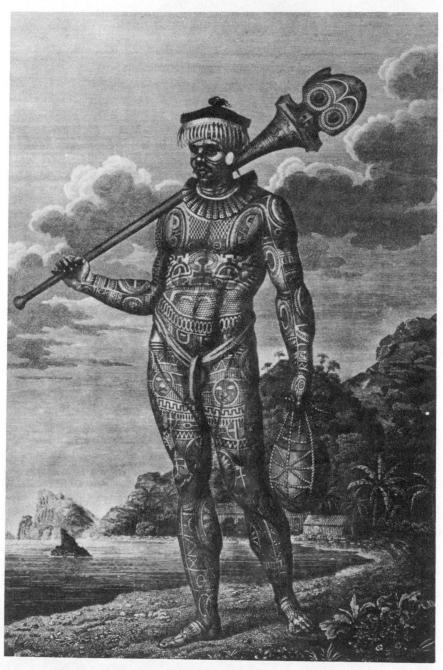

Tattooing was the highest Marquesan art. Melville had to flee the tribal artist who yearned to exert his skill on an expanse of white skin.

Richard Tobias Greene, Melville's fellow deserter on Nuku-Hiva

A European vessel moored among native canoes in a bay of Tahiti, where Bougain-ville and other seekers of the "noble savage" thought to find an earthly paradise (National Library of Australia, Canberra)

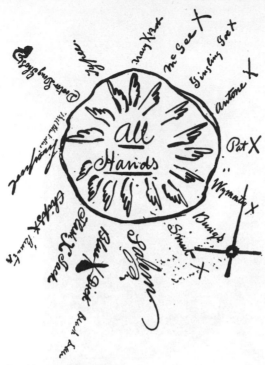

The "round robin," with signatures and marks of the mutineers in a circle, so that no "ringleader" could be singled out for punishment (see *Omoo,* Chapter 20)

The British Consulate at Papeete, where the mutineers faced Charles B. Wilson, acting consul (J. W. Earnshaw, Sydney, Australia)

The "Broom Road" circling Tahiti, described by Melville in *Omoo*

Native canoes off the Punaauia coast of the island of Tahiti (Tyerman & Bennet)

The valley of Punaauia in Tahiti, where Paul Gauguin painted the islanders half a century after Melville's visit (Tyerman & Bennet)

Pomaré, Queen of Tahiti, the persecuted Christian, surrounded by her family at the moment when the French forces were landing to set up a protectorate (National Library of Australia, Canberra)

Papetoai Valley on Mooréa, where Melville visited a mission church and signed on the *Charles and Henry* whaler as a boatsteerer (Tyerman & Bennet)

Lahaina, Maui, where Melville was discharged from the *Charles and Henry*. He climbed the heights to visit the missionary high school at Lahainaluna.

The port of Honolulu, sketched during the month when Melville enlisted on the frigate *United States;* Diamond Head is seen to the right, with Punchbowl in the foreground. (Reprinted by permission of Duke University Press)

"I shall never forget a robust, red-faced, and very ladylike personage, a missionary's spouse, who day after day for months together took her regular airings in a little go-cart drawn by two of the [Hawaiian] islanders."—*Typee,* Chapter 26

King Kamehameha III, the first royal ruler whom Melville met, was less than thirty years old when Melville saw him in Honolulu. (Archives of Hawaii)

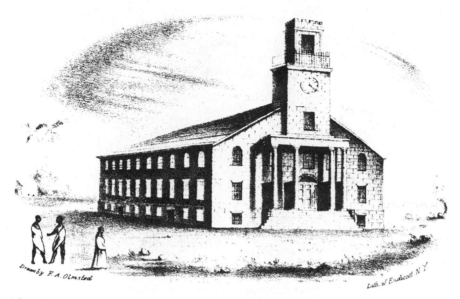

The old stone church of Kawaiahao in the town of Honolulu

The precipice of the Pali above the town of Honolulu, as seen by a naval artist during Melville's stay in Hawaii (Reprinted by permission of Duke University Press)

The "rare sport" of surfboard-riding, as described in Chapter 90 of *Mardi* (Ellis, *Polynesian Researches*)

Hawaiian Islanders sporting in the surf: a sketch by F. A. Olmsted

The ancient Hawaiian sport of surfboard-riding has now become an international challenge to skill.

The frigate *United States,* in which Melville served before the mast, leading the Pacific Squadron under press of sail (Reprinted by permission of Duke University Press)

Melville's man-of-war, the frigate *United States,* rounding the island of Molokai in the Hawaiian group (Reprinted by permission of Duke University Press)

Herman (left) and his brother Thomas, captain of the clipper *Meteor,* before their departure in 1860 on Herman's second Pacific voyage (Reprinted by permission of Harvard University Library)

PART IV

A PASSAGE
TO ALLEGORY:
Mardi
(1849)

INTRODUCTION

Had Melville wished to follow up the marketplace success of *Typee* and *Omoo,* he should have written a book about his adventures in the Hawaiian Islands. True, he spent less than four months at Lahaina and Honolulu; but he had spent less than a month in the Marquesas, and only six weeks in Tahiti. He could have followed his custom of fleshing out his narrative by drawing on printed and verbal sources, of which there were more available on Hawaii than on either the Marquesas or the Society groups.

There are a number of traces in his next book of his Hawaii experiences.[1] But these were on the whole not congenial to him. He found in the islands neither unspoiled primitives nor wholehearted Christian converts, despite the labors of the missionaries he so disliked. As a deserter from a ship, he was not free to rove among the more enchanting parts of the islands. He finally threw in his lot not with the American colony but with the British; his attitude toward his compatriots in Honolulu led not to literature but to such outbursts as his "Appendix" to *Typee.*

The main reason why we have no book by Melville about Hawaii, however, lay in his attitude in the year 1848, critical in world history as well as in Melvillian biography. Herman had now become a husband, a voracious reader, and a budding philosopher. He had embraced writing as a profession, but did not wish to follow up the easy career of travel writer. As he proclaimed in January, 1849, in his wry "Author's Preface" to *Mardi: and a Voyage Thither:* "Having published two narratives of voyages in the Pacific, which, in many quarters, were received with incredulity, the thought occurred to me of indeed writing a romance of Polynesian adventure, and publishing it as such; to see whether the fiction might not, possibly, be received for a verity: in some degree the reverse of my previous experience. This thought was the germ of others, which have resulted in *Mardi.*" Those who had doubted the facts of his earlier books would now have to acknowledge the truth of his fantasy.

The tone of the opening of *Mardi* is comparable to that of *Omoo*. The narrator, unhappy in a whale ship lying "something more than sixty degrees to the west of the Gallipagos [sic]," embarks in an open boat with Jarl, a Viking sailor from Skye, as companion, intent on seeking the groups now known as the Ellice, Gilbert, and Marshall chains. They flee less to escape the discipline of the ship than to find freedom to adventure in the beckoning west, where lay Melville's course of empire. They rescue two Polynesians, Samoa and Annatoo, a couple of lovers, survivors on a sinking ship from Lahaina, Maui. Through its fortieth chapter, *Mardi* might well be read as the start of a rousing sea adventure by Frederick Marryat or W. Clark Russell. Then the story is swallowed, like Jonah, by a whale named Allegory.

A languid, pale beauty named Yillah (the name suggests a yellow lily)[2] is rescued from sacrifice at the cost of killing her guardian priest Aleema, whose three sons thereafter pursue the hero to his death. She is no Polynesian, and indeed is "more than mortal," born in Oroolia, the Island of Delights, and magically transformed into a flower blossom. The company now have entered the spreading, fantastic archipelago of Mardi, world within a world. For a time the adventurer and Yillah live an Edenlike existence on the island of Odo, whose king, Media, welcomes him as the god Taji, a divine emissary of the sun, even as Captain James Cook was greeted in the Hawaiian Islands as the returned god Lono. The narrator's earthy companions—Jarl, Samoa, and Annatoo —gradually fade from the foreground as he draws to him a more intellectual entourage consisting of Media, man of moderation and mind; Mohi, braid-bearded historian; Yoomy, a minstrel; and Babbalanja, a prattling philosopher.

Yillah mysteriously disappears, and the remainder of the long book concerns the search for her. This quest is diverted dozens of times, however, as the company visits allegorical islands representing Swiftian exaggerations of human nature or satirical pictures of the countries of Melville's century. (Great Britain is Dominora, for example; Verdanna is Ireland, Franco is France, and Vivenza is the United States.) Taji is menaced by floral messages from the prideful Queen Hautia, who embodies the temptations of the flesh as Yillah represents the spiritual side of femininity. But Yillah also represents the ideal of absolute truth, and therefore cannot again be found in this world.

At the ending, Taji's comrades are content to compromise and remain on the island of Serenia, a loving Christian commonwealth. But Taji has in him the stuff of Captain Ahab of *Moby Dick*. He flees the temptations of Hautia, and steers toward the reef, seeking the drifting white corpse of Yillah. "Let *me*, then, be the unreturning wanderer," he cries. "The helm! By Oro, I will steer my own fate, old man.—Mardi, farewell!" Unable to strike through the mask of appearances, Taji, pursued by the three sons of the murdered priest Aleema, commits symbolic suicide. "Now, I am my own soul's emperor; and my first act is abdication!" Like Ahab, he will seek the truth even through murder, madness, and death.

A synopsis of this world-viewing romance is unfair to Melville. *Mardi,* which the author called a "chartless voyage," disappointed not only his followers but himself; but it presents a region of fancy which many readers still enjoy exploring. Its historical eminence cannot be gainsaid. James Baird says of the book that it is "the most important of all experimental works documenting the development of the symbolistic imagination."[3] It is a truism that had there been no *Mardi* there could have been no *Moby Dick.* In grappling with his Mardian microcosm, Melville did not always fix upon T. S. Eliot's "objective correlative," but he painfully taught himself much about this art of welding the symbol to the metaphysics.

The dilemma of Taji is that he seeks spiritual truth by rational means, and is doomed to fail. His predicament was well described by a remark about Melville by his friend Nathaniel Hawthorne: "He can neither believe, nor be comfortable in his unbelief; and he is too honest and courageous not to try to do one or the other."[4]

The appreciation of *Mardi* depends not only upon untangling the opinions of the author but upon the understanding that in this book he attempted not only satire but a type of writing new for him, challenging all the world's narrators of the legendary journey. This genre runs from the Greek romancer Lucian's *Veracious History* to the latest star quest of science fictionists. Undoubtedly Melville was influenced by his reading of Dante, *Gulliver's Travels,* Edmund Spenser (whose Duessa and other false ladies resemble Queen Hautia), and the voyagings of the Pantagruel of Rabelais.[5] These are intermingled with Germanic fancies like *Undine,* as well as his wife Elizabeth's "language of flowers" books. Herman's own experiences in courtship and marriage are undoubtedly reflected in the Yillah-Hautia contrasts in this volume concocted some months after the honeymoon. All these bookish and personal intrusions do not jibe at all with the plain, sailorly opening of *Mardi.* "Melville was trying to compose three or four books simultaneously: he failed, in the strict sense, to compose even one."[6]

Our point here is that, outwardly, *Mardi* is a romance of South Sea adventure, and it is remarkable how much of the Polynesian background Melville retained in this sprawling volume.[7] He was, after all, as Newton Arvin notes, "the first

Western writer of genius who had lived in the South Seas himself. . . . So the seascape and landscape of *Mardi* is that of the Pacific world, of Hawaii or the Marquesas or Tahiti. . . . Nor is the Polynesianism of *Mardi* a matter only of scene; it is a matter also of custom and conduct, of legend and myth."[8]

The islands of Mardi are volcanic, oceanic peaks, ringed with coral reefs, overflowing with lagoons rimmed with palms and breadfruit trees. The subjects of the "kings" dwell in thatched huts furnished with tapa cloth and pandanus mats and hung with calabashes. The feasts are Polynesian feasts, and the celebrants wear flower garlands and feather ornaments like those of Hawaii. The Hawaiian capital island of Oahu appears as "Ohonoo," which Melville translates in Chapter 89 as "the isle of Rogues." The surfboard riders at Ohonoo recall those Melville had seen at Waikiki beach. The precipice of Mondo compares with the cliff beneath the Nuuanu Pali over which, in 1795, the conquering Kamehameha drove many of the defenders of Oahu to death on the rocks below. "To the right of the brink of the precipice," Melville says in Chapter 92, "and far over it, projects a narrow ledge. The test of legitimacy in the Ohonoo monarchs is to stand hereon, arms folded, and javelins darting by." This custom, noted by William Ellis,[9] was followed even by the great Kamehameha, who, as Archibald Campbell and Captain George Vancouver remarked, was adept at countering the javelins during this deadly ordeal.

Fishponds such as those cultivated by the gluttonous monarch of Mondoldo may be seen today on the shores of several Hawaiian islands. Melville refers in Chapter 57 to the story of Captain Cook, "hailed by the Hawaiians as one of their demi-gods." The name of Hevaneva, the businesslike idol maker in Chapter 114, is clearly taken from that of Hevaheva, high priest of the Hawaiian war god at the time the missionaries arrived in 1820. Marjora the usurper of Juam may well be based on Kamehameha I, who won the throne through warfare rather than legitimate claim. The young king Donjalolo of Juam in Chapters 71–85 bears several points of resemblance to Kamehameha III, reigning monarch during Melville's visit in 1843. Young Donjalolo is also comparable to Uhia, king of Ohonoo. Although both Donjalolo and Uhia are fictional monarchs, both may have been modeled somewhat on the only Polynesian king that Melville saw with his own eyes—His Hawaiian Majesty Kamehameha III.

Borrowings from the customs and lore of the Marquesas and Tahiti can also be found in *Mardi*. Kannakoko, New Zealand tribal ruler, is symbolically wedded to the sea. A church in the novel is called a morai, or temple platform like those measured by Cook at Tahiti. Oro, synonymous in the book with

Jehovah, is a powerful god in Polynesian religion.[10] The world of *Mardi* is first of all a Pacific world.

Murray in London refused to publish this strange new venture, and the first edition appeared in London in three volumes under the imprint of Richard Bentley, selling at the rather high price of half a guinea each. Harper put out the American edition in two volumes a month later. "It was probably the first 'three-decker' novel by an American published in England and one of the most expensive American books to be issued by an English press."[11] Its lack of financial or critical success did little to encourage Melville on his career as a professional novelist.

❁ ❁ ❁

CHAPTER 30

My original intention to touch at the Kingsmill Chain, or the countries adjacent, was greatly strengthened by thus encountering Samoa; and the more I had to do with my Belisarius, the more I was pleased with him. Nor could I avoid congratulating myself, upon having fallen in with a hero, who in various ways could not fail of proving exceedingly useful.

Like any man of mark, Samoa best speaks for himself; but we may as well convey some idea of his person. Though manly enough, nay, an obelisk in stature, the savage was far from being sentimentally prepossessing. Be not alarmed; but he wore his knife in the lobe of his dexter ear, which by constant elongation almost drooped upon his shoulder. A mode of sheathing it exceedingly handy, and far less brigandish than the Highlander's dagger concealed in his leggings.

But it was the mother of Samoa, who at a still earlier day had punctured him through and through in still another direction. The middle cartilage of his nose was slightly pendent, peaked, and Gothic, and perforated with a hole; in which, like a Newfoundland dog carrying a cane, Samoa sported a trinket: a well-polished nail.

In other respects he was equally a coxcomb. In his style of tattooing, for instance, which seemed rather incomplete; his marks embracing but a vertical half of his person, from crown to sole; the other side being free from the slightest stain. Thus clapped together, as it were, he looked like a union of the unmatched moieties of two distinct beings; and your fancy was lost in conjecturing, where roamed the absent ones. When he turned round upon you suddenly, you thought you saw someone else, not him whom you had been regarding before.

But there was one feature in Samoa beyond the reach of the innovations of art:—his eye; which in civilised man or savage, ever shines in the head, just as it shone at birth. Truly, our eyes are miraculous things. But alas, that in so many instances, these divine organs should be mere lenses inserted into the socket, as glasses in spectacle rims.

But my Islander had a soul in his eye; looking out upon you there, like somebody in him. What an eye, to be sure! At times, brilliantly changeful as opal; in anger, glowing like steel at white heat.

Belisarius, be it remembered, had but very recently lost an arm. But you would have thought he had been born without it; so Lord Nelson-like and cavalierly did he sport the honourable stump.

But no more of Samoa; only this: that his name had been given him by a sea-captain; to whom it had been suggested by the native designation of the islands to which he belonged; the Saviian or Samoan Group, otherwise known as the Navigator Islands. The island of Upolua, one of that cluster, claiming the special honour of his birth, as Corsica does Napoleon's, we shall occasionally hereafter speak of Samoa as the Upoluan; by which title he most loved to be called.

It is ever ungallant to pass over a lady. But what shall be said of Annatoo! As I live, I can make no pleasing portrait of the dame; for as in most ugly subjects, flattering would but make the matter worse. Furthermore, unalleviated ugliness should ever go unpainted, as something unnecessary to duplicate. But the only ugliness is that of the heart, seen through the face. And though beauty be obvious, the only loveliness is invisible.

CHAPTER 52

Five suns rose and set. And Yillah pining for the shore, we turned our prow due west, and next morning came in sight of land.

It was innumerable islands; lifting themselves bluely through the azure air, and looking upon the distant sea, like haycocks in a hazy field. Towering above all, and midmost, rose a mighty peak; one fleecy cloud sloping against its summit; a column wreathed. Beyond, like purple steeps in heaven at set of sun, stretched far away, what seemed lands on lands, in infinite perspective.

Gliding on, the islands grew more distinct; rising up from the billows to greet us; revealing hills, vales, and peaks, grouped within a milk-white zone of reef, so vast, that in the distance all was dim. The jewelled vapours, erewhile hovering over these violet shores, now seemed to be shedding their gems; and as the almost level rays of the sun, shooting through the air like a variegated prism, touched the verdant land, it trembled all over with dewy sparkles.

Still nearer we came: our sail faintly distended as the breeze died away from our vicinity to the isles. The billows rolled listlessly by, as if conscious that their long task was nigh done; while gleamed the white reef, like the trail of a great fish in a calm. But as yet, no sign of paddle or canoe; no distant smoke; no shining thatch. Bravo! good comrades, we've discovered some new constellation in the sea.

Sweet Yillah, no more of Oroolia; see you not this flowery land? Nevermore shall we desire to roam.

Voyaging along the zone, we came to an opening; and quitting the firmament blue of the open sea, we glided in upon the still, green waters of the wide lagoon. Mapped out in the broad shadows of the isles, and tinted here and there with the reflected hues of the sun clouds, the mild waters stretched all around us like another sky. Near by the break in the reef, was a little island, with palm-trees harping in the breeze; an aviary of alluring sounds, that seemed calling upon us to land. And here, Yillah, whom the sight of the verdure had made glad, threw out a merry suggestion. Nothing less, than to plant our mast, sail-set, upon the highest hill; and fly away, island and all; trees rocking, birds carolling, flowers springing; away, away, across the wide waters, to Oroolia! But alas! how weigh the isle's coral anchor, leagues down in the fathomless sea?

We glanced around, but all the islands seemed slumbering in the flooding light.

"A canoe! a canoe!" cried Samoa, as three proas showed themselves rounding a neighbouring shore. Instantly we sailed for them; but after shooting to and fro for a time, and standing up and gazing at us, the Islanders retreated behind the headland. Hardly were they out of sight, when from many a shore round about, other proas pushed off. Soon the water all round us was enlivened by fleets of canoes, darting hither and thither like frighted water-fowls. Presently they all made for one island.

From their actions we argued that these people could have had but little or no intercourse with whites; and most probably knew not how to account for our appearance among them. Desirous, therefore, of a friendly meeting, ere any hostile suspicions might arise, we pointed our craft for the island, whither all the canoes were now hastening. Whereupon, those which had not yet reached their destination, turned and fled; while the occupants of the proas that had landed, ran into the groves, and were lost to view.

Crossing the distinct outer line of the isle's shadow on the water, we gained the shore; and gliding along its margin, passing canoe after canoe, hauled up on the silent beach, which otherwise seemed entirely innocent of man.

A dilemma. But I decided at last upon disembarking Jarl and Samoa, to seek out and conciliate the natives. So, landing them upon a jutting buttress of coral, whence they waded to the shore, I pushed off with Yillah into the water beyond, to await the event.

Full an hour must have elapsed; when, to our great joy, loud shouts were heard; and there burst into view a tumultuous crowd, in the midst of which my

Viking was descried, mounted upon the shoulders of two brawny natives; while the Upoluan, striding on in advance, seemed resisting a similar attempt to elevate him in the world.

Good omens both.

"Come ashore!" cried Jarl. "Aramai!" cried Samoa; while storms of interjections went up from the Islanders, who with extravagant gestures danced about the beach.

Further caution seemed needless: I pointed our prow for the shore. No sooner was this perceived, than, raising an applauding shout, the Islanders ran up to their waists in the sea. And skimming like a gull over the smooth lagoon, the light shallop darted in among them. Quick as thought, fifty hands were on the gunwale: and, with all its contents lifted bodily into the air, the little *Chamois,* upon many a dripping shoulder, was borne deep into the groves. Yillah shrieked at the rocking motion, and when the boughs of the trees brushed against the tent.

With his staff, an old man now pointed to a couple of twin-like trees, some four paces apart; and a little way from the ground conveniently crotched.

And here, eftsoons, they deposited their burden; lowering the *Chamois* gently between the forks of the trees, whose willow-like foliage fringed the tent and its inmate.

CHAPTER 53

Until now, enveloped in her robe, and crouching like a fawn, Yillah had been well-nigh hidden from view. But presently she withdrew her hood.

What saw the Islanders, that they so gazed and adored in silence; some retreating, some creeping nearer, and the women all in a flutter? Long they gazed; and following Samoa's example, stretched forth their arms in reverence.

The adoration of the maiden was extended to myself. Indeed, from the singular gestures employed, I had all along suspected, that we were being received with unwonted honours.

I now sought to get speech of my comrades. But so obstreperous was the crowd, that it was next to impossible. Jarl was still in his perch in the air; his enthusiastic bearers not yet suffering him to alight. Samoa, however, who had managed to keep out of the saddle, by and by contrived to draw nearer to the *Chamois.*

He advised me, by no means to descend for the present; since in any event we were sure of remaining unmolested therein; the Islanders regarding it as sacred.

The Upoluan attracted a great deal of attention; chiefly from his style of tattooing, which, together with other peculiarities, so interested the natives, that they were perpetually hanging about him, putting eager questions, and all the time keeping up a violent clamour.

But despite the large demand upon his lungs, Samoa made out to inform me, that notwithstanding the multitude assembled, there was no high chief, or person of consequence present; the king of the place, also those of the islands adjacent, being absent at a festival in another quarter of the Archipelago. But upon the first distant glimpse of the *Chamois,* fleet canoes had been dispatched to announce the surprising event that had happened.

In good time, the crowd becoming less tumultuous, and abandoning the siege of Samoa, I availed myself of this welcome lull, and called upon him and my Viking to enter the *Chamois;* desirous of condensing our forces against all emergencies.

Samoa now gave me to understand, that from all he could learn, the Islanders regarded me as a superior being. They had inquired of him, whether I was not White Taji, a sort of half-and-half deity, now and then an Avatar among them, and ranking among their inferior ex-officio demi-gods. To this, Samoa had said ay; adding, moreover, all he could to encourage the idea.

He now entreated me, at the first opportunity, to announce myself as Taji: declaring that if once received under that title, the unbounded hospitality of our final reception would be certain; and our persons fenced about from all harm.

Encouraging this. But it was best to be wary. For although among some barbarians the first strangers landing upon their shores, are frequently hailed as divine; and in more than one wild land have been actually styled gods, as a familiar designation; yet this has not exempted the celestial visitants from peril, when too much presuming upon the reception extended to them. In sudden tumults they have been slain outright, and while full faith in their divinity had in no wise abated. The sad fate of an eminent navigator is a well-known illustration of this unaccountable waywardness.

With no small anxiety, therefore, we awaited the approach of some of the dignitaries of Mardi; for by this collective appellation, the people informed us, their islands were known.

We waited not long. Of a sudden, from the seaside, a single shrill cry was heard. A moment more, and the blast of numerous conch-shells startled the air; a confused clamour drew nearer and nearer; and fixing our eyes in the direction of these sounds, we impatiently awaited what was to follow.

CHAPTER 54

Never before had I seen the deep foliage of woodlands navigated by canoes. But on they came sailing through the leaves; two abreast; borne on men's shoulders; in each a chief, carried along to the measured march of his bearers; paddle-blades reversed under arms. As they emerged, the multitude made gestures of homage. At the distance of some eight or ten paces the procession halted; when the kings alighted to the ground.

They were fine-looking men, arrayed in various garbs. Rare the show of stained feathers, and jewels, and other adornments. Brave the floating of dyed mantles.

The regal bearing of these personages, the deference paid them, and their entire self-possession, not a little surprised me. And it seemed preposterous, to assume a divine dignity in the presence of these undoubted potentates of *terra firma*. Taji seemed oozing from my fingers' ends. But courage! and erecting my crest, I strove to look every inch the character I had determined to assume.

For a time, it was almost impossible to tell with what emotions precisely the chiefs were regarding me. They said not a word.

But plucking up heart of grace, I crossed my cutlass on my chest, and reposing my hand on the hilt, addressed their High Mightinesses thus. "Men of Mardi, I come from the sun. When this morning it rose and touched the wave, I pushed my shallop from its golden beach, and hither sailed before its level rays. I am Taji."

More would have been added, but I paused for the effect of my exordium.

Stepping back a pace or two, the chiefs eagerly conversed.

Emboldened, I returned to the charge, and laboured hard to impress them with just such impressions of me and mine, as I deemed desirable. The gentle Yillah was a seraph from the sun; Samoa I had picked off a reef in my route from that orb; and as for the Skyeman, why, as his name imported, he came from above. In a word, we were all strolling divinities.

Advancing toward the *Chamois,* one of the kings, a calm old man, now addressed me as follows:—"Is this indeed Taji? he, who according to a tradition, was to return to us after five thousand moons? But that period is yet unexpired. What bring'st thou hither then, Taji, before thy time? Thou wast but a quarrel-some demi-god, say the legends, when thou dwelt among our sires. But wherefore comest thou, Taji? Truly, thou wilt interfere with the worship of thy images, and we have plenty of gods besides thee. But comest thou to fight?—We have plenty of spears, and desire not thine. Comest thou to dwell?—Small are the houses of Mardi. Or comest thou to fish in the sea? Tell us, Taji."

Now, all this was a series of posers hard to be answered; furnishing a curious example, moreover, of the reception given to strange demi-gods when they travel without their portmanteaus; and also of the familiar manner in which these kings address the immortals. Much I mourned that I had not previously studied better my part, and learned the precise nature of my previous existence in the land.

But nothing like carrying it bravely.

"Attend. Taji comes, old man, because it pleases him to come. And Taji will depart when it suits him. Ask the shades of your sires whether Taji thus scurvily greeted them, when they came stalking into his presence in the land of spirits. No. Taji spread the banquet. He removed their mantles. He kindled a fire to drive away the damp. He said not, 'Come you to fight, you fogs and vapours? come you to dwell? or come you to fish in the sea?' Go to, then, kings of Mardi!"

Upon this, the old king fell back; and his place was supplied by a noble chief, of a free, frank bearing. Advancing quickly toward the boat, he exclaimed—"I am Media, the son of Media. Thrice welcome, Taji. On my island of Odo hast thou an altar. I claim thee for my guest." He then reminded the rest that the strangers had voyaged far, and needed repose. And, furthermore, that he proposed escorting them forthwith to his own dominions; where, next day, he would be happy to welcome all visitants.

And good as his word, he commanded his followers to range themselves under the *Chamois*. Springing out of our prow, the Upoluan was followed by Jarl; leaving Yillah and Taji to be borne therein toward the sea.

Soon we were once more afloat; by our side, Media sociably seated; six of his paddlers, perched upon the gunwale, swiftly urging us over the lagoon.

The transition from the grove to the sea was instantaneous. All seemed a dream.

The place to which we were hastening, being some distance away, as we rounded isle after isle, the extent of the Archipelago grew upon us greatly.

CHAPTER 55

Upon at last drawing nigh to Odo, its appearance somewhat disappointed me. A small island, of moderate elevation.

But plumb not the height of the house that feasts you.

The beach was lined with expectant natives, who, lifting the *Chamois,* carried us up the beach.

Alighting, as they were bearing us along, King Media, designating a canoe-house hard by, ordered our craft to be deposited therein. This being done, we stepped upon the soil. It was the first we had pressed in very many days. It sent a sympathetic thrill through our frames.

Turning his steps inland, Media signed us to follow.

Soon we came to a rude sort of enclosure, fenced in by an imposing wall. Here a halt was sounded, and in great haste the natives proceeded to throw down a portion of the stones. This accomplished, we were signed to enter the fortress thus carried by storm. Upon an artificial mound, opposite the breach, stood a small structure of bamboo, open in front. Within, was a long pedestal, like a settee, supporting three images, also of wood, and about the size of men; bearing, likewise, a remote resemblance to that species of animated nature. Before these idols was an altar, and at its base many fine mats.

Entering the temple, as if he felt very much at home, Media disposed these mats so as to form a very pleasant lounge; where he deferentially entreated Yillah to recline. Then deliberately removing the first idol, he motioned me to seat myself in its place. Setting aside the middle one, he quietly established himself in its stead. The displaced ciphers, meanwhile, standing upright before us, and their blank faces looking upon this occasion unusually expressive. As yet, not a syllable as to the meaning of this cavalier treatment of their wooden godships.

We now tranquilly awaited what next might happen, and I earnestly prayed, that if sacrilege was being committed, the vengeance of the gods might be averted from an ignoramus like me; notwithstanding the petitioner himself hailed from the other world. Perfect silence was preserved: Jarl and Samoa standing a little without the temple; the first looking quite composed, but his comrade casting wondering glances at my sociable apotheosis with Media.

Now happening to glance upon the image last removed, I was not long in detecting a certain resemblance between it and our host. Both were decorated in the same manner; the carving on the idol exactly corresponding with the tattooing of the king.

Presently, the silence was relieved by a commotion without: and a butler approached, staggering under an immense wooden trencher; which, with profound genuflections, he deposited upon the altar before us. The tray was loaded like any harvest wain; heaped up with good things sundry and divers; breadfruit, and cocoa-nuts, and plaintains, and guavas; all pleasant to the eye, and furnishing good earnest of something equally pleasant to the palate.

Transported at the sight of these viands, after so long an estrangement from full indulgence in things green, I was forthwith proceeding to help Yillah and myself, when, like lightning, a most unwelcome query obtruded. Did deities dine? Then also recurred what Media had declared about my shrine in Odo.

Was this it? Self-sacrilegious demigod that I was, was I going to gluttonise on the very offerings, laid before me in my own sacred fane? Give heed to thy ways, oh Taji, lest thou stumble and be lost.

But hereupon, what saw we, but his cool majesty of Odo tranquilly proceeding to lunch in the temple?

How now? Was Media too a god? Egad, it must be so. Else, why his image here in the fane, and the original so entirely at his ease, with legs full cosily tucked away under the very altar itself. This put to flight all appalling apprehensions of the necessity of starving to keep up the assumption of my divinity. So without more ado I helped myself right and left; taking the best care of Yillah; who ever fed her flushed beauty with juicy fruits, thereby transferring to her cheek the sweet glow of the guava.

Our hunger appeased, and Media in token thereof celestially laying his hand upon the appropriate region, we proceeded to quit the enclosure. But coming to the wall where the breach had been made, lo, and behold, no breach was to be seen. But down it came tumbling again, and forth we issued.

This overthrowing of walls, be it known, is an incidental compliment paid distinguished personages in this part of Mardi. It would seem to signify, that such gentry can go nowhere without creating an impression; even upon the most obdurate substances.

Sublimate, as you will, the idea of our ethereality as intellectual beings; no sensible man can harbour a doubt, but that there is a vast deal of satisfaction in dining. More: there is a savour of life and immortality in substantial fare. Like balloons, we are nothing till filled.

And well knowing this, nature has provided this jolly round board, our globe, which in an endless sequence of courses and crops, spreads a perpetual feast. Though, as with most public banquets, there is no small crowding, and many go away famished from plenty.

CHAPTER 63

Time now to enter upon some further description of the island and its lord.

And first for Media: a gallant gentleman and king. From a goodly stock he came. In his endless pedigree, reckoning deities by decimals, innumerable kings, and scores of great heroes, chiefs, and priests. Nor in person, did he belie his origin. No far-descended dwarf was he, the least of a receding race. He stood like a palm-tree; about whose acanthus capital droops not more gracefully the silken fringes, than Media's locks upon his noble brow. Strong was his arm to wield the club, or hurl the javelin; and potent, I ween, round a maiden's waist.

Thus much here for Media. Now comes his isle.

Our pleasant ramble found it a little round world by itself; full of beauties as a garden; chequered by charming groves; watered by roving brooks; and fringed all round by a border of palm-trees, whose roots drew nourishment from the water. But though abounding in other quarters of the Archipelago, not a solitary bread-fruit grew in Odo. A noteworthy circumstance, observable in these regions, where islands close adjoining so differ in their soil, that certain fruits growing genially in one, are foreign to another. But Odo was famed for its guavas, whose flavour was likened to the flavour of new-blown lips; and for its grapes, whose juices prompted many a laugh and many a groan.

Beside the city where Media dwelt, there were few other clusters of habitations in Odo. The higher classes living, here and there, in separate households; but not as eremites. Some buried themselves in the cool, quivering bosoms of the groves. Others, fancying a marine vicinity, dwelt hard by the beach in little cages of bamboo; whence of mornings they sallied out with jocund cries, and went plunging into the refreshing bath, whose frothy margin was the threshold of their dwellings. Others still, like birds, built their nests among the sylvan nooks of the elevated interior; whence all below, and hazy green, lay steeped in languor the island's throbbing heart.

Thus dwelt the chiefs and merry men of mark. The common sort, including serfs, and Helots, war-captives held in bondage, lived in secret places, hard to find. Whence it came, that, to a stranger, the whole isle looked care-free and beautiful. Deep among the ravines and the rocks, these beings lived in noisome caves, lairs for beasts, not human homes; or built them coops of rotten boughs— living trees were banned them—whose mouldy hearts hatched vermin. Fearing infection of some plague, born of this filth, the chiefs of Odo seldom passed that way; and looking round within their green retreats, and pouring out their wine, and plucking from orchards of the best, marvelled how these swine could grovel in the mire, and wear such sallow cheeks. But they offered no sweet homes; from that mire they never sought to drag them out; they open threw no orchard; and intermitted not the mandates that condemned their drudges to a life of deaths. Sad sight! to see those round-shouldered Helots, stooping in their trenches: artificial, three in number, and concentric: the isle well-nigh surrounding. And herein, fed by oozy loam, and kindly dew from heaven, and bitter sweat from men, grew as in hot-beds the nutritious Taro.

Toil is man's allotment; toil of brain, or toil of hands, or a grief that's more than either, the grief and sin of idleness. But when man toils and slays himself for masters who withhold the life he gives to them—then, then, the soul screams out, and every sinew cracks. So with these poor serfs. And few of them could choose but be the brutes they seemed.

Now needs it to be said, that Odo was no land of pleasure unalloyed, and plenty without a pause?—Odo, in whose lurking-places infants turned from breasts, whence flowed no nourishment.—Odo, in whose inmost haunts, dark groves were brooding, passing which you heard most dismal cries, and voices cursing Media. There, men were scourged; their crime, a heresy; the heresy, that Media was no demi-god. For this they shrieked. Their fathers shrieked before; their fathers, who, tormented, said, "Happy we to groan, that our children's children may be glad." But their children's children howled. Yet these, too, echoed previous generations, and loudly swore, "The pit that's dug for us may prove another's grave."

But let all pass. To look at, and to roam about of holydays, Odo seemed a happy land. The palm-trees waved—though here and there you marked one sear and palsy-smitten; the flowers bloomed—though dead ones mouldered in decay; the waves ran up the strand in glee—though, receding, they sometimes left behind bones mixed with shells.

But else than these, no sign of death was seen throughout the isle. Did men in Odo live for aye? Was Ponce de Leon's fountain there? For near and far, you saw no ranks and files of graves, no generations harvested in winrows. In Odo, no hard-hearted nabob slept beneath a gentle epitaph; no *requiescat in pace* mocked a sinner damned; no *memento mori* admonished men to live while yet they might. Here Death hid skull; and hid it in the sea, the common sepulchre of Odo. Not dust to dust, but dust to brine; not hearses but canoes. For all who died upon that isle were carried out beyond the outer reef, and there were buried with their sires' sires. Hence came the thought, that of gusty nights, when round the isles, and high toward heaven, flew the white reef's rack and foam, that then and there, kept chattering watch and ward the myriads that were ocean-tombed.

But why these watery obsequies?

Odo was but a little isle, and must the living make way for the dead, and Life's small colony be dislodged by Death's grim hosts; as the gaunt tribes of Tamerlane o'erspread the tented pastures of the Khan?

And now, what follows, said these Islanders: "Why sow corruption in the soil which yields us life? We would not pluck our grapes from over graves. This earth's an urn for flowers, not for ashes."

They said that Oro, the supreme, had made a cemetery of the sea.

And what more glorious grave? Was Mausolus more sublimely urned? Or do the minster-lamps that burn before the tomb of Charlemagne, show more of pomp than all the stars that blaze above the shipwrecked mariner?

But no more of the dead; men shrug their shoulders, and love not their company; though full soon we shall all have them for fellows.

CHAPTER 71

Crossing the lagoon, our course now lay along the reef to Juam; a name bestowed upon one of the largest islands hereabout; and also, collectively, upon several wooded isles engirdling it, which together were known as the dominions of one monarch. That monarch was Donjalolo. Just turned of twenty-five, he was accounted not only the handsomest man in his dominions, but throughout the lagoon. His comeliness, however, was so feminine, that he was sometimes called "Fonoo," or the Girl.

Our first view of Juam was imposing. A dark green pile of cliffs, towering some one hundred toises; at top, presenting a range of steep, gable-pointed projections; as if some Titanic hammer and chisel had shaped the mass.

Sailing nearer, we perceived an extraordinary rolling of the sea, which bursting into the lagoon through an adjoining breach in the reef, surged toward Juam in enormous billows. At last, dashing against the wall of the cliff, they played there in unceasing fountains. But under the brow of a beetling crag, the spray came and went unequally. There, the blue billows seemed swallowed up, and lost.

Right regally was Juam guarded. For, at this point, the rock was pierced by a cave, into which the great waves chased each other like lions; after a hollow, subterraneous roaring issuing forth with manes dishevelled.

Cautiously evading the dangerous currents here ruffling the lagoon, we rounded the wall of cliff, and shot upon a smooth expanse: on one side, hemmed in by the long, verdant, northern shore of Juam; and across the water, sentinelled by its tributary islets.

With sonorous Vee-Vee in the shark's-mouth, we swept toward the beach, tumultuous with a throng.

Our canoes were secured. And surrounded by eager glances, we passed the lower ends of several populous valleys; and crossing a wide, open meadow, gradually ascending, came to a range of light-green bluffs. Here, we wended our way down a narrow defile, almost cleaving this quarter of the island to its base. Black crags frowned overhead; among them the shouts of the Islanders reverberated. Yet steeper grew the defile, and more overhanging the crags; till at last, the keystone of the arch seemed dropped into its place. We found ourselves in a subterranean tunnel, dimly lighted by a span of white day at the end.

Emerging, what a scene was revealed! All round, embracing a circuit of some three leagues, stood heights inaccessible, here and there, forming buttresses, sheltering deep recesses between. The bosom of the place was vivid with verdure.

Shining aslant into this wild hollow, the afternoon sun lighted up its eastern side with tints of gold. But opposite brooded a sombre shadow, double-shading the secret places between the salient spurs of the mountains. Thus cut in twain by masses of day and night, it seemed as if some Last Judgment had been enacted in the glen.

No sooner did we emerge from the defile, than we became sensible of a dull, jarring sound; and Yoomy was almost tempted to turn and flee, when informed that the sea-cavern, whose mouth we had passed, was believed to penetrate deep into the opposite hills; and that the surface of the amphitheatre was depressed beneath that of the lagoon. But all over the lowermost hillsides, and sloping into the glen, stood grand old groves; still and stately, as if no insolent waves were throbbing in the mountain's heart.

Such was Willamilla, the hereditary abode of the young monarch of Juam.

Was Yillah immured in this strange retreat? But from those around us naught could we learn.

Our attention was now directed to the habitations of the glen; comprised in two handsome villages; one to the west, the other to the east; both stretching along the base of the cliffs.

Said Media, "Had we arrived at Willamilla in the morning, we had found Donjalolo and his court in the eastern village; but being afternoon, we must travel farther, and seek him in his western retreat; for that is now in the shade."

Wending our way, Media added, that aside from his elevated station as a monarch, Donjalolo was famed for many uncommon traits; but more especially for certain peculiar deprivations, under which he laboured.

Whereupon Braid-Beard unrolled his old chronicles; and regaled us with the history, which will be found in the following chapter.

CHAPTER 72

Many ages ago, there reigned in Juam a king called Teei. This Teei's succession to the sovereignty was long disputed by his brother Marjora; who at last rallying round him an army, after many vicissitudes, defeated the unfortunate monarch in a stout fight of clubs on the beach.

In those days, Willamilla during a certain period of the year was a place set apart for royal games and diversions; and was furnished with suitable accom-modations for king and court. From its peculiar position, moreover, it was re-garded as the last stronghold of the Juam monarchy: in remote times having twice withstood the most desperate assaults from without. And when Roonoonoo, a famous upstart, sought to subdue all the isles in this part of the Archipelago, it was to Willamilla that the banded kings had repaired to take counsel to-gether; and while there conferring, were surprised at the sudden onslaught of

Roonoonoo in person. But in the end, the rebel was captured, he and all his army, and impaled on the tops of the hills.

Now, defeated and fleeing for his life, Teei with his surviving followers was driven across the plain toward the mountains. But to cut him off from all escape to inland Willamilla, Marjora dispatched a fleet band of warriors to occupy the entrance of the defile. Nevertheless, Teei the pursued ran faster than his pursuers; first gained the spot; and with his chiefs fled swiftly down the gorge, closely hunted by Marjora's men. But arriving at the farther end, they in vain sought to defend it. And after much desperate fighting, the main body of the foe coming up, with great slaughter the fugitives were driven into the glen.

They ran to the opposite wall of cliff; where turning, they fought at bay, blood for blood, and life for life, till at last, overwhelmed by numbers, they were all put to the point of the spear.

With fratricidal hate, singled out by the ferocious Marjora, Teei fell by that brother's hand. When stripping from the body the regal girdle, the victor wound it round his own loins; thus proclaiming himself king over Juam.

Long torn by this intestine war, the island acquiesced in the new sovereignty. But at length a sacred oracle declared, that since the conqueror had slain his brother in deep Willamilla, so that Teei never more issued from that refuge of death; therefore, the same fate should be Marjora's; for never thenceforth, from that glen, should he go forth; neither Marjora; nor any son of his girdled loins; nor his son's sons; nor the uttermost scion of his race.

But except this denunciation, naught was denounced against the usurper; who, mindful of the tenure by which he reigned, ruled over the island for many moons; at his death bequeathing the girdle to his son.

In those days, the wildest superstitions concerning the interference of the gods in things temporal prevailed to a much greater extent than at present. Hence Marjora himself, called sometimes in the traditions of the island, The-Heart-of-Black-Coral, even unscrupulous Marjora had quailed before the oracle. "He bowed his head," say the legends. Nor was it then questioned, by his most devoted adherents, that had he dared to act counter to that edict, he had dropped dead, the very instant he went under the shadow of the defile. This persuasion also guided the conduct of the son of Marjora, and that of his grandson.

But there at last came to pass a change in the popular fancies concerning this ancient anathema. The penalty denounced against the posterity of the usurper should they issue from the glen, came to be regarded as only applicable to an invested monarch, not to his relatives, or heirs.

A most favourable construction of the ban; for all those related to the king freely passed in and out of Willamilla.

From the time of the usurpation, there had always been observed a certain ceremony upon investing the heir to the sovereignty with the girdle of Teei. Upon these occasions, the chief priests of the island were present, acting an important part. For the space of as many days as there had reigned kings of Marjora's dynasty, the inner mouth of the defile remained sealed; the new monarch placing the last stone in the gap. This symbolised his relinquishment forever of all purpose of passing out of the glen. And without this observance, was no king girdled in Juam.

It was likewise an invariable custom, for the heir to receive the regal investiture immediately upon the decease of his sire. No delay was permitted. And instantly upon being girdled, he proceeded to take part in the ceremony of closing the cave; his predecessor yet remaining uninterred on the purple mat where he died. . . .

CHAPTER 73

Previous to recording our stay in his dominions, it only remains to be related of Donjalolo, that after assuming the girdle, a change came over him.

During the lifetime of his father, he had been famed for his temperance and discretion. But when Mardi was forever shut out; and he remembered the law of his isle, interdicting abdication to its kings; he gradually fell into desperate courses, to drown the emotions at times distracting him.

His generous spirit thirsting after some energetic career, found itself narrowed down within the little glen of Willamilla, where ardent impulses seemed idle. But these are hard to die; and repulsed all around, recoil upon themselves.

So with Donjalolo; who, in many a riotous scene, wasted the powers which might have compassed the noblest designs.

Not many years had elapsed since the death of the king, his father. But the still youthful prince was no longer the bright-eyed and elastic boy who at the dawn of day had sallied out to behold the landscapes of the neighbouring isles.

Not more effeminate Sardanapalus, than he. And, at intervals, he was the victim of unaccountable vagaries; haunted by spectres, and beckoned to by the ghosts of his sires.

At times, loathing his vicious pursuits, which brought him no solid satisfaction, but ever filled him with final disgust, he would resolve to amend his ways; solacing himself for his bitter captivity, by the society of the wise and discreet. But brief the interval of repentance. Anew, he burst into excesses, a hundredfold more insane than ever.

Thus vacillating between virtue and vice; to neither constant, and upbraided by both; his mind, like his person in the glen, was continually passing and repassing between opposite extremes.

CHAPTER 74

From the mouth of the cavern, a broad shaded way overarched by fraternal trees embracing in mid-air, conducted us to a cross-path, on either hand leading to the opposite cliffs, shading the twin villages before mentioned.

Level as a meadow, was the bosom of the glen. Here, nodding with green orchards of the bread-fruit and the palm; there, flashing with golden plantations of the banana. Emerging from these, we came out upon a grassy mead, skirting a projection of the mountain. And soon we crossed a bridge of boughs, spanning a trench, thickly planted with roots of the tara, like alligators, or Hollanders, revelling in the soft alluvial. Strolling on, the wild beauty of the mountains excited our attention. The topmost crags poured over with vines; which, undulating in the air, seemed leafy cascades; their sources the upland groves.

Midway up the precipice, along a shelf of rock, sprouted the multitudinous roots of an apparently trunkless tree. Shooting from under the shallow soil, they spread all over the rocks below, covering them with an intricate network. While far aloft, great boughs—each a copse—clambered to the very summit of the mountain; then bending over, struck anew into the soil; forming along the verge an interminable colonnade; all manner of antic architecture standing against the sky.

According to Mohi, this tree was truly wonderful; its seed having been dropped from the moon; where were plenty more similar forests, causing the dark spots on its surface.

Here and there, the cool fluid in the veins of the mountains gushed forth in living springs; their waters received in green mossy tanks, half buried in grasses.

In one place, a considerable stream, bounding far out from a wooded height, ere reaching the ground was dispersed in a wide misty shower, falling so far from the base of the cliff, that walking close underneath, you felt little moisture. Passing this fall of vapours, we spied many Islanders taking a bath.

But what is yonder swaying of the foliage? And what now issues forth, like a habitation astir? Donjalolo drawing nigh to his guests.

He came in a fair sedan; a bower resting upon three long, parallel poles, borne by thirty men, gaily attired; five at each pole-end. Decked with dyed tappas, and looped with garlands of newly-plucked flowers, from which, at every step, the fragrant petals were blown; with a sumptuous, elastic motion the gay sedan came on; leaving behind it a long, rosy wake of fluttering leaves and odours.

Drawing near, it revealed a slender, enervate youth, of pallid beauty, reclining upon a crimson mat, near the festooned arch of the bower. His anointed head was resting against the bosom of a girl; another stirred the air, with a fan of Pintado plumes. The pupils of his eyes were as floating isles in the sea. In a soft low tone he murmured "Media!"

The bearers paused; and Media advancing, the Island Kings bowed their foreheads together.

Through tubes ignited at the end, Donjalolo's reclining attendants now blew an aromatic incense around him. These were composed of the stimulating leaves of the "aina," mixed with the long yellow blades of a sweet-scented upland grass; forming a hollow stem. In general, the agreeable fumes of the "aina" were created by one's own inhalations; but Donjalolo deeming the solace too dearly purchased by any exertion of the royal lungs, regaled himself through those of his attendants, whose lips were as moss-rose buds after a shower.

In silence the young prince now eyed us attentively; meanwhile gently waving his hand, to obtain a better view through the wreaths of vapour. He was about to address us, when chancing to catch a glimpse of Samoa, he suddenly started; averted his glance; and wildly commanded the warrior out of sight. Upon this, his attendants would have soothed him; and Media desired the Upoluan to withdraw.

While we were yet lost in wonder at this scene, Donjalolo, with eyes closed, fell back into the arms of his damsels. Recovering, he fetched a deep sigh, and gazed vacantly around.

It seems, that he had fancied Samoa the noonday spectre of his. ancestor Marjora; the usurper having been deprived of an arm in the battle which gained him the girdle. Poor prince: this was one of those crazy conceits, so puzzling to his subjects.

Media now hastened to assure Donjalolo, that Samoa, though no cherub to behold, was good flesh and blood, nevertheless. And soon the king unconcernedly gazed; his monomania having departed as a dream.

But still suffering from the effects of an overnight feast, he presently murmured forth a desire to be left to his women; adding that his people would not fail to provide for the entertainment of his guests.

The curtains of the sedan were now drawn; and soon it disappeared in the groves. Journeying on, ere long we arrived at the western side of the glen; where one of the many little arbours scattered among the trees, was assigned for our abode. Here, we reclined to an agreeable repast. After which, we strolled forth to view the valley at large; more especially the far-famed palaces of the prince.

CHAPTER 76

Whether the hard condition of their kingly state, very naturally demanding some luxurious requital, prevailed upon the monarchs of Juam to house themselves so delightfully as they did; whether buried alive in their glen, they sought to centre therein a secret world of enjoyment; however it may have been, throughout the Archipelago this saying was a proverb—"You are lodged like the king in Willamilla." Hereby was expressed the utmost sumptuousness of a palace.

A well-warranted saying; for of all the bright places, where my soul loves to linger, the haunts of Donjalolo are most delicious.

In the eastern quarter of the glen was the House of Morning. This fanciful palace was raised upon a natural mound, many rods square, almost completely filling up a deep recess between deep-green and projecting cliffs, overlooking many abodes distributed in the shadows of the groves beyond.

Now, if it indeed be, that from the time employed in its construction, any just notion may be formed of the stateliness of an edifice, it must needs be determined that this retreat of Donjalolo could not be otherwise than imposing.

Full five hundred moons was the palace in completing; for by some architectural arborist, its quadrangular foundations had been laid in seed cocoa-nuts, requiring that period to sprout up into pillars. In front, these were horizontally connected by elaborately carved beams, of a scarlet hue, inserted into the vital wood; which, swelling out, and overlapping, firmly secured them. The beams supported the rafters, inclining from the rear; while over the aromatic grasses covering the roof, waved the tufted tops of the palms, green capitals to their dusky shafts.

Through and through this vibrating verdure, bright birds flitted and sang; the scented and variegated thatch seemed a hanging garden; and between it and the palm tops, was leaf-hung an arbour in the air.

Without these columns, stood a second and third colonnade, forming the most beautiful bowers; advancing through which, you fancied that the palace beyond must be chambered in a fountain, or frozen in a crystal. Three sparkling rivulets flowing from the heights were led across its summit, through great trunks half buried in the thatch; and emptying into a sculptured channel, running along the eaves, poured over in one wide sheet, plaited and transparent. Received into a basin beneath, they were thence conducted down the vale.

The sides of the palace were hedged by Diomi bushes bearing a flower, from its perfume, called Lenora, or Sweet Breath; and within these odorous hedges were heavy piles of mats, richly dyed and embroidered.

Here lounging of a glowing noon, the plaited cascade playing, the verdure waving, and the birds melodious, it was hard to say whether you were an inmate of a garden in the glen, or a grotto in the sea.

But enough for the nonce of the House of the Morning. Cross we the hollow, to the House of the Afternoon.

CHAPTER 77

For the most part, the House of the Afternoon was but a wing built against a mansion wrought by the hand of Nature herself; a grotto running into the side of the mountain.

From high over the mouth of this grotto, sloped a long arbour, supported by great blocks of stone, rudely chiselled into the likeness of idols, each bearing a carved lizard on its chest: a sergeant's guard of the gods condescendingly doing duty as posts.

From the grotto thus vestibuled, issued hilariously forth the most considerable stream of the glen; which, seemingly overjoyed to find daylight in Willamilla, sprang into the arbour with a cheery, white bound. But its youthful enthusiasm was soon repressed; its waters being caught in a large stone basin, scooped out of the natural rock; whence, staid and decorous, they traversed sundry moats; at last meandering away, to join floods with the streams trained to do service at the other end of the vale.

Truant streams: the livelong day wending their loitering path to the subterraneous outlet, flowing into which, they disappeared. But no wonder they loitered; passing such ravishing landscapes. Thus with life: man bounds out of night; runs and babbles in the sun; then returns to his darkness again; though, peradventure, once more to emerge.

But the grotto was not a mere outlet to the stream. Flowing through a dark flume in the rock, on both sides it left a dry, elevated shelf, to which you ascend from the arbour by three artificially wrought steps, sideways disposed to avoid the spray of the rejoicing cataract. Mounting these, and pursuing the edge of the flume, the grotto gradually expands and heightens; your way lighted by rays in the inner distance. At last you come to a lofty subterraneous dome, lit from above by a cleft in the mountain; while full before you, in the opposite wall, from a low, black arch, midway up, and inaccessible, the stream, with a hollow ring and a dash, falls in a long, snowy column into a bottomless pool, whence, after many an eddy and whirl, it entered the flume, and away with a rush. Half hidden from view by an overhanging brow of the rock, the white fall looked like the sheeted ghost of the grotto.

Yet gallantly bedecked was the cave, as any old armorial hall hung round with banners and arras. Streaming from the cleft, vines swung in the air; or crawled along the rocks, wherever a tendril could be fixed. High up, their leaves were green; but lower down, they were shrivelled; and dyed of many colours; and tattered and torn with much rustling; as old banners again; sore ravelled with much triumphing.

In the middle of this hall in the hill was incarcerated the stone image of one Demi, the tutelar deity of Willamilla. All green and oozy like a stone under water, poor Demi looked as if sore harassed with sciatics and lumbagos.

But he was cheered from aloft, by the promise of receiving a garland all blooming on his crown; the dryads sporting in the woodlands above, forever peeping down the cleft, and essaying to drop him a coronal.

Now, the still, panting glen of Willamilla, nested so close by the mountains, and a goodly green mark for the archer in the sun, would have been almost untenable were it not for the grotto. Hereby, it breathed the blessed breezes of Omi; a mountain promontory buttressing the island to the east, receiving the cool stream of the upland Trades; much pleasanter than the currents beneath.

At all times, even in the brooding noon-day, a gush of cool air came hand-in-hand with the cool waters, that burst with a shout into the palace of Donjalolo. And as, after first refreshing the king, as in loyalty bound, the stream flowed at large through the glen, and bathed its verdure; so, the blessed breezes of Omi, not only made pleasant the House of the Afternoon; but finding ample outlet in its wide, open front, blew forth upon the bosom of all Willamilla.

"Come let us take the air of Omi," was a very common saying in the glen. And the speaker would hie with his comrade toward the grotto; and flinging himself on the turf, pass his hand through his locks, and recline; making a joy and a business of breathing; for truly the breezes of Omi were as air-wine to the lungs.

Yet was not this breeze over-cool; though at times the zephyrs grew boisterous. Especially at the season of high sea, when the strong Trades, drawn down the cleft in the mountain, rushed forth from the grotto with wonderful force. Crossing it then, you had much ado to keep your robe on your back.

Thus much for the House of the Afternoon. Whither—after spending the shady morning under the eastern cliffs of the glen—daily, at a certain hour, Donjalolo in his palanquin was borne; there, finding new shades; and there tarrying till evening; when again he was transported whence he came: thereby anticipating the revolution of the sun. Thus dodging day's luminary through life, the prince hied to and fro in his dominions; on his smooth, spotless brow Sol's rays never shining.

CHAPTER 89

Judge not things by their names. This, the maxim illustrated respecting the isle toward which we were sailing.

Ohonoo was its designation, in other words the Land of Rogues. So what but a nest of villains and pirates could one fancy it to be: a downright Tortuga, swarming with "Brethren of the Coast,"—such as Montbars, L'Ollonais, Bartolomeo, Peter of Dieppe, and desperadoes of that kidney. But not so. The men of Ohonoo were as honest as any in Mardi. They had a suspicious appellative for their island, true; but not thus seemed it to them. For, upon nothing did they so much plume themselves as upon this very name. Why? Its origin went back to old times; and being venerable they gloried therein; though they disclaimed its present applicability to any of their race; showing, that words are but algebraic signs, conveying no meaning except what you please. And to be called one thing, is oftentimes to be another.

But how came the Ohonoose by their name?

Listen, and Braid-Beard, our Herodotus, will tell.

Long and long ago, there were banished to Ohonoo all the bucaniers, filibusters, thieves, and malefactors of the neighbouring islands; who, becoming at last quite a numerous community, resolved to make a stand for their dignity, and number one among the nations of Mardi. And even as before they had been weeded out of the surrounding countries; so now, they went to weeding out themselves; banishing all objectionable persons to still another island. These events happened at a period so remote, that at present it was uncertain whether those twice banished, were thrust into their second exile by reason of their superlative knavery, or because of their comparative honesty. If the latter, then must the residue have been a precious enough set of scoundrels.

However it was, the commonwealth of knaves now mustered together their gray-beards, and wise-pates, and knowing-ones, of which last there was a plenty, chose a king to rule over them, and went to political housekeeping for themselves.

And in the fulness of time, this people became numerous and mighty. And the more numerous and mighty they waxed, by so much the more did they take pride and glory in their origin, frequently reverting to it with manifold boastings. The proud device of their monarch was a hand with the forefinger crooked, emblematic of the peculatory propensities of his ancestors.

And all this, at greater length, said Mohi.

"It would seem, then, my lord," said Babbalanja, reclining, "as if these men of Ohonoo had canonised the derelictions of their progenitors, though the same traits are deemed scandalous among themselves. But it is time that makes the difference. The knave of a thousand years ago seems a fine old fellow full of spirit and fun, little malice in his soul; whereas, the knave of to-day seems a sour-visaged wight, with nothing to redeem him. Many great scoundrels of our chronicler's chronicles are heroes to us:—witness, Marjora the usurper. Ay, time truly works wonders. It sublimates wine; it sublimates fame; nay, is the creator thereof; it enriches and darkens our spears of the palm; enriches and enlightens the mind; it ripens cherries and young lips; festoons old ruins, and ivies old heads; imparts a relish to old yams, and a pungency to the Ponderings of old Bardianna; of fables distils truths; and finally, smooths, levels, glosses, softens, melts, and meliorates all things. Why, my lord, round Mardi itself is all the better for its antiquity, and the more to be revered; to the cosy-minded, more comfortable to dwell in. Ah! if ever it lay in embryo like a green seed in the pod, what a damp, shapeless thing it must have been, and how unpleasant from the traces of its recent creation. The first man, quoth old Bardianna, must have felt like one going into a new habitation, where the bamboos are green. Is there not a legend in Maramma, that his family were long troubled with influenzas and catarrhs?"

"Oh Time, Time, Time!" cried Yoomy—"it is Time, old midsummer Time, that has made the old world what it is. Time hoared the old mountains, and balded their old summits, and spread the old prairies, and built the old forests, and moulded the old vales. It is Time that has worn glorious old channels for the glorious old rivers, and rounded the old lakes, and deepened the old sea! It is Time——"

"Ay, full time to cease," cried Media. "What have you to do with cogitations not in verse, minstrel? Leave prose to Babbalanja, who is prosy enough."

"Even so," said Babbalanja, "Yoomy, you have overstepped your province. My lord Media well knows, that your business is to make the metal in you jingle in tags, not ring in the ingot."

CHAPTER 90

Approached from the northward, Ohonoo, midway cloven down to the sea, one half a level plain; the other, three mountain terraces—Ohonoo looks like the first steps of a gigantic way to the sun. And such, if Braid-Beard spoke truth, it had formerly been.

"Ere Mardi was made," said that true old chronicler, "Vivo, one of the genii, built a ladder of mountains whereby to go up and go down. And of this ladder, the island of Ohonoo was the base. But wandering here and there, incognito in a vapour, so much wickedness did Vivo spy out, that in high dudgeon he hurried up his ladder, knocking the mountains from under him as he went. These here and there fell into the lagoon, forming many isles, now green and luxuriant; which, with those sprouting from seeds dropped by a bird from the moon, comprise all the groups in the reef."

Surely, oh, surely, if I live till Mardi be forgotten by Mardi, I shall not forget the sight that greeted us, as we drew nigh the shores of this same island of Ohonoo; for was not all Ohonoo bathing in the surf of the sea?

But let the picture be painted.

Where eastward the ocean rolls surging against the outer reef of Mardi, there, facing the flood-gate in the barrier, stands cloven Ohonoo; her plains sloping outward to the sea, her mountains a bulwark behind. As at Juam, where the wild billows from seaward roll in upon its cliffs; much more at Ohonoo, in billowy battalions charge they hotly into the lagoon, and fall on the isle like an army from the deep. But charge they never so boldly, and charge they forever, old Ohonoo gallantly throws them back till all before her is one scud and rack. So charged the bright billows of cuirassiers at Waterloo: so hurled them off the long line of living walls, whose base was as the sea-beach, wreck-strewn, in a gale.

Without the break in the reef, wide banks of coral shelve off, creating the bar, where the waves muster for the onset, thundering in water-bolts, that shake the whole reef, till its very spray trembles. And then is it, that the swimmers of Ohonoo most delight to gambol in the surf.

For this sport, a surf-board is indispensable: some five feet in length; the width of a man's body; convex on both sides; highly polished; and rounded at the ends. It is held in high estimation; invariably oiled after use; and hung up conspicuously in the dwelling of the owner.

Ranged on the beach, the bathers by hundreds dash in; and diving under the swells, make straight for the outer sea, pausing not till the comparatively smooth expanse beyond has been gained. Here, throwing themselves upon their boards, tranquilly they wait for a billow that suits. Snatching them up, it hurries them landward, volume and speed both increasing, till it races along a watery wall, like the smooth, awful verge of Niagara. Hanging over this scroll, looking down from it as from a precipice, the bathers halloo; every limb in motion to preserve their place on the very crest of the wave. Should they fall behind, the squadrons that follow would whelm them; dismounted, and thrown forward, as certainly would they be run over by the steed they ride. 'Tis like charging at the head of cavalry: you must on.

An expert swimmer shifts his position on his plank; now half striding it; and anon, like a rider in the ring, poising himself upright in the scud, coming on like a man in the air.

At last all is lost in scud and vapour, as the overgrown billow bursts like a bomb. Adroitly emerging, the swimmers thread their way out; and like seals at the Orkneys, stand dripping upon the shore.

Landing in smooth water, some distance from the scene, we strolled forward; and meeting a group resting, inquired for Uhia, their king. He was pointed out in the foam. But presently drawing nigh, he embraced Media, bidding all welcome.

The bathing over, and evening at hand, Uhia and his subjects repaired to their canoes; and we to ours.

Landing at another quarter of the island, we journeyed up a valley called Monlova, and were soon housed in a very pleasant retreat of our host.

Soon supper was spread. But though the viands were rare, and the red wine went round and round like a foaming bay horse in the ring; yet we marked, that despite the stimulus of his day's good sport, and the stimulus of his brave good cheer, Uhia our host was moody and still.

Said Babbalanja, "My lord, he fills wine-cups for others to quaff."

But whispered King Media, "Though Uhia be sad, be we merry, merry men."

And merry some were, and merrily went to their mats.

CHAPTER 92

One object of interest in Ohonoo was the original image of Keevi, the god of Thieves; hence, from time immemorial, the tutelar deity of the isle.

His shrine was a natural niche in a cliff, walling in the valley of Monlova. And here stood Keevi, with his five eyes, ten hands, and three pair of legs, equipped at all points for the vocation over which he presided. Of mighty girth, his arms terminated in hands, every finger a limb, spreading in multiplied digits: palms twice five, and fifty fingers.

According to the legend, Keevi fell from a golden cloud, burying himself to the thighs in the earth, tearing up the soil all round. Three meditative mortals, strolling by at the time, had a narrow escape.

A wonderful recital; but none of us voyagers durst flout it. Did they not show us the identical spot where the idol fell? We descended into the hollow, now verdant. Questionless, Keevi himself would have vouched for the truth of the miracle, had he not been unfortunately dumb. But by far the most cogent and pointed argument advanced in support of this story, is a spear which the priests of Keevi brought forth, for Babbalanja to view.

"Let me look at it closer," said Babbalanja.

And turning it over and over and curiously inspecting it, "Wonderful spear," he cried. "Doubtless, my reverends, this self-same spear must have persuaded many recusants!"

"Nay, the most stubborn," they answered.

"And all afterward quoted as additional authority for the truth of the legend?"

"Assuredly."

From the sea to the shrine of this god, the fine valley of Monlova ascends with a gentle gradation, hardly perceptible; but upon turning round toward the water, one is surprised to find himself high elevated above its surface. Pass on, and the same silent ascent deceives you; and the valley contracts; and on both sides the cliffs advance; till at last you come to a narrow space, shouldered by buttresses of rock. Beyond, through this cleft, all is blue sky. If the Trades blow high, and you came unawares upon the spot, you would think Keevi himself pushing you forward with all his hands; so powerful is the current of air rushing through this elevated defile. But expostulate not with the tornado that blows you along; sail on; but soft; look down; the land breaks off in one sheer descent of a thousand feet, right down to the wide plain below. So sudden and profound this precipice, that you seem to look off from one world to another. In a dreamy, sunny day, the spangled plain beneath assumes an uncertain fleeting aspect. Had you a deep-sea lead you would almost be tempted to sound the ocean-haze at your feet.

This, mortal! is the precipice of Mondo.

From this brink, spear in hand, sprang fifty rebel warriors, driven back into the vale by a superior force. Finding no spot to stand at bay, with a fierce shout they took the fatal leap.

Said Mohi, "Their souls ascended, ere their bodies touched."

This tragical event took place many generations gone by, and now a dizzy, devious way conducts one, firm of foot, from the verge to the plain. But none ever ascended. So perilous, indeed, is the descent itself, that the Islanders venture not the feat, without invoking supernatural aid. Flanking the precipice, beneath beetling rocks, stand the guardian deities of Mondo; and on altars before them, are placed the propitiatory offerings of the traveller.

To the right of the brink of the precipice, and far over it, projects a narrow ledge. The test of legitimacy in the Ohonoo monarchs is to stand hereon, arms folded, and javelins darting by.

And there in his youth Uhia stood.

"How felt you, cousin?" asked Media.

"Like the King of Ohonoo," he replied. "As I *shall* again feel, when King of all Mardi."

CHAPTER 94

Drawing near Mondoldo, our next place of destination, we were greeted by six fine canoes, gaily tricked out with streamers, and all alive with the gestures of their occupants. King Borabolla and court were hastening to welcome our approach; Media, unbeknown to all, having notified him at the Banquet of the Five-and-Twenty Kings, of our intention to visit his dominions.

Soon, side by side, these canoes floated with ours; each barge of Odo courteously flanked by those of Mondoldo.

Not long were we in identifying Borabolla: the portly, pleasant old monarch, seated cross-legged upon a dais, projecting over the bow of the largest canoe of the six, close-grappling to the side of the *Sea-Elephant*.

Was he not a goodly round sight to behold? Round all over; round of eye and of head; and like the jolly round Earth, roundest and biggest about the Equator. A girdle of red was his Equinoctial Line, giving a compactness to his plumpness.

This old Borabolla permitted naught to come between his head and the sun; not even gray hairs. Bald as a gourd, right down on his brazen skull the rays of the luminary converged.

He was all hilarity: full of allusions to the feast at Willamilla, where he had done royal execution. Rare old Borabolla! thou wert made for dining out; thy ample mouth an inlet for good cheer, and a sally-port for good humour.

Bustling about on his dais, he now gave orders for the occupants of our canoes to be summarily emptied into his own; saying, that in that manner only did he allow guests to touch the beach of Mondoldo.

So, with no little trouble—for the waves were grown somewhat riotous—we proceeded to comply; bethinking ourselves all the while how annoying is sometimes an overstrained act of hospitality.

We were now but little less than a mile from the shore. But what of that? There was plenty of time, thought Borabolla, for a hasty lunch, and the getting of a subsequent appetite ere we effected a landing. So viands were produced; to which the guests were invited to pay heedful attention; or take the consequences, and famish till the long voyage in prospect was ended.

Soon the water shoaled (approaching land is like nearing truth in metaphysics), and ere we yet touched the beach, Borabolla declared, that we were already landed. Which paradoxical assertion implied, that the hospitality of Mondoldo was such, that in all directions it radiated far out upon the lagoon, embracing a great circle; so that no canoe could sail by the island, without its occupants being so long its guests.

In most hospitable vicinity to the water, was a fine large structure, enclosed by a stockade; both rather dilapidated; as if the cost of entertaining its guests prevented outlays for repairing the place. But it was one of Borabolla's maxims, that generally your tumble-down old homesteads yield the most entertainment; their very dilapidation betokening their having seen good service in hospitality; whereas, spruce-looking, finical portals have a phiz full of meaning; for niggards are oftentimes neat.

Now, after what has been said, who so silly as to fancy, that because Borabolla's mansion was enclosed by a stockade, that the same was intended as a defence against guests? By no means. In the palisade was a mighty breach, not an entrance-way, wide enough to admit six Daniel Lamberts abreast.

"Look," cried Borabolla, as landing we stepped toward the place. "Look, Media! look all. These gates, you here see, lashed back with osiers, have been so lashed during my lifetime; and just where they stand shall they rot; ay, they shall perish wide open."

"But why have them at all?" inquired Media.

"Ah! there you have old Borabolla," cried the other.

"No," said Babbalanja, "a fence whose gate is ever kept open, seems unnecessary, I grant; nevertheless, it gives a notable hint, otherwise not so aptly conveyed; for is not the open gate the sign of the open heart?"

"Right, right," cried Borabolla; "so enter both, cousin Media"; and with one hand smiting his chest, with the other he waved us on.

But if the stockade seemed all open gate, the structure within seemed only a roof; for nothing but a slender pillar here and there supported it.

"This is my mode of building," said Borabolla; "I will have no outside to my palaces. Walls are superfluous. And to a high-minded guest, the entering a narrow doorway is like passing under a yoke; every time he goes in, or comes out, it reminds him that he is being entertained at the cost of another. So storm in all round."

Within, was one wide field-bed; where reclining, we looked up to endless rows of brown calabashes, and trenchers suspended along the rafters; promissory of ample cheer as regiments of old hams in a baronial refectory.

They were replenished with both meat and drink; the trenchers readily accessible by means of cords; but the gourds containing arrack, suspended neck downward, were within easy reach where they swung.

Seeing all these indications of hard roystering; like a cautious young bridegroom at his own marriage merrymaking, Taji stood on his guard. And when Borabolla urged him to empty a gourd or two, by way of making room in him for the incidental repast about to be served, Taji civilly declined; not wishing to cumber the floor, before the cloth was laid.

Jarl, however, yielding to importunity, and unmindful of the unities of time and place, went freely about, from gourd to gourd, concocting in him a punch. At which, Samoa expressed much surprise, that he should be so unobservant as not to know, that in Mardi, guests might be pressed to demean themselves, without its being expected that so they would do. A true toss-pot himself, he bode his time.

The second lunch over, Borabolla placed both hands to the ground, and giving the sigh of the fat man, after three vigorous efforts, succeeded in gaining his pins; which pins of his were but small for his body; insomuch that they hugely staggered about, under the fine old load they carried.

The specific object of his thus striving after an erect posture, was to put himself in motion, and conduct us to his fish ponds, famous throughout the Archipelago as the hobby of the king of Mondoldo. Furthermore, as the great repast of the day, yet to take place, was to be a grand piscatory one, our host was all anxiety, that we should have a glimpse of our fish, while yet alive and hearty.

We were alarmed at perceiving, that certain servitors were preparing to accompany us with trenchers of edibles. It begat the notion that our trip to the fish ponds was to prove a long journey. But they were not three hundred yards distant; though Borabolla being a veteran traveller, never stirred from his abode without his battalion of butlers.

The ponds were four in number, close bordering the water, embracing about an acre each, and situated in a low fen, draining several valleys. The excavated soil was thrown up in dykes, made tight by being beaten all over, while in a soft state, with the heavy, flat ends of palm stalks. Lying side by side, by three connecting trenches, these ponds could be made to communicate at pleasure; while two additional canals afforded means of letting in upon them the salt waters of the lagoon on one hand, or those of an inland stream on the other. And by a third canal with four branches, together or separately, they could be partially drained. Thus, the waters could be mixed to suit any gills; and the young fish taken from the sea, passed through a stated process of freshening; so that by the time they graduated, the salt was well out of them, like the brains out of some diplomaed collegians.

Fresh-water fish are only to be obtained in Mondoldo by the artificial process above mentioned; as the streams and brooks abound not in trout or other Waltonian prey.

Taken all floundering from the sea, Borabolla's fish, passing through their regular training for the table, and daily tended by their keepers, in course of time became quite tame and communicative. To prove which, calling his head ranger, the king bade him administer the customary supply of edibles.

Accordingly, mouthfuls were thrown into the ponds. Whereupon, the fish darted in a shoal toward the margin; some leaping out of the water in their eagerness. Crouching on the bank, the ranger now called several by name, patted their scales, carrying on some heathenish nursery talk, like St. Anthony, in ancient Coptic, instilling virtuous principles into his finny flock on the sea-shore.

But alas, for the hair-shirted old dominie's backsliding disciples. For, of all nature's animated kingdoms, fish are the most unchristian, inhospitable, heart-less, and cold-blooded of creatures. At least, so seem they to strangers; though at bottom, somehow, they must be all right. And truly it is not to be wondered at, that the very reverend Anthony strove after the conversion of fish. For, whoso shall Christianise, and by so doing humanise the sharks, will do a greater good, by the saving of human life in all time to come, than though he made catechumens of the head-hunting Dyaks of Borneo, or the blood-bibbing Battas of Sumatra. And are these Dyaks and Battas one whit better than tiger-sharks? Nay, are they so good? Were a Batta your intimate friend, you would often mistake an orang-outang for him; and have orang-outangs immortal souls? True, the Battas believe in a hereafter; but of what sort? Full of Blue-Beards and bloody bones. So, also, the sharks; who hold that Paradise is one vast Pacific, ploughed by navies of mortals, whom an endless gale forever drops into their maws.

Not wholly a surmise. For, does it not appear a little unreasonable to imagine, that there is any creature, fish, flesh, or fowl, so little in love with life, as not to cherish hopes of a future state? Why does man believe in it? One reason, reckoned cogent, is, that he desires it. Who shall say, then, that the leviathan this day harpooned on the coast of Japan, goes not straight to his ancestor, who rolled all Jonah, as a sweet morsel, under his tongue?

Though herein, some sailors are slow believers, or at best hold themselves in a state of philosophical suspense. Say they—"That catastrophe took place in the Mediterranean; and the only whales frequenting the Mediterranean, are of a sort having not a swallow large enough to pass a man entire; for those Mediter-ranean whales feed upon small things, as horses upon oats." But hence, the sailors draw a rash inference. Are not the Straits of Gibraltar wide enough to admit a sperm-whale, even though none have sailed through, since Nineveh and the gourd in its suburbs dried up?

As for the possible hereafter of the whales; a creature eighty feet long with-out stockings, and thirty feet round the waist before dinner, is not inconsiderately to be consigned to annihilation.

PART V

A PASSAGE
BEFORE THE MAST:
White Jacket
(1850)

INTRODUCTION

The book Melville wrote previous to *Moby Dick* was *White-Jacket: or The World in a Man-of-War.* Therein the author left behind the unwieldy macrocosm of *Mardi* and limited his scope to a close examination of the microcosm of an American naval vessel in the days when captains were kings and any of America's defenders on the sea could be summarily flogged to death.

Melville embodied in *White Jacket* with rare unity his experiences during fourteen months within the wooden walls of the U.S.S. *United States,* but the story begins with the ship leaving Callao for its three-month run homeward. The book is again a novel rather than pure autobiography or "documentary" (as one scholar labeled it), and again Herman drew heavily on dogwatch yarns and printed sources.[1] Revelation of the strong amount of invented incidents in what appears to be a narrative of routine service in the American Navy is found in the researches of Charles R. Anderson, especially *Melville in the South Seas* (Baltimore: Johns Hopkins University Press, 1941; New York: Dover, 1966). Earlier Dr. Anderson had remarked: "More than a dozen of the most important scenes, making up almost half of the volume, were manufactured out of whole cloth. Several of them, at least, found their source in contemporary travel books; many more, perhaps, were revampings of sailor-lore, garnered from the tall tales he had heard in the maintop on pleasant nights. Some of these concoctions are the brightest bits of foolery in this best-humored of all Melville's volumes; some are given as lurid personal experiences, traps for the unwary biographer; some are vehicles for his most incisive attacks on naval abuses."[2]

The theme of *White Jacket* is clearly propagandistic, aiming to abolish or mitigate the many abuses to which Melville's fellow seamen were subjected. Its immediate effect upon the passage of a reform bill by Congress can be exaggerated, although the book drew indignant replies from three rear admirals. Melville's achievement, in retrospect, is in my opinion the publication of the finest book by an enlisted man in any navy at any time. On his homeward voyage one can share the joys and terrors of a man-of-warsman, admire hearty heroes like Jack Chase, and shiver at the tyranny of "Captain Claret" and "Surgeon Cadwallader Cuticle, M.D." Melville's ear for odd lingo was keen, and his use of naval slang and technical jargon in this book made it a treasure chest for lexicographers.[3]

Late in 1849, during which year were published both *Mardi* and *Redburn: His First Voyage*—the story of an Atlantic voyage by an impressionable young sailor—Melville decided to go abroad again. He took along the American proof sheets of *White Jacket* furnished him by Harpers, to arrange copyright and sell the rights to an English publisher, but could not get better terms than those offered by Bentley, by now his regular British firm. After a stay in London, Melville visited the Continent and returned home to New York City early in 1850, the year in which *White Jacket* was published there and in London. Herman was pleased to find that both *Redburn* and *White Jacket,* which he had turned out as potboilers, had been surprisingly well received (except by rear admirals). Soon Melville's friend Richard Henry Dana suggested that he should do a popular book on the whale fishery, as Dana had achieved popularity a decade earlier with *Two Years Before the Mast,* his book on the merchant seamen of the Pacific. Melville pondered, and settled down to write *Moby Dick*.

In *White Jacket,* the U.S.S. *Neversink,* as Melville calls it, spends only a few weeks in the Pacific, and new scenes dealing with the South Seas are scarce. One should include, however, his description of the difficulties of escaping from the Pacific by way of Cape Horn. The grand ocean was reluctant, it would seem, to permit its most famous celebrant to depart from its dominion without a final show of its unpacific powers.

❀ ❀ ❀

CHAPTER 24

And now, through drizzling fogs and vapors, and under damp, double-reefed top-sails, our wet-decked frigate drew nearer and nearer to the squally Cape.

Who has not heard of it? Cape Horn, Cape Horn—a *horn* indeed, that has tossed many a good ship. Was the descent of Orpheus, Ulysses, or Dante into Hell, one whit more hardy and sublime than the first navigator's weathering of that terrible Cape?

Turned on her heel by a fierce West Wind, many an outward-bound ship has been driven across the Southern Ocean to the Cape of Good Hope—*that* way to seek a passage to the Pacific. And that stormy Cape, I doubt not, has sent many a fine craft to the bottom, and told no tales. At those ends of the earth are no chronicles. What signify the broken spars and shrouds that, day after day, are driven before the prows of more fortunate vessels? or the tall masts, imbedded in icebergs, that are found floating by? They but hint the old story—of ships that have sailed from their ports, and never more have been heard of.

Impracticable Cape! You may approach it from this direction or that—in any way you please—from the East, or from the West; with the wind astern, or abeam, or on the quarter; and still Cape Horn is Cape Horn. Cape Horn it is that takes the conceit out of fresh-water sailors, and steeps in a still salter brine the saltest. Woe betide the tyro! the foolhardy, Heaven preserve!

Your Mediterranean captain, who with a cargo of oranges has hitherto made merry runs across the Atlantic, without so much as furling a t'-gallant-sail, often-times, off Cape Horn, receives a lesson which he carries to the grave; though the grave—as is too often the case—follows so hard on the lesson that no benefit comes from the experience.

Other strangers who draw nigh to this Patagonia termination of our Continent, with their souls full of its shipwrecks and disasters—top-sails cautiously reefed, and every thing guardedly snug—these strangers at first unexpectedly encountering a tolerably smooth sea, rashly conclude that the Cape, after all, is but a bugbear; they have been imposed upon by fables, and founderings and sinkings hereabouts are all cock-and-bull stories.

"Out reefs, my hearties; fore and aft set t'-gallant-sails! stand by to give her the fore-top-mast stun'-sail!"

But Captain Rash, those sails of yours were much safer in the sail-maker's loft. For now, while the heedless craft is bounding over the billows, a black cloud rises out of the sea; the sun drops down from the sky; a horrible mist far and wide spreads over the water.

"Hands by the halyards! Let go! Clew up!"

Too late.

For ere the ropes' ends can be cast off from the pins, the tornado is blowing down to the bottom of their throats. The masts are willows, the sails ribbons, the cordage wool; the whole ship is brewed into the yeast of the gale.

And now, if, when the first green sea breaks over him, Captain Rash is not swept overboard, he has his hands full, be sure. In all probability his three masts have gone by the board, and, raveled into list, his sails are floating in the air. Or, perhaps, the ship *broaches to,* or is *brought by the lee.* In either case, Heaven help the sailors, their wives, and their little ones; and Heaven help the under-writers.

Familiarity with danger makes a brave man braver, but less daring. Thus with seamen: he who goes the oftenest round Cape Horn goes the most circumspectly. A veteran mariner is never deceived by the treacherous breezes which sometimes waft him pleasantly toward the latitude of the Cape. No sooner does he come within a certain distance of it—previously fixed in his own mind—than all hands are turned to setting the ship in storm-trim; and, never mind how light the breeze, down come his t'-gallant-yards. He "bends" his strongest storm-sails, and lashes every thing on deck securely. The ship is then ready for the worst; and if, in reeling round the headland, she receives a broadside, it generally goes well with her. If ill, all hands go to the bottom with quiet consciences.

Among sea-captains, there are some who seem to regard the genius of the Cape as a willful, capricious jade, that must be courted and coaxed into complaisance. First, they come along under easy sail; do not steer boldly for the headland, but tack this way and that—sidling up to it. Now they woo the Jezebel with a t'-gallant-studding-sail; anon, they deprecate her wrath with double-reefed-top-sails. When, at length, her unappeasable fury is fairly aroused, and all round the dismantled ship the storm howls and howls for days together, they still persevere in their efforts. First, they try unconditional submission; furling every rag and *heaving to;* laying like a log, for the tempest to toss wheresoever it pleases.

This failing, they set a *spencer* or *try-sail,* and shift on the other tack. Equally vain! The gale sings as hoarsely as before. At last, the wind comes round fair; they drop the fore-sail; square the yards, and scud before it: their implacable foe chasing them with tornadoes, as if to show her insensibility to the last.

Other ships, without encountering these terrible gales, spend week after week endeavoring to turn this boisterous world-corner against a continual head-wind. Tacking hither and thither, in the language of sailors, they *polish* the Cape by beating about its edges so long.

Le Mair and Schouten, two Dutchmen, were the first navigators who weathered Cape Horn. Previous to this, passages had been made to the Pacific by the Straits of Magellan; nor, indeed, at that period, was it known to a certainty that there was any other route, or that the land now called Terra Del Fuego was an island. A few leagues southward from Terra Del Fuego is a cluster of small islands, the Diegoes; between which and the former island are the Straits of Le Mair, so called in honor of their discoverer, who first sailed through them into the Pacific. Le Mair and Schouten, in their small, clumsy vessels, encountered a series of tremendous gales, the prelude to the long train of similar hardships which most of their followers have experienced. It is a significant fact, that Schouten's vessel, the *Horne,* which gave its name to the Cape, was almost lost in weathering it.

The next navigator round the Cape was Sir Francis Drake, who, on Raleigh's Expedition, beholding for the first time, from the Isthmus of Darien, the "goodlie South Sea," like a true-born Englishman, vowed, please God, to sail an English ship thereon; which the gallant sailor did, to the sore discomfiture of the Spaniards on the coasts of Chili and Peru.

But perhaps the greatest hardships on record, in making this celebrated passage, were those experienced by Lord Anson's squadron in 1736. Three remarkable and most interesting narratives record their disasters and sufferings. The first, jointly written by the carpenter and gunner of the Wager; the second, by young Byron, a midshipman in the same ship; the third, by the chaplain of the Centurion. White-Jacket has them all; and they are fine reading of a boisterous March night, with the casement rattling in your ear, and the chimney-stacks blowing down upon the pavement, bubbling with rain-drops.

But if you want the best idea of Cape Horn, get my friend Dana's unmatchable "Two Years Before the Mast." But you can read, and so you must have read it. His chapters describing Cape Horn must have been written with an icicle.

At the present day the horrors of the Cape have somewhat abated. This is owing to a growing familiarity with it; but, more than all, to the improved condition of ships in all respects, and the means now generally in use of preserving the health of the crews in times of severe and prolonged exposure.

CHAPTER 25

Colder and colder; we are drawing nigh to the Cape. Now gregoes, pea jackets, monkey jackets, reefing jackets, storm jackets, oil jackets, paint jackets, round jackets, short jackets, long jackets, and all manner of jackets, are the order of the day, not excepting the immortal white jacket, which begins to be sturdily buttoned up to the throat, and pulled down vigorously at the skirts, to bring them well over the loins.

But, alas! those skirts were lamentably scanty; and though, with its quiltings, the jacket was stuffed out about the breasts like a Christmas turkey, and of a dry cold day kept the wearer warm enough in that vicinity, yet about the loins it was shorter than a ballet-dancer's skirts; so that while my chest was in the temperate zone, close adjoining the torrid, my hapless thighs were in Nova Zembla, hardly an icicle's toss from the Pole.

Then, again, the repeated soakings and dryings it had undergone, had by this time made it shrink woefully all over, especially in the arms, so that the wristbands had gradually crawled up near to the elbows; and it required an energetic thrust to push the arm through, in drawing the jacket on.

I endeavored to amend these misfortunes by sewing a sort of canvass ruffle round the skirts, by way of a continuation or supplement to the original work, and by doing the same with the wristbands.

This is the time for oil-skin suits, dread-naughts, tarred trowsers and overalls, sea-boots, comforters, mittens, woolen socks, Guernsey frocks, Havre shirts, buffalo-robe shirts, and moose-skin drawers. Every man's jacket is his wigwam, and every man's hat his caboose.

Perfect license is now permitted to the men respecting their clothing. Whatever they can rake and scrape together they put on—swaddling themselves in old sails, and drawing old socks over their heads for night-caps. This is the time for smiting your chest with your hand, and talking loud to keep up the circulation.

Colder, and colder, and colder, till at last we spoke a fleet of icebergs bound North. After that, it was one incessant *"cold snap,"* that almost snapped off our fingers and toes. Cold! It was cold as *Blue Flujin,* where sailors say fire freezes.

And now coming up with the latitude of the Cape, we stood southward to give it a wide berth, and while so doing were becalmed; ay, becalmed off Cape Horn, which is worse, far worse, than being becalmed on the Line.

Here we lay forty-eight hours, during which the cold was intense. I wondered at the liquid sea, which refused to freeze in such a temperature. The clear, cold sky overhead looked like a steel-blue cymbal, that might ring, could you smite it. Our breath came and went like puffs of smoke from pipe-bowls. At first there was a long, gawky swell, that obliged us to furl most of the sails, and even send down t'-gallant-yards, for fear of pitching them overboard.

Out of sight of land, at this extremity of both the inhabitable and uninhabitable world, our peopled frigate, echoing with the voices of men, the bleating of lambs, the cackling of fowls, the gruntings of pigs, seemed like Noah's old ark itself, becalmed at the climax of the Deluge.

There was nothing to be done but patiently to await the pleasure of the elements, and "whistle for a wind," the usual practice of seamen in a calm. No fire was allowed, except for the indispensable purpose of cooking, and heating bottles of water to toast Selvagee's feet. He who possessed the largest stock of vitality, stood the best chance to escape freezing. It was horrifying. In such weather any man could have undergone amputation with great ease, and helped take up the arteries himself.

Indeed, this state of affairs had not lasted quite twenty-four hours, when the extreme frigidity of the air, united to our increased tendency to inactivity, would very soon have rendered some of us subjects for the surgeon and his mates, had not a humane proceeding of the Captain suddenly impelled us to vigorous exercise.

And here be it said, that the appearance of the Boatswain, with his silver whistle to his mouth, at the main hatchway of the gun-deck, is always regarded by the crew with the utmost curiosity, for this betokens that some general order is about to be promulgated through the ship. What now? is the question that runs on from man to man. A short preliminary whistle is then given by "Old Yarn," as they call him, which whistle serves to collect round him, from their various stations, his four mates. Then Yarn, or Pipes, as leader of the orchestra, begins a peculiar call, in which his assistants join. This over, the order, whatever it may be, is loudly sung out and prolonged, till the remotest corner echoes again. The Boatswain and his mates are the town-criers of a man-of-war.

The calm had commenced in the afternoon; and the following morning the ship's company were electrified by a general order, thus set forth and declared: *"D'ye hear there, fore and aft! all hands skylark!"*

This mandate, nowadays never used except upon very rare occasions, produced the same effect upon the men that Exhilarating Gas would have done, or an extra allowance of "grog." For a time, the wonted discipline of the ship was broken through, and perfect license allowed. It was a Babel here, a Bedlam there, and a Pandemonium every where. The Theatricals were nothing compared with it. Then the faint-hearted and timorous crawled to their hiding-places, and the lusty and bold shouted forth their glee. Gangs of men, in all sorts of outlandish habiliments, wild as those worn at some crazy carnival, rushed to and fro, seizing upon whomsoever they pleased—warrant-officers and dangerous pugilists excepted—pulling and hauling the luckless tars about, till fairly baited into a genial warmth. Some were made fast to, and hoisted aloft with a will; others, mounted upon oars, were ridden fore and aft on a rail, to the boisterous mirth of the spectators, any one of whom might be the next victim. Swings were rigged from the tops, or the masts; and the most reluctant wights being purposely selected, spite of all struggles, were swung from East to West, in vast arcs of circles, till almost breathless. Hornpipes, fandangoes, Donnybrook-jigs, reels, and quadrilles, were danced under the very nose of the most mighty captain, and upon the very quarter-deck and poop. Sparring and wrestling, too, were all the vogue; *Kentucky bites* were given, and the *Indian hug* exchanged. The din frightened the sea-fowl, that flew by with accelerated wing.

It is worth mentioning that several casualities occurred, of which, however, I will relate but one. While the "skylarking" was at its height, one of the fore-top-men—an ugly-tempered devil of a Portuguese, looking on—swore that he would be the death of any man who laid violent hands upon his inviolable person. This threat being overheard, a band of desperadoes, coming up from behind, tripped him up in an instant, and in the twinkling of an eye the Portuguese was straddling an oar, borne aloft by an uproarious multitude, who rushed him along the deck at a rail-road gallop. The living mass of arms all round and beneath him was so dense, that every time he inclined to one side he was instantly pushed upright, but only to fall over again, to receive another push from the contrary direction. Presently, disengaging his hands from those who held them, the enraged seaman drew from his bosom an iron belaying-pin, and recklessly laid about him to right and left. Most of his persecutors fled; but some eight or ten still stood their ground, and, while bearing him aloft, endeavored to wrest the weapon from his hands. In this attempt, one man was struck on the head, and dropped insensible. He was taken up for dead, and carried below to Cuticle, the surgeon, while the Portuguese was put under guard. But the wound did not prove very serious; and in a few days the man was walking about the deck, with his head well bandaged.

This occurrence put an end to the "skylarking," further head-breaking being strictly prohibited. In due time the Portuguese paid the penalty of his rashness at the gangway; while once again the officers *shipped their quarter-deck faces*.

CHAPTER 26

Ere the calm had yet left us, a sail had been discerned from the fore-top-mast-head, at a great distance, probably three leagues or more. At first it was a mere speck, altogether out of sight from the deck. By the force of attraction, or something else equally inscrutable, two ships in a calm, and equally affected by the currents, will always approximate, more or less. Though there was not a breath of wind, it was not a great while before the strange sail was descried from our bulwarks; gradually, it drew still nearer.

What was she, and whence? There is no object which so excites interest and conjecture, and, at the same time, baffles both, as a sail, seen as a mere speck on these remote seas off Cape Horn.

A breeze! a breeze! for lo! the stranger is now perceptibly nearing the frigate; the officer's spy-glass pronounces her a full-rigged ship, with all sail set, and coming right down to us, though in our own vicinity the calm still reigns.

She is bringing the wind with her. Hurrah! Ay, there it is! Behold how mincingly it creeps over the sea, just ruffling and crisping it.

Our top-men were at once sent aloft to loose the sails, and presently they faintly began to distend. As yet we hardly had steerage-way. Toward sunset the stranger bore down before the wind, a complete pyramid of canvas. Never before, I venture to say, was Cape Horn so audaciously insulted. Stun'-sails alow and aloft; royals, moon-sails, and every thing else. She glided under our stern, within hailing distance, and the signal-quarter-master ran up our ensign to the gaff.

"Ship ahoy!" cried the Lieutenant of the Watch, through his trumpet.

"Halloa!" bawled an old fellow in a green jacket, clapping one hand to his mouth, while he held on with the other to the mizzen-shrouds.

"What ship's that?"

"The Sultan, Indiaman, from New York, and bound to Callao and Canton, sixty days out, all well. What frigate's that?"

"The United States ship Neversink, homeward bound."

"Hurrah! hurrah! hurrah!" yelled our enthusiastic countryman, transported with patriotism.

By this time the Sultan had swept past, but the Lieutenant of the Watch could not withhold a parting admonition.

"D'ye hear? You'd better take in some of your flying-kites there. Look out for Cape Horn!"

But the friendly advice was lost in the now increasing wind. With a suddenness by no means unusual in these latitudes, the light breeze soon became a succession of sharp squalls, and our sail-proud braggadocio of an Indiaman was observed to let every thing go by the run, his t'-gallant stun'-sails and flying-jib taking quick leave of the spars; the flying-jib was swept into the air, rolled together for a few mintues, and tossed about in the squalls like a foot-ball. But the wind played no such pranks with the more prudently managed canvas of the Neversink, though before many hours it was stirring times with us.

About midnight, when the starboard watch, to which I belonged, was below, the boatswain's whistle was heard, followed by the shrill cry for "*All hands take in sail!* jump, men, and save ship!"

Springing from our hammocks, we found the frigate leaning over to it so steeply, that it was with difficulty we could climb the ladders leading to the upper deck.

Here the scene was awful. The vessel seemed to be sailing on her side. The main deck guns had several days previous been run in and housed, and the port-holes closed, but the lee carronades on the quarter-deck and forecastle were plunging through the sea, which undulated over them in milk-white billows of foam. With every lurch to leeward the yard-arm-ends seemed to dip in the sea, while forward the spray dashed over the bows in cataracts, and drenched the men who were on the fore-yard. By this time the deck was alive with the whole strength of the ship's company, five hundred men, officers and all, mostly clinging to the weather bulwarks. The occasional phosphorescence of the yeasting sea cast a glare upon their uplifted faces, as a night fire in a populous city lights up the panic-stricken crowd.

In a sudden gale, or when a large quantity of sail is suddenly to be furled, it is the custom for the First Lieutenant to take the trumpet from whoever happens then to be officer of the deck. But Mad Jack had the trumpet that watch; nor did the First Lieutenant now seek to wrest it from his hands. Every eye was upon him, as if we had chosen him from among us all, to decide this battle with the elements, by single combat with the spirit of the Cape; for Mad Jack was the saving genius of the ship, and so proved himself that night. I owe this right hand, that is this moment flying over my sheet, and all my present being to Mad Jack. The ship's bows were now butting, battering, ramming, and thundering over and upon the head seas, and with a horrible wallowing sound our whole hull was rolling in the trough of the foam. The gale came athwart the deck, and every sail seemed bursting with its wild breath.

All the quarter-masters, and several of the forecastle-men, were swarming round the double-wheel on the quarter-deck. Some jumping up and down, with their hands upon the spokes; for the whole helm and galvanized keel were fiercely feverish, with the life imparted to them by the tempest.

"Hard *up* the helm!" shouted Captain Claret, bursting from his cabin like a ghost in his night-dress.

"Damn you!" raged Mad Jack to the quarter-masters; "hard *down*—hard *down,* I say, and be damned to you!"

Contrary orders! but Mad Jack's were obeyed. His object was to throw the ship into the wind, so as the better to admit of close-reefing the top-sails. But though the halyards were let go, it was impossible to clew down the yards, owing to the enormous horizontal strain on the canvas. It now blew a hurricane. The spray flew over the ship in floods. The gigantic masts seemed about to snap under the world-wide strain of the three entire top-sails.

"Clew down! clew down!" shouted Mad Jack, husky with excitement, and in a frenzy, beating his trumpet against one of the shrouds. But, owing to the slant of the ship, the thing could not be done. It was obvious that before many minutes something must go—either sails, rigging, or sticks; perhaps the hull itself, and all hands.

Presently a voice from the top exclaimed that there was a rent in the main-top-sail. And instantly we heard a report like two or three muskets discharged together: the vast sail was rent up and down like the Veil of the Temple. This saved the main-mast; for the yard was now clewed down with comparative ease, and the top-men laid out to stow the shattered canvas. Soon, the two remaining top-sails were also clewed down and close reefed.

Above all the roar of the tempest and the shouts of the crew, was heard the dismal tolling of the ship's bell—almost as large as that of a village church—which the violent rolling of the ship was occasioning. Imagination can not conceive the horror of such a sound in a night-tempest at sea.

"Stop that ghost!" roared Mad Jack; "away, one of you, and wrench off the clapper!"

But no sooner was this ghost gagged, than a still more appalling sound was heard, the rolling to and fro of the heavy shot, which, on the gun-deck, had broken loose from the gun-racks, and converted that part of the ship into an immense bowling-alley. Some hands were sent down to secure them; but it was as much as their lives were worth. Several were maimed; and the midshipmen who were ordered to see the duty performed reported it impossible, until the storm abated.

The most terrific job of all was to furl the main-sail, which, at the commencement of the squalls, had been clewed up, coaxed and quieted as much as possible with the bunt-lines and slab-lines. Mad Jack waited some time for a lull, ere he gave an order so perilous to be executed. For to furl this enormous sail, in such a gale, required at least fifty men on the yard; whose weight, superadded to that of the ponderous stick itself, still further jeopardized their lives. But there was no prospect of a cessation of the gale, and the order was at last given.

At this time a hurricane of slanting sleet and hail was descending upon us; the rigging was coated with a thin glare of ice, formed within the hour.

"Aloft, main-yard-men! and all you main-top-men! and furl the main-sail!" cried Mad Jack.

I dashed down my hat, slipped out of my quilted jacket in an instant, kicked the shoes from my feet, and, with a crowd of others, sprang for the rigging. Above the bulwarks (which in a frigate are so high as to afford much protection to those on deck) the gale was horrible. The sheer force of the wind flattened us to the rigging as we ascended, and every hand seemed congealing to the icy shrouds by which we held.

"Up—up, my brave hearties!" shouted Mad Jack; and up we got, some way or other, all of us, and groped our way out on the yard-arms.

"Hold on, every mother's son!" cried an old quarter-gunner at my side. He was bawling at the top of his compass; but in the gale, he seemed to be whispering; and I only heard him from his being right to windward of me.

But his hint was unnecessary; I dug my nails into the *jack-stays,* and swore that nothing but death should part me and them until I was able to turn round and look to windward. As yet this was impossible; I could scarcely hear the man to leeward at my elbow; the wind seemed to snatch the words from his mouth and fly away with them to the South Pole.

All this while the sail itself was flying about, sometimes catching over our head, and threatening to tear us from the yard in spite of all our hugging. For about three quarters of an hour we thus hung suspended right over the rampant billows, which curled their very crests under the feet of some four or five of us clinging to the lee yard-arm, as if to float us from our place.

Presently, the word passed along the yard from windward, that we were ordered to come down and leave the sail to blow, since it could not be furled. A midshipman, it seemed, had been sent up by the officer of the deck to give the order, as no trumpet could be heard where we were.

Those on the weather yard-arm managed to crawl upon the spar and scramble down the rigging; but with us, upon the extreme leeward side, this feat was out of the question; it was, literally, like climbing a precipice to get to windward in order to reach the shrouds; besides, the entire yard was now encased in ice, and our hands and feet were so numb that we dared not trust our lives to them. Nevertheless, by assisting each other, we contrived to throw ourselves prostrate along the yard, and embrace it with our arms and legs. In this position, the stun'-sail-booms greatly assisted in securing our hold. Strange as it may appear, I do not suppose that, at this moment, the slightest sensation of fear was felt by one man on that yard. We clung to it with might and main; but this was instinct. The truth is, that, in circumstances like these, the sense of fear is annihilated in the unutterable sights that fill all the eye, and the sounds that fill all the ear. You become identified with the tempest; your insignificance is lost in the riot of the stormy universe around.

Below us, our noble frigate seemed thrice its real length—a vast black wedge, opposing its widest end to the combined fury of the sea and wind.

At length the first fury of the gale began to abate, and we at once fell to pounding our hands, as a preliminary operation to going to work; for a gang of men had now ascended to help secure what was left of the sail; we somehow packed it away, at last, and came down.

About noon the next day, the gale so moderated that we shook two reefs out of the top-sails, set new courses, and stood due east, with the wind astern.

Thus, all the fine weather we encountered after first weighing anchor on the pleasant Spanish coast, was but the prelude to this one terrific night; more especially, that treacherous calm immediately preceding it. But how could we reach our long-promised homes without encountering Cape Horn? by what possibility avoid it? And though some ships have weathered it without these perils, yet by far the greater part must encounter them. Lucky it is that it comes about midway in the homeward-bound passage, so that the sailors have time to prepare for it, and time to recover from it after it is astern.

But, sailor or landsman, there is some sort of a Cape Horn for all. Boys! beware of it; prepare for it in time. Graybeards! thank God it is passed. And ye lucky livers, to whom, by some rare fatality, your Cape Horns are placid as Lake Lemans, flatter not yourselves that good luck is judgment and discretion; for all the yolk in your eggs, you might have floundered and gone down, had the Spirit of the Cape said the word.

PART VI

A PASSAGE TO INFINITY: *Moby Dick* (1851)

❀ ❀ ❀

INTRODUCTION

Moby Dick is one of the world's great novels. It is readily available in good editions, and has been interpreted with probably more acuteness (and disagreement) than any other work of fiction.

Thus an anthology that omits *Moby Dick* because of its ready availability is not unthinkable. In a collection concerned with Melville's view of the South Seas, however, the book should not be overlooked, for many passages are revealing. The *Pequod* does not enter this ocean, though, until Chapter 111, and thereafter does not sight land. The view of the region is thus from the deck on the whaling grounds—a view common to many early visitors to the ocean, but one scarcely lending itself to scene sketching.

The most likeable person aboard the *Pequod* is a noble Polynesian. In Queequeg, Melville gives a full-length portrait of what he must have considered, after years of observation and reflection, to be his view of a Pacific Island "savage," a seagoing Mehevi with a harpoon forever at his side. Selection of certain passages showing Ishmael's early acquaintance at the Spouter Inn in New Bedford with Queequeg (hardly a typical Polynesian name) reveals a nature uncontaminated by cities and naturally religious, even though he worships an idol carved with his own hands.[1]

Another choice, with a South Sea setting, presents a bower in the Arsacides (an early name for the Solomon group, derived from a Parthian dynasty; a Cape Arsacides is still marked on the map of the island of Malaita). This imaginary scene shows Melville's conception of a Melanesian court near which the skeleton of a giant sperm whale can be measured.

Finally, one should certainly not omit the invocation in Chapter 111 to the Pacific Ocean.

A comparison of the maps showing the routes of Melville's actual ships and that of the *Pequod* of *Moby Dick* reveals much about Melville's creativity. The *Acushnet,* departing from New Bedford, cruised among the Cape Verde Islands, stopped at Rio de Janeiro, rounded Cape Horn, stopped at Tumbes in Peru, cruised near the Galápagos, and then went to the Marquesas, where Melville deserted. Joining the *Lucy Ann,* he sailed on an aimless run westward before being put ashore in Papeete. In the *Charles and Henry,* he probably went south of the twentieth parallel and then along the equatorial grounds and north to Hawaii. On the *United States,* after a North Pacific run, he revisited the Marquesas and the Society groups, went to Valparaiso and Paita, ran north to Mazatlán in Mexico, rounded the Horn eastward, and after a stop at Rio was discharged at Boston.

The presumed route of the *Pequod* scarcely overlaps this route at any point. Leaving New Bedford, she cruised the Azores and Cape Verdes, as well as the "Plate ground" off Rio, and then went to St. Helena and around the Cape of Good Hope. The Indian Ocean left in her wake, she threaded the isles of Indonesia, burst into the Pacific through the "Bashee isles" (the Bashi Channel between Formosa and the southern Philippines), and cruised east of Japan. The catastrophe came near the Equator somewhere between the Marshall group and Fanning Island.

Melville on his various passages saw almost none of the places visited by the legendary *Pequod.* Would it not have been easier for him to guide his fictional craft in his own tracks, rather than to set it afloat on the other side of the world? It is possible that his intentions in the novel and the use of his many sources—which describe whaling scenes in other oceans than the Pacific—may have impelled him to send the *Pequod* around the Cape of Good Hope. At any rate, the itinerary of that vessel is less a report of Melville's own voyaging than a triumph of his imagination. As in *Typee* and *Omoo,* the quantity of autobiography shrinks under scrutiny.

Melville spent nearly two years writing *Moby Dick*—a longer time than he spent on any other work, putting in regular hours at composition, revision, and proofreading, and limiting family and social demands on his energy. Financial troubles required him to borrow more than two thousand dollars to finish his work ("dollars damn me," he said), but he finally gave his book to the press. It was as usual published in England first—on October 18, 1851, by Richard Bentley, in three volumes entitled *The Whale.* In October it was put out by Harper & Brothers as *Moby-Dick or, The Whale.* The reviewers, despite an appreciative letter from Hawthorne, showed no realization that one of the world's masterpieces was under their noses.

CHAPTER 3

. . . Folding back the counterpane, I stooped over the bed. Though none of the most elegant, it yet stood the scrutiny tolerably well. I then glanced round the room; and besides the bedstead and centre table, could see no other furniture belonging to the place, but a rude shelf, the four walls, and a papered fireboard representing a man striking a whale. Of things not properly belonging to the room, there was a hammock lashed up, and thrown upon the floor in one corner; also a large seaman's bag, containing the harpooneer's wardrobe, no doubt in lieu of a land trunk. Likewise, there was a parcel of outlandish bone fish hooks on the shelf over the fire-place, and a tall harpoon standing at the head of the bed.

But what is this on the chest? I took it up, and held it close to the light, and felt it, and smelt it, and tried every way possible to arrive at some satisfactory conclusion concerning it. I can compare it to nothing but a large door mat, ornamented at the edges with little tinkling tags something like the stained porcupine quills round an Indian moccasin. There was a hole or slit in the middle of this mat, as you see the same in South American ponchos. But could it be possible that any sober harpooneer would get into a door mat, and parade the streets of any Christian town in that sort of guise? I put it on, to try it, and it weighed me down like a hamper, being uncommonly shaggy and thick, and I thought a little damp, as though this mysterious harpooneer had been wearing it of a rainy day. I went up in it to a bit of glass against the wall, and I never saw such a sight in my life. I tore myself out of it in such a hurry that I gave myself a kink in the neck.

I sat down on the side of the bed, and commenced thinking about this head-peddling harpooneer, and his door mat. After thinking some time on the bed-side, I got up and took off my monkey jacket, and then stood in the middle of the room thinking. I then took off my coat, and thought a little more in my shirt sleeves. But beginning to feel very cold now, half undressed as I was, and remembering what the landlord said about the harpooneer's not coming home at all that night, it being so very late, I made no more ado, but jumped out of my pantaloons and boots, and then blowing out the light tumbled into bed, and commended myself to the care of heaven.

Whether that mattress was stuffed with corn-cobs or broken crockery, there is no telling, but I rolled about a good deal, and could not sleep for a long time. At last I slid off into a light doze, and had pretty nearly a good offing towards the land of Nod, when I heard a heavy footfall in the passage, and saw a glimmer of light come into the room from under the door.

Lord save me, thinks I, that must be the harpooneer, the infernal head-peddler. But I lay perfectly still, and resolved not to say a word till spoken to. Holding a light in one hand, and that identical New Zealand head in the other, the stranger entered the room, and without looking towards the bed, placed his candle a good way off from me on the floor in one corner, and then began working away at the knotted cords of the large bag I before spoke of as being in the room. I was all eagerness to see his face, but he kept it averted for some time while employed in unlacing the bag's mouth. This accomplished, however, he turned round—when, good heavens! what a sight! Such a face! It was of a dark, purplish, yellow color, here and there stuck over with large, blackish looking squares. Yes, it's just as I thought, he's a terrible bedfellow; he's been in a fight, got dreadfully cut, and here he is, just from the surgeon. But at that moment he chanced to turn his face so towards the light, that I plainly saw they could not be sticking-plasters at all, those black squares on his cheeks. They were stains of some sort or other. At first I knew not what to make of this; but soon an inkling of the truth occurred to me. I remembered a story of a white man—a whaleman too—who, falling among the cannibals, had been tattooed by them. I concluded that this harpooneer, in the course of his distant voyages, must have met with a similar adventure. And what is it, thought I, after all! It's only his outside; a man can be honest in any sort of skin. But then, what to make of his unearthly complexion, that part of it, I mean, lying round about, and completely independent of the squares of tattooing. To be sure, it might be nothing but a good coat of tropical tanning; but I never heard of a hot sun's tanning a white man into a purplish yellow one. However, I had never been in the South Seas; and perhaps the sun there produced these extraordinary effects upon the skin. Now, while all these ideas were passing through me like lightning, the harpooneer never noticed me at all. But, after some difficulty having opened his bag, he commenced fumbling in it, and presently pulled out a sort of tomahawk, and a seal-skin wallet with the hair on. Placing these on the old chest in the middle of the room, he then took the New Zealand head—a ghastly thing enough—and crammed it down into the bag. He now took off his hat—a new beaver hat—when I came nigh singing out with fresh surprise. There was no hair on his head—none to speak of at least—nothing but a small scalp-knot twisted up on his forehead. His bald purplish head now looked for all the world like a mildewed skull. Had not the stranger stood between me and the door, I would have bolted out of it quicker than ever I bolted a dinner.

Even as it was, I thought something of slipping out of the window, but it was the second floor back. I am no coward, but what to make of this head-peddling purple rascal altogether passed my comprehension. Ignorance is the parent of fear, and being completely nonplussed and confounded about the stranger, I confess I was now as much afraid of him as if it was the devil himself who had thus broken into my room at the dead of night. In fact, I was so afraid of him that I was not game enough just then to address him, and demand a satisfactory answer concerning what seemed inexplicable in him.

Meanwhile, he continued the business of undressing, and at last showed his chest and arms. As I live, these covered parts of him were checkered with the same squares as his face; his back, too, was all over the same dark squares; he seemed to have been in a Thirty Years' War, and just escaped from it with a sticking-plaster shirt. Still more, his very legs were marked, as if a parcel of dark green frogs were running up the trunks of young palms. It was now quite plain that he must be some abominable savage or other shipped aboard of a whaleman in the South Seas, and so landed in this Christian country. I quaked to think of it. A peddler of heads too—perhaps the heads of his own brothers. He might take a fancy to mine—heavens! look at that tomahawk!

But there was no time for shuddering, for now the savage went about something that completely fascinated my attention, and convinced me that he must indeed be a heathen. Going to his heavy grego, or wrapall, or dreadnaught, which he had previously hung on a chair, he fumbled in the pockets, and produced at length a curious little deformed image with a hunch on its back, and exactly the color of a three days' old Congo baby. Remembering the embalmed head, at first I almost thought that this black manikin was a real baby preserved in some similar manner. But seeing that it was not at all limber, and that it glistened a good deal like polished ebony, I concluded that it must be nothing but a wooden idol, which indeed it proved to be. For now the savage goes up to the empty fireplace, and removing the papered fire-board, sets up this little hunchbacked image, like a tenpin, between the andirons. The chimney jambs and all the bricks inside were very sooty, so that I thought this fire-place made a very appropriate little shrine or chapel for his Congo idol.

I now screwed my eyes hard towards the half hidden image, feeling but ill at ease meantime—to see what was next to follow. First he takes about a double handful of shavings out of his grego pocket, and places them carefully before the idol; then laying a bit of ship biscuit on top and applying the flame from the lamp, he kindled the shavings into a sacrificial blaze. Presently, after many hasty snatches into the fire, and still hastier withdrawals of his fingers (whereby he seemed to be scorching them badly), he at last succeeded in drawing out the biscuit; then blowing off the heat and ashes a little, he made a polite offer of it to the little negro. But the little devil did not seem to fancy such dry sort of fare at all; he never moved his lips. All these strange antics were accompanied by still stranger guttural noises from the devotee, who seemed to be praying in a sing-song or else singing some pagan psalmody or other, during which his face twitched about in the most unnatural manner. At last extinguishing the fire, he took the idol up very unceremoniously, and bagged it again in his grego pocket as carelessly as if he were a sportsman bagging a dead woodcock.

All these queer proceedings increased my uncomfortableness, and seeing him now exhibiting strong symptoms of concluding his business operations, and jumping into bed with me, I thought it was high time, now or never, before the light was put out, to break the spell in which I had so long been bound.

But the interval I spent in deliberating what to say, was a fatal one. Taking up his tomahawk from the table, he examined the head of it for an instant, and then holding it to the light, with his mouth at the handle, he puffed out great clouds of tobacco smoke. The next moment the light was extinguished, and this wild cannibal, tomahawk between his teeth, sprang into bed with me. I sang out, I could not help it now; and giving a sudden grunt of astonishment he began feeling me.

Stammering out something, I knew not what, I rolled away from him against the wall, and then conjured him, whoever or whatever he might be, to keep quiet, and let me get up and light the lamp again. But his guttural responses satisfied me at once that he but ill comprehended my meaning.

"Who-e debel you?"—he at last said—"you no speak-e, dam-me, I kill-e." And so saying the lighted tomahawk began flourishing about me in the dark.

"Landlord, for God's sake, Peter Coffin!" shouted I. "Landlord! Watch! Coffin! Angels! save me!"

"Speak-e! tell-ee me who-ee be, or dam-me, I kill-e!" again growled the cannibal, while his horrid flourishings of the tomahawk scattered the hot to-bacco ashes about me till I thought my linen would get on fire. But thank heaven, at that moment the landlord came into the room light in hand, and leaping from the bed I ran up to him.

"Don't be afraid now," said he, grinning again. "Queequeg here wouldn't harm a hair of your head."

"Stop your grinning," shouted I, "and why didn't you tell me that that infernal harpooneer was a cannibal?"

"I thought ye know'd it;—didn't I tell ye, he was peddlin' heads around town?—but turn flukes again and go to sleep. Queequeg, look here—you sabbee me, I sabbee you—this man sleepe you—you sabbee?"—

"Me sabbee plenty"—grunted Queequeg, puffing away at his pipe and sitting up in bed.

"You gettee in," he added, motioning to me with his tomahawk, and throwing the clothes to one side. He really did this in not only a civil but a really kind and charitable way. I stood looking at him a moment. For all his tattooings he was on the whole a clean, comely looking cannibal. What's all this fuss I have been making about, thought I to myself—the man's a human being just as I am: he has just as much reason to fear me, as I have to be afraid of him. Better sleep with a sober cannibal than a drunken Christian.

"Landlord," said I, "tell him to stash his tomahawk there, or pipe, or whatever you call it; tell him to stop smoking, in short, and I will turn in with him. But I don't fancy having a man smoking in bed with me. It's dangerous. Besides, I aint insured."

This being told to Queequeg, he at once complied, and again politely motioned me to get into bed—rolling over to one side as much as to say—I wont touch a leg of ye.

"Good night, landlord," said I, "you may go."

I turned in, and never slept better in my life.

CHAPTER 4

Upon waking next morning about daylight, I found Queequeg's arm thrown over me in the most loving and affectionate manner. You had almost thought I had been his wife. The counterpane was of patchwork, full of odd little parti-colored squares and triangles; and this arm of his tattooed all over with an interminable Cretan labyrinth of a figure, no two parts of which were of one precise shade—owing I suppose to his keeping his arm at sea unmethodically in sun and shade, his shirt sleeves irregularly rolled up at various times—this same arm of his, I say, looked for all the world like a strip of that same patchwork quilt. Indeed, partly lying on it as the arm did when I first awoke, I could hardly tell it from the quilt, they so blended their hues together; and it was only by the sense of weight and pressure that I could tell that Queequeg was hugging me.

My sensations were strange. Let me try to explain them. When I was a child, I well remember a somewhat similar circumstance that befell me; whether it was a reality or a dream, I never could entirely settle. The circumstance was this. I had been cutting up some caper or other—I think it was trying to crawl up the chimney, as I had seen a little sweep do a few days previous; and my stepmother who, somehow or other, was all the time whipping me, or sending me to bed supperless,—my mother dragged me by the legs out of the chimney and packed me off to bed, though it was only two o'clock in the afternoon of the 21st June, the longest day in the year in our hemisphere. I felt dreadfully.

But there was no help for it, so up stairs I went to my little room in the third floor, undressed myself as slowly as possible so as to kill time, and with a bitter sigh got between the sheets.

I lay there dismally calculating that sixteen entire hours must elapse before I could hope for a resurrection. Sixteen hours in bed! the small of my back ached to think of it. And it was so light too; the sun shining in at the window, and a great rattling of coaches in the streets, and the sound of gay voices all over the house. I felt worse and worse—at last I got up, dressed, and softly going down in my stockinged feet, sought out my stepmother, and suddenly threw myself at her feet, beseeching her as a particular favor to give me a good slippering for my misbehavior; anything indeed but condemning me to lie abed such an unendurable length of time. But she was the best and most conscientious of stepmothers, and back I had to go to my room. For several hours I lay there broad awake, feeling a great deal worse than I have ever done since, even from the greatest subsequent misfortunes. At last I must have fallen into a troubled nightmare of a doze; and slowly waking from it—half steeped in dreams—I opened my eyes, and the before sun-lit room was now wrapped in outer darkness. Instantly I felt a shock running through all my frame; nothing was to be seen, and nothing was to be heard; but a supernatural hand seemed placed in mine. My arm hung over the counterpane, and the nameless, unimaginable, silent form or phantom, to which the hand belonged, seemed closely seated by my bedside. For what seemed ages piled on ages, I lay there, frozen with the most awful fears, not daring to drag away my hand; yet ever thinking that if I could but stir it one single inch, the horrid spell would be broken. I knew not how this consciousness at last glided away from me; but waking in the morning, I shudderingly remembered it all, and for days and weeks and months afterwards I lost myself in confounding attempts to explain the mystery. Nay, to this very hour, I often puzzle myself with it.

Now, take away the awful fear, and my sensations at feeling the supernatural hand in mine were very similar, in their strangeness, to those which I experienced on waking up and seeing Queequeg's pagan arm thrown round me. But at length all the past night's events soberly recurred, one by one, in fixed reality, and then I lay only alive to the comical predicament. For though I tried to move his arm—unlock his bridegroom clasp—yet, sleeping as he was, he still hugged me tightly, as though naught but death should part us twain. I now strove to rouse him—"Queequeg!—but his only answer was a snore. I then rolled over, my neck feeling as if it were in a horse-collar; and suddenly felt a slight scratch. Throwing aside the counterpane, there lay the tomahawk sleeping by the savage's side, as if it were a hatchet-faced baby. A pretty pickle, truly, thought I; abed here in a strange house in the broad day, with a cannibal and a tomahawk! "Queequeg!—in the name of goodness, Queequeg, wake!" At length, by dint of much wriggling, and loud and incessant expostulations upon the unbecomingness of his hugging a fellow male in that matrimonial sort of style, I succeeded in extracting a grunt; and presently, he drew back his arm, shook himself all over like a Newfoundland dog just from the water, and sat up in bed, stiff as a pike-staff, looking at me, and rubbing his eyes as if he did not altogether remember how I came to be there, though a dim consciousness of knowing something about me seemed slowly dawning over him. Meanwhile, I lay quietly eyeing him, having no serious misgivings now, and bent upon narrowly observing so curious a creature. When, at last, his mind seemed made up touching the character of his bedfellow, and he became, as it were, reconciled to the fact; he jumped out upon the floor, and by certain signs and sounds gave me to understand that, if it pleased me, he would dress first and then leave me to dress afterwards, leaving the whole apartment to myself. Thinks I, Queequeg, under the circumstances, this is a very civilized overture; but, the truth is, these savages have an innate sense of delicacy, say what you will; it is marvellous how essentially polite they are. I pay this particular compliment to Queequeg, because he treated me with so much civility and consideration, while I was guilty of great rudeness; staring at him from the bed, and watching all his toilette motions; for the time my curiosity getting the better of my breeding. Nevertheless, a man like Queequeg you don't see every day, he and his ways were well worth unusual regarding.

He commenced dressing at top by donning his beaver hat, a very tall one, by the by, and then—still minus his trowsers—he hunted up his boots. What under the heaven he did it for, I cannot tell, but his next movement was to crush himself—boots in hand, and hat on—under the bed; when, from sundry violent gaspings and strainings, I inferred he was hard at work booting himself; though by no law of propriety that I ever heard of, is any man required to be private when putting on his boots. But Queequeg, do you see, was a creature in the transition state—neither caterpiller nor butterfly. He was just enough civilized to show off his outlandishness in the strangest possible manner. His education was not yet completed. He was an undergraduate. If he had not been a small degree civilized, he very probably would not have troubled himself with boots at all; but then, if he had not been still a savage, he never would have dreamt of getting under the bed to put them on. At last, he emerged with his hat very much dented and crushed down over his eyes, and began creaking and limping about the room, as if, not being much accustomed to boots, his pair of damp, wrinkled cowhide ones—probably not made to order either—rather pinched and tormented him at the first go off of a bitter cold morning.

Seeing, now, that there were no curtains to the window, and that the street being very narrow, the house opposite commanded a plain view into the room, and observing more and more the indecorous figure that Queequeg made, staving about with little else but his hat and boots on; I begged him as well as I could, to accelerate his toilet somewhat, and particularly to get into his pantaloons as soon as possible. He complied, and then proceeded to wash himself. At that time in the morning any Christian would have washed his face; but Queequeg, to my amazement, contented himself with restricting his ablutions to his chest, arms, and hands. He then donned his waistcoat, and taking up a piece of hard soap on the wash-stand centre-table, dipped it into water and commenced lathering his face. I was watching to see where he kept his razor, when lo and behold, he takes the harpoon from the bed corner, slips out the long wooden stock, unsheathes the head, whets it a little on his boot, and striding up to the bit of mirror against the wall, begins a vigorous scraping, or rather harpooning of his cheeks. Thinks I, Queequeg, this is using Rogers's best cutlery with a vengeance. Afterwards I wondered the less at this operation when I came to know of what fine steel the head of a harpoon is made, and how exceedingly sharp the long straight edges are always kept.

The rest of his toilet was soon achieved, and he proudly marched out of the room, wrapped up in his great pilot monkey jacket, and sporting his harpoon like a marshal's baton.

CHAPTER 10

Returning to the Spouter-Inn from the Chapel, I found Queequeg there quite alone; he having left the Chapel before the benediction some time. He was sitting on a bench before the fire, with his feet on the stove hearth, and in one hand was holding close up to his face that little negro idol of his; peering hard into its face, and with a jack-knife gently whittling away at its nose, meanwhile humming to himself in his heathenish way.

But being now interrupted, he put up the image; and pretty soon, going to the table, took up a large book there, and placing it on his lap began counting the pages with deliberate regularity; at every fiftieth page—as I fancied—stopping a moment, looking vacantly around him, and giving utterance to a long-drawn gurgling whistle of astonishment. He would then begin again at the next fifty; seeming to commence at number one each time, as though he could not count more than fifty, and it was only by such a large number of fifties being found together, that his astonishment at the multitude of pages was excited.

With much interest I sat watching him. Savage though he was, and hideously marred about the face—at least to my taste—his countenance yet had a something in it which was by no means disagreeable. You cannot hide the soul. Through all his unearthly tattooings, I thought I saw the traces of a simple honest heart; and in his large, deep eyes, fiery black and bold, there seemed tokens of a spirit that would dare a thousand devils. And besides all this, there was a certain lofty bearing about the Pagan, which even his uncouthness could not altogether maim. He looked like a man who had never cringed and never had had a creditor. Whether it was, too, that his head being shaved, his forehead was drawn out in freer and brighter relief, and looked more expansive than it otherwise would, this I will not venture to decide; but certain it was his head was phrenologically an excellent one. It may seem ridiculous, but it reminded me of General Washington's head, as seen in the popular busts of him. It had the same long regularly graded retreating slope from above the brows, which were likewise very projecting, like two long promontories thickly wooded on top. Queequeg was George Washington cannibalistically developed.

Whilst I was thus closely scanning him, half-pretending meanwhile to be looking out at the storm from the casement, he never troubled himself with so much as a single glance; but appeared wholly occupied with counting the pages of the marvellous book. Considering how sociably we had been sleeping together the night previous, and especially considering the affectionate arm I had found thrown over me upon waking in the morning, I thought this indifference of his very strange. But savages are strange beings; at times you do not know exactly how to take them. At first they are overawing; their calm self-collectedness of simplicity seems a Socratic wisdom. I had noticed also that Queequeg never consorted at all, or but very little, with the other seamen in the inn. He made no advances whatever; appeared to have no desire to enlarge the circle of his acquaintances. All this struck me as mighty singular; yet, upon second thoughts, there was something almost sublime in it. Here was a man some twenty thousand miles from home, by the way of Cape Horn, that is—which was the only way he could get there—thrown among people as strange to him as though he were in the planet Jupiter; and yet he seemed entirely at his ease; preserving the utmost serenity; content with his own companionship; always equal to himself. Surely this was a touch of fine philosophy; though no doubt he had never heard there was such a thing as that. But, perhaps, to be true philosophers, we mortals should not be conscious of so living or so striving. So soon as I hear that such or such a man gives himself out for a philosopher, I conclude that, like the dyspeptic old woman, he must have "broken his digester."

As I sat there in that now lonely room; the fire burning low, in that mild stage when, after its first intensity has warmed the air, it then only glows to be looked at; the evening shades and phantoms gathering round the casements, and peering in upon us silent, solitary twain; the storm booming without in solemn swells; I began to be sensible of strange feelings. I felt a melting in me. No more my splintered heart and maddened hand were turned against the wolfish world. This soothing savage had redeemed it. There he sat, his very indifference speaking a nature in which there lurked no civilized hypocrisies and bland deceits. Wild he was; a very sight of sights to see; yet I began to feel myself mysteriously drawn towards him. And those same things that would have repelled most others, they were the very magnets that thus drew me. I'll try a pagan friend, thought I, since Christian kindness has proved but hollow courtesy. I drew my bench near him, and made some friendly signs and hints, doing my best to talk with him meanwhile. At first he little noticed these advances; but presently, upon my referring to his last night's hospitalities, he made out to ask me whether we were again to be bedfellows. I told him yes; whereat I thought he looked pleased, perhaps a little complimented.

We then turned over the book together, and I endeavored to explain to him the purpose of the printing, and the meaning of the few pictures that were in it. Thus I soon engaged his interest; and from that we went to jabbering the best we could about the various outer sights to be seen in this famous town. Soon I proposed a social smoke; and, producing his pouch and tomahawk, he quietly offered me a puff. And then we sat exchanging puffs from that wild pipe of his, and keeping it regularly passing between us.

If there yet lurked any ice of indifference towards me in the Pagan's breast, this pleasant, genial smoke we had, soon thawed it out, and left us cronies. He seemed to take to me quite as naturally and unbiddenly as I to him; and when our smoke was over, he pressed his forehead against mine, clasped me round the waist, and said that henceforth we were married; meaning, in his country's phrase, that we were bosom friends; he would gladly die for me, if need should be. In a countryman, this sudden flame of friendship would have seemed far too premature, a thing to be much distrusted; but in this simple savage those old rules would not apply.

After supper, and another social chat and smoke, we went to our room together. He made me a present of his embalmed head; took out his enormous tobacco wallet, and groping under the tobacco, drew out some thirty dollars in silver; then spreading them on the table, and mechanically dividing them into two equal portions, pushed one of them towards me, and said it was mine. I was going to remonstrate; but he silenced me by pouring them into my trowsers' pockets. I let them stay. He then went about his evening prayers, took out his idol, and removed the paper fireboard. By certain signs and symptoms, I thought he seemed anxious for me to join him; but well knowing what was to follow, I deliberated a moment whether, in case he invited me, I would comply or otherwise.

I was a good Christian; born and bred in the bosom of the infallible Presbyterian Church. How then could I unite with this wild idolator in worshipping his piece of wood? But what is worship? thought I. Do you suppose now, Ishmael, that the magnanimous God of heaven and earth—pagans and all included—can possibly be jealous of an insignificant bit of black wood? Impossible! But what is worship?—to do the will of God—*that* is worship. And what is the will of God?—to do to my fellow man what I would have my fellow man to do to me—*that* is the will of God. Now, Queequeg is my fellow man. And what do I wish that this Queequeg would do to me? Why, unite with me in my particular Presbyterian form of worship. Consequently, I must then unite with him in his; ergo, I must turn idolator. So I kindled the shavings; helped prop up the innocent little idol; offered him burnt biscuit with Queequeg; salamed before him twice or thrice; kissed his nose; and that done, we undressed and went to bed, at peace with our own consciences and all the world. But we did not go to sleep without some little chat.

How it is I know not; but there is no place like a bed for confidential disclosures between friends. Man and wife, they say, there open the very bottom of their souls to each other; and some old couples often lie and chat over old times till nearly morning. Thus, then, in our hearts' honeymoon, lay I and Queequeg—a cozy, loving pair.

CHAPTER 11

We had lain thus in bed, chatting and napping at short intervals, and Queequeg now and then affectionately throwing his brown tattooed legs over mine, and then drawing them back; so entirely sociable and free and easy were we; when, at last, by reason of our confabulations, what little nappishness remained in us altogether departed, and we felt like getting up again, though day-break was yet some way down the future.

Yes, we became very wakeful; so much so that our recumbent position began to grow wearisome, and by little and little we found ourselves sitting up; the clothes well tucked around us, leaning against the head-board with our four knees drawn up close together, and our two noses bending over them, as if our knee-pans were warming-pans. We felt very nice and snug, the more so since it was so chilly out of doors; indeed out of bed-clothes too, seeing that there was no fire in the room. The more so, I say, because truly to enjoy bodily warmth, some small part of you must be cold, for there is no quality in this world that is not what it is merely by contrast. Nothing exists in itself. If you flatter yourself that you are all over comfortable, and have been so a long time, then you cannot be said to be comfortable any more. But if, like Queequeg and me in the bed, the tip of your nose or the crown of your head be slightly chilled, why then, indeed, in the general consciousness you feel most delightfully and unmistakably warm. For this reason a sleeping apartment should never be furnished with a fire, which is one of the luxurious discomforts of the rich. For

the height of this sort of deliciousness is to have nothing but the blanket between you and your snugness and the cold of the outer air. Then there you lie
like the one warm spark in the heart of an arctic crystal.

We had been sitting in this crouching manner for some time, when all at
once I thought I would open my eyes; for when between sheets, whether by
day or by night, and whether asleep or awake, I have a way of always keeping
my eyes shut, in order the more to concentrate the snugness of being in bed.
Because no man can ever feel his own identity aright except his eyes be closed;
as if darkness were indeed the proper element of our essences, though light be
more congenial to our clayey part. Upon opening my eyes then, and coming out
of my own pleasant and self-created darkness into the imposed and coarse outer
gloom of the unilluminated twelve-o'clock-at-night, I experienced a disagreeable
revulsion. Nor did I at all object to the hint from Queequeg that perhaps it
were best to strike a light, seeing that we were so wide awake; and besides he
felt a strong desire to have a few quiet puffs from his Tomahawk. Be it said,
that though I had felt such a strong repugnance to his smoking in the bed the
night before, yet see how elastic our stiff prejudices grow when love once comes
to bend them. For now I liked nothing better than to have Queequeg smoking
by me, even in bed, because he seemed to be full of such serene household joy
then. I no more felt unduly concerned for the landlord's policy of insurance. I
was only alive to the condensed confidential comfortableness of sharing a pipe
and a blanket with a real friend. With our shaggy jackets drawn about our
shoulders, we now passed the Tomahawk from one to the other, till slowly
there grew over us a blue hanging tester of smoke, illuminated by the flame of
the new-lit lamp.

Whether it was that this undulating tester rolled the savage away to far
distant scenes, I know not, but he now spoke of his native island; and, eager to
hear his history, I begged him to go on and tell it. He gladly complied. Though
at the time I but ill comprehended not a few of his words, yet subsequent
disclosures, when I had become more familiar with his broken phraseology, now
enable me to present the whole story such as it may prove in the mere skeleton
I give.

CHAPTER 12

Queequeg was a native of Kokovoko, an island far away to the West and South.
It is not down in any map; true places never are.

When a new-hatched savage running wild about his native woodlands in a
grass clout, followed by the nibbling goats, as if he were a green sapling; even
then, in Queequeg's ambitious soul, lurked a strong desire to see something more

of Christendom than a specimen whaler or two. His father was a High Chief, a King; his uncle a High Priest; and on the maternal side he boasted aunts who were the wives of unconquerable warriors. There was excellent blood in his veins—royal stuff; though sadly vitiated, I fear, by the cannibal propensity he nourished in his untutored youth.

A Sag Harbor ship visited his father's bay, and Queequeg sought a passage to Christian lands. But the ship, having her full complement of seamen, spurned his suit; and not all the King his father's influence could prevail. But Queequeg vowed a vow. Alone in his canoe, he paddled off to a distant strait, which he knew the ship must pass through when she quitted the island. On one side was a coral reef; on the other a low tongue of land, covered with mangrove thickets that grew out into the water. Hiding his canoe, still afloat, among these thickets, with its prow seaward, he sat down in the stern, paddle low in hand; and when the ship was gliding by, like a flash he darted out; gained her side; with one backward dash of his foot capsized and sank his canoe; climbed up the chains; and throwing himself at full length upon the deck, grappled a ringbolt there, and swore not to let it go, though hacked in pieces.

In vain the captain threatened to throw him overboard; suspended a cutlass over his naked wrists; Queequeg was the son of a King, and Queequeg budged not. Struck by his desperate dauntlessness, and his wild desire to visit Christendom, the captain at last relented, and told him he might make himself at home. But this fine young savage—this sea Prince of Wales, never saw the captain's cabin. They put him down among the sailors, and made a whaleman of him. But like Czar Peter content to toil in the shipyards of foreign cities, Queequeg disdained no seeming ignominy, if thereby he might happily gain the power of enlightening his untutored countrymen. For at bottom—so he told me—he was actuated by a profound desire to learn among the Christians, the arts whereby to make his people still happier than they were; and more than that, still better than they were. But, alas! the practices of whalemen soon convinced him that even Christians could be both miserable and wicked; infinitely more so, than all his father's heathens. Arrived at last in old Sag Harbor; and seeing what the sailors did there; and then going on to Nantucket, and seeing how they spent their wages in *that* place also, poor Queequeg gave it up for lost. Thought he, it's a wicked world in all meridians; I'll die a pagan.

And thus an old idolator at heart, yet he lived among these Christians, wore their clothes, and tried to talk their gibberish. Hence the queer ways about him, though now some time from home.

By hints, I asked him whether he did not propose going back, and having a coronation; since he might now consider his father dead and gone, he being very old and feeble at the last accounts. He answered no, not yet; and added that he was fearful Christianity, or rather Christians, had unfitted him for ascending the pure and undefiled throne of thirty pagan Kings before him. But by and by, he said, he would return,—as soon as he felt himself baptized again. For the nonce, however, he proposed to sail about, and sow his wild oats in all four oceans. They had made a harpooneer of him, and that barbed iron was in lieu of a sceptre now.

I asked him what might be his immediate purpose, touching his future movements. He answered, to go to sea again, in his old vocation. Upon this, I told him that whaling was my own design, and informed him of my intention to sail out of Nantucket, as being the most promising port for an adventurous whaleman to embark from. He at once resolved to accompany me to that island, ship aboard the same vessel, get into the same watch, the same boat, the same mess with me, in short to share my every hap; with both my hands in his, boldly dip into the Potluck of both worlds. To all this I joyously assented; for besides the affection I now felt for Queequeg, he was an experienced harpooneer, and as such, could not fail to be of great usefulness to one, who, like me, was wholly ignorant of the mysteries of whaling, though well acquainted with the sea, as known to merchant seamen.

His story being ended with his pipe's last dying puff, Queequeg embraced me, pressed his forehead against mine, and blowing out the light, we rolled over from each other, this way and that, and very soon were sleeping.

CHAPTER 101

. . . And as for my exact knowledge of the bones of the leviathan in their gigantic, full grown development, for that rare knowledge I am indebted to my late royal friend Tranquo, king of Tranque, one of the Arsacides. For being at Tranque, years ago, when attached to the trading-ship Dey of Algiers, I was invited to spend part of the Arsacidean holidays with the lord of Tranque, at his retired palm villa at Pupella; a sea-side glen not very far distant from what our sailors called Bamboo-Town, his capital.

Among many other fine qualities, my royal friend Tranquo, being gifted with a devout love for all matters of barbaric vertù, had brought together in Pupella whatever rare things the more ingenious of his people could invent; chiefly carved woods of wonderful devices, chiselled shells, inlaid spears, costly paddles, aromatic canoes; and all these distributed among whatever natural wonders, the wonder-freighted, tribute-rendering waves had cast upon his shores.

Chief among these latter was a great Sperm Whale, which, after an unusually long raging gale, had been found dead and stranded, with his head against a cocoa-nut tree, whose plumage-like, tufted droopings seemed his verdant jet. When the vast body had at last been stripped of its fathom-deep enfoldings, and the bones become dust dry in the sun, then the skeleton was carefully transported up the Pupella glen, where a grand temple of lordly palms now sheltered it.

The ribs were hung with trophies; the vertebrae were carved with Arsacidean annals, in strange hieroglyphics; in the skull, the priests kept up an unextinguished aromatic flame, so that the mystic head again sent forth its vapory spout; while, suspended from a bough, the terrific lower jaw vibrated over all the devotees, like the hair-hung sword that so affrighted Damocles.

It was a wondrous sight. The wood was green as mosses of the Icy Glen; the trees stood high and haughty, feeling their living sap; the industrious earth beneath was as a weaver's loom, with a gorgeous carpet on it, whereof the ground-vine tendrils formed the warp and woof, and the living flowers the figures. All the trees, with all their laden branches; all the shrubs, and ferns, and grasses; the message-carrying air; all these unceasingly were active. Through the lacings of the leaves, the great sun seemed a flying shuttle weaving the unwearied verdure. Oh, busy weaver! unseen weaver!—pause!—one word!—whither flows the fabric? what palace may it deck? wherefore all these ceaseless toilings? Speak, weaver!—stay thy hand!—but one single word with thee! Nay—the shuttle flies—the figures float from forth the loom; the freshet-rushing carpet for ever slides away. The weaver-god, he weaves; and by that weaving is he deafened, that he hears no mortal voice; and by that humming, we, too, who look on the loom are deafened; and only when we escape it shall we hear the thousand voices that speak through it. For even so it is in all material factories. The spoken words that are inaudible among the flying spindles; those same words are plainly heard without the walls, bursting from the opened casements. Thereby have villanies been detected. Ah, mortal! then, be heedful; for so, in all this din of the great world's loom, thy subtlest thinkings may be overheard afar.

Now, amid the green, life-restless loom of that Arsacidean wood, the great, white, worshipped skeleton lay lounging—a gigantic idler! Yet, as the ever-woven verdant warp and woof intermixed and hummed around him, the mightly idler seemed the cunning weaver; himself all woven over with the vines; every month assuming greener, fresher verdure; but himself a skeleton. Life folded Death; Death trellised Life; the grim god wived with youthful Life, and begat him curly-headed glories.

Now, when with royal Tranquo I visited this wondrous whale, and saw the skull an altar, and the artificial smoke ascending from where the real jet had issued, I marvelled that the king should regard a chapel as an object of vertù. He laughed. But more I marvelled that the priests should swear that smoky jet of his was genuine. To and fro I paced before this skeleton—brushed the vines aside—broke through the ribs—and with a ball of Arsacidean twine, wandered, eddied long amid its many winding, shaded collonades and arbors. But soon my line was out; and following it back, I emerged from the opening where I entered. I saw no living thing within; naught was there but bones.

Cutting me a green measuring-rod, I once more dived within the skeleton. From their arrow-slit in the skull, the priests perceived me taking the altitude of the final rib. "How now!" they shouted; "Dar'st thou measure this our god! That's for us." "Aye, priests—well, how long do ye make him, then?" But hereupon a fierce contest rose among them, concerning feet and inches; they cracked each other's sconces with their yard-sticks—the great skull echoed—and seizing that lucky chance, I quickly concluded my own admeasurements.

These admeasurements I now propose to set before you. But first, be it recorded, that, in this matter, I am not free to utter any fancied measurement I please. Because there are skeleton authorities you can refer to, to test my accuracy. There is a Leviathanic Museum, they tell me, in Hull, England, one of the whaling ports of that country, where they have some fine specimens of finbacks and other whales. Likewise, I have heard that in the museum of Manchester, in New Hampshire, they have what the proprietors call "the only perfect specimen of a Greenland or River Whale in the United States." Moreover, at a place in Yorkshire, England, Burton Constable by name, a certain Sir Clifford Constable has in his possession the skeleton of a Sperm Whale, but of moderate size, by no means of the full-grown magnitude of my friend King Tranquo's.

In both cases, the stranded whales to which these two skeletons belonged, were originally claimed by their proprietors upon similar grounds. King Tranquo seizing his because he wanted it; and Sir Clifford, because he was lord of the seignories of those parts. Sir Clifford's whale has been articulated throughout; so that, like a great chest of drawers, you can open and shut him, in all his bony cavities—spread out his ribs like a gigantic fan—and swing all day upon his lower jaw. Locks are to be put upon some of his trap-doors and shutters; and a footman will show round future visitors with a bunch of keys at his side. Sir Clifford thinks of charging twopence for a peep at the whispering gallery in the spinal column; threepence to hear the echo in the hollow of his cerebellum; and sixpence for the unrivalled view from his forehead.

The skeleton dimensions I shall now proceed to set down are copied verbatim from my right arm, where I had them tattooed; as in my wild wanderings at that period, there was no other secure way of preserving such valuable statistics. But as I was crowded for space, and wished the other parts of my body to remain a blank page for a poem I was then composing—at least, what untattooed parts might remain—I did not trouble myself with the odd inches; nor, indeed, should inches at all enter into a congenial admeasurement of the whale.

CHAPTER 103

In the first place, I wish to lay before you a particular, plain statement, touching the living bulk of this leviathan, whose skeleton we are briefly to exhibit. Such a statement may prove useful here.

According to a careful calculation I have made, and which I partly base upon Captain Scoresby's estimate, of seventy tons for the largest sized Greenland whale of sixty feet in length; according to my careful calculation, I say, a Sperm Whale of the largest magnitude, between eighty-five and ninety feet in length, and something less than forty feet in its fullest circumference, such a whale will weigh at least ninety tons; so that reckoning thirteen men to a ton, he would considerably outweigh the combined population of a whole village of one thousand one hundred inhabitants.

Think you not then that brains, like yoked cattle, should be put to this leviathan, to make him at all budge to any landsman's imagination?

Having already in various ways put before you his skull, spout-hole, jaw, teeth, tail, forehead, fins, and divers other parts, I shall now simply point out what is most interesting in the general bulk of his unobstructed bones. But as the colossal skull embraces so very large a proportion of the entire extent of the skeleton; as it is by far the most complicated part; and as nothing is to be repeated concerning it in this chapter, you must not fail to carry it in your mind, or under your arm, as we proceed, otherwise you will not gain a complete notion of the general structure we are about to view.

In length, the Sperm Whale's skeleton at Tranque measured seventy-two feet; so that when fully invested and extended in life, he must have been ninety feet long; for in the whale, the skeleton loses about one fifth in length compared with the living body. Of this seventy-two feet, his skull and jaw comprised some twenty feet, leaving some fifty feet of plain back-bone. Attached to this backbone, for something less than a third of its length, was the mighty circular basket of ribs which once enclosed his vitals.

To me this vast ivory-ribbed chest, with the long, unrelieved spine, extending far away from it in a straight line, not a little resembled the hull of a great ship new-laid upon the stocks, when only some twenty of her naked bow-ribs are inserted, and the keel is otherwise, for the time, but a long, disconnected timber.

The ribs were ten on a side. The first, to begin from the neck, was nearly six feet long; the second, third, and fourth were each successively longer, till you came to the climax of the fifth, or one of the middle ribs, which measured eight feet and some inches. From that part, the remaining ribs diminished, till the tenth and last only spanned five feet and some inches. In general thickness, they all bore a seemly correspondence to their length. The middle ribs were the most arched. In some of the Arsacides they are used for beams whereon to lay foot-path bridges over small streams.

In considering these ribs, I could not but be struck anew with the circumstance, so variously repeated in this book, that the skeleton of the whale is by no means the mould of his invested form. The largest of the Tranque ribs, one of the middle ones, occupied that part of the fish which, in life, is greatest in depth. Now, the greatest depth of the invested body of this particular whale must have been at least sixteen feet; whereas, the corresponding rib measured but little more than eight feet. So that this rib only conveyed half of the true notion of the living magnitude of that part. Besides, for some way, where I now saw but a naked spine, all that had been once wrapped round with tons of added bulk in flesh, muscle, blood, and bowels. Still more, for the ample fins, I here saw but a few disordered joints; and in place of the weighty and majestic, but boneless flukes, an utter blank!

How vain and foolish, then, thought I, for timid untravelled man to try to comprehend aright this wondrous whale, by merely poring over his dead attenuated skeleton, stretched in this peaceful wood. No. Only the heart of quickest perils; only when within the eddyings of his angry flukes; only on the profound unbounded sea, can the fully invested whale be truly and livingly found out.

But the spine. For that, the best way we can consider it is, with a crane, to pile its bones high up on end. No speedy enterprise. But now it's done, it looks much like Pompey's Pillar.

There are forty and odd vertebrae in all, which in the skeleton are not locked together. They mostly lie like the great knobbed blocks on a Gothic spire, forming solid courses of heavy masonry. The largest, a middle one, is in width something less than three feet, and in depth more than four. The smallest, where the spine tapers away into the tail, is only two inches in width, and looks something like a white billiard-ball. I was told that there were still smaller ones, but they had been lost by some little cannibal urchins, the priest's children, who had stolen them to play marbles with. Thus we see how that the spine of even the hugest of living things tapers off at last into simple child's play.

CHAPTER III

. . . When gliding by the Bashee isles we emerged at last upon the great South Sea; were it not for other things, I could have greeted my dear Pacific with uncounted thanks, for now the long supplication of my youth was answered; that serene ocean rolled eastwards from me a thousand leagues of blue.

There is one knows not what sweet mystery about this sea, whose gently awful stirrings seem to speak of some hidden soul beneath; like those fabled undulations of the Ephesian sod over the buried Evangelist St. John. And meet it is that over these sea-pastures, wide-rolling watery prairies and Potters' Fields of all four continents, the waves should rise and fall, and ebb and flow unceasingly; for here, millions of mixed shades and shadows, drowned dreams, somnambulisms, reveries; all that we call lives and souls, lie dreaming, dreaming, still; tossing like slumberers in their beds; the ever-rolling waves but made so by their restlessness.

To any meditative Magian rover, this serene Pacific, once beheld, must ever after be the sea of his adoption. It rolls the midmost waters of the world, the Indian Ocean and Atlantic being but its arms. The same waves wash the moles of the new-built Californian towns, but yesterday planted by the recentest race of men, and lave the faded but still gorgeous skirts of Asiatic lands, older than Abraham; while all between float milky-ways of coral isles, and low-lying, endless, unknown archipelagoes, and impenetrable Japans. Thus this mysterious, divine Pacific zones the world's whole bulk about; makes all coasts one bay to it; seems the tide-beating heart of earth. Lifted by those eternal swells, you needs must own the seductive god, bowing your head to Pan. . . .

PART VII

A PASSAGE TO
THE ENCHANTED ISLES:
Las Encantadas
(1854)

$$\text{❈ ❈ ❈}$$

INTRODUCTION

"My own interest in the *Encantadas* began when I conducted an expedition to the Galápagos Islands, the scene of these ten sketches. Since we intended to remain six months on these isolated islands, our scientific impedimenta were augmented with books. And among these was a copy of *Piazza Tales*. While I was on these islands, I had the pleasure of visiting every part mentioned in the *Encantadas*. Reading these haunting sketches in the very midst of the inferno that inspired them, I thought then, as I do now, that they are the finest descriptive pieces of writing concerning this volcanic archipelago. The bibliography of Galápagos literature is vast, and as a naturalist preparing a book on the islands I have had recourse to all of it. There are, of course, chapters in books on the Galápagos that are more accurate, there are zoological treatises that deal exhaustively with the curious lost-world fauna, but in all the vast range of its literature, I know of nothing that describes the islands as poetically and, I am almost tempted to say, as realistically, as Herman Melville's *Encantadas* or *Enchanted Isles*."[1]

This tribute by Victor Wolfgang von Hagen, eminent zoologist, stresses the authenticity of Melville's treatment of the first group of Pacific islands that he encountered. Early critics, inclined to consider "The Encantadas," along with "Benito Cereno," as "the final momentary brightening of the embers before they sank into blackness and ash,"[2] were forced by better judges to appreciate the artistry of these later works. "Benito Cereno" was termed by Edmund O'Brien "the noblest short story in American literature." Michael Sadlier, English bookman, was the first, without denying the eminence of *Moby Dick,* to "venture that his genius is more perfectly and skillfully revealed in a volume of stories belonging to the so-called decadence"—specifically "Benito Cereno" and "Las Encantadas," which "held in the small compass of their beauty the essence of their author's supreme artistry."[3]

"Benito Cereno" takes place off an island at the southern end of Chile—a spot that hardly qualifies as a part of the South Seas. In any event, that story is too long for inclusion. No justification is needed, however, for presenting here in full Melville's panorama of the equatorial islands of the Galápagos. His ten canvases from the "archipelago of aridities" reveal not only his painterly eye but his profound feeling that his life had become a prison house. Chained to his desk, writing to pay off debts, he could not prevent his pen from uttering images of isolation, desolation, servitude, punishment, endurance, and despair.

Melville during the early 1850's, despite the success of his first books, owed money and had to support a wife and four children. Without any other resource than his writing, he began shaping his work to suit the magazine market. *The Piazza Tales* (1854) included some of these pieces, among them "The Encantadas, or Enchanted Isles." The germ of this work was an assignment to do a book for Harpers on "tortoises or tortoise-hunting"; but the memory of the giant creatures on the deck of the *Acushnet* developed instead into a series of sketches that viewed the cindery island cluster from a variety of points of view.

"The Encantadas," which has rightly been called Melville's *Inferno,* first appeared in *Putnam's Monthly Magazine* from March through May, 1854, under the Poesque pen name of Salvator R. Tarnmoor. The sketches, read consecutively, give a sort of documentary film of a group which is today more accessible than during the whaling era; indeed, Pacific cruise ships now make the Galápagos their goal. Outstanding among the ten pieces, however, is the story of "Norfolk Island and the Chola Widow."

Melville had for several years been probing the theme of a forsaken but enduringly faithful woman. He had offered the materials for such a story to Nathaniel Hawthorne at Pittsfield in 1852, but his friend had returned these, saying rightly that Melville was the one to shape this subject. The "Agatha" theme, drawn from a true episode, was still in Melville's mind when he was writing about the hellish isles. What better place could be found in which to isolate a young bride, who would be faithful for years to the memory of the husband she had buried? The quotations heading the sketches are drawn— sometimes with changes that might be copying errors—from *The Faerie Queen* of Edmund Spenser, an epic in which the themes of patience and resistance to despair appear and were pondered under Melville's reading lamp. The unpublished story of Agatha, emblematic of Christian faith, was transfigured into the story of Hunilla. Its concluding scene, in which the Chola widow rides a small gray ass toward her native Peruvian village and "eyes the jointed workings of the beast's armorial cross," seemed to James Russell Lowell to be the finest touch of genius he had seen in prose.

As he had previously done, Melville sought sources to supplement his own experience. Two of these he acknowledged in a footnote: David Porter[4] and James Colnett.[5] He did not mention a third, the four-volume set concerning the British scientific expedition of 1826–36.[6] The impressions of Robert Fitzroy, captain of the *Beagle* and author of the first two volumes, must have been helpful; and the third volume, by Charles Darwin, who examined the Galápagos group in October, 1835, aided Melville in keeping in order his fauna and flora. He also refers to William Ambrose Cowley, buccaneer and author.[7] At this time Melville was also planning to write "Benito Cereno," based on a true incident during a voyage by Captain Amasa Delano, whose *Narratives of Voyages and Travels* gives in Chapter XXI a summary of his visits to the Galápagos group. As was customary with him, though, Melville took these sources as starting points for his own evocations and meditations.

SKETCH FIRST

The Isles at Large

That may not be, said then the Ferryman,
Least we unweeting hap to be fordonne:
For those same Islands, seeming now and than,
Are not firme land, nor any certein wonne,
But stragling plots, which to and fro do ronne
In the wide waters; therefore are they hight
The Wandring Islands: Therefore doe them shonne;
For they have oft drawne many a wandring wight
Into most deadly daunger and distressed plight;
For whosoever once hath fastened
His foot thereon, may never it recure,
But wandreth evermore uncertein and unsure.

Darke, dolefull, dreary, like a greedy grave,
That still for carrion carcases doth crave:
On top whereof ay dwelt the ghastly owle,
Shrieking his balefull note, which ever drave
Far from that haunt all other chearefull fowle;
And all about it wandring ghostes did wayle and howle.

Take five-and-twenty heaps of cinders dumped here and there in an outside city lot; imagine some of them magnified into mountains, and the vacant lot the sea; and you will have a fit idea of the general aspect of the Encantadas, or Enchanted Isles. A group rather of extinct volcanoes than of isles; looking much as the world at large might, after a penal conflagration.

It is to be doubted whether any spot of earth can, in desolateness, furnish a parallel to this group. Abandoned cemeteries of long ago, old cities by piecemeal tumbling to their ruin, these are melancholy enough; but, like all else which has but once been associated with humanity, they still awaken in us some thoughts of sympathy, however sad. Hence, even the Dead Sea, along with whatever other emotions it may at times inspire, does not fail to touch in the pilgrim some of his less unpleasurable feelings.

And as for solitariness; the great forests of the north, the expanses of unnavigated waters, the Greenland ice-fields, are the profoundest of solitudes to a human observer; still the magic of their changeable tides and seasons mitigates their terror; because, though unvisited by men, these forests are visited by the May; the remotest seas reflect familiar stars even as Lake Erie does; and in the clear air of a fine Polar day, the irradiated, azure ice shows beautifully as malachite.

But the special curse, as one may call it, of the Encantadas, that which exalts them in desolation above Idumea and the Pole, is, that to them change never comes; neither the change of seasons nor of sorrows. Cut by the Equator, they know not autumn, and they know not spring; while already reduced to the lees of fire, ruin itself can work little more upon them. The showers refresh the deserts; but in these isles, rain never falls. Like split Syrian gourds left withering in the sun, they are cracked by an everlasting drought beneath a torrid sky. "Have mercy on me," the wailing spirit of the Encantadas seems to cry, "and send Lazarus that he may dip the tip of his finger in water and cool my tongue, for I am tormented in this flame."

Another feature in these isles is their emphatic uninhabitableness. It is deemed a fit type of all-forsaken overthrow, that the jackal should den in the wastes of weedy Babylon; but the Encantadas refuse to harbor even the outcasts of the beasts. Man and wolf alike disown them. Little but reptile life is here found: tortoises, lizards, immense spiders, snakes, and that strangest anomaly of outlandish nature, the *iguana*. No voice, no low, no howl is heard; the chief sound of life here is a hiss.

On most of the isles where vegetation is found at all, it is more ungrateful than the blankness of Atacama. Tangled thickets of wiry bushes, without fruit and without a name, springing up among deep fissures of calcined rock, and treacherously masking them; or a parched growth of distorted cactus trees.

In many places the coast is rock-bound, or, more properly, clinker-bound; tumbled masses of blackish or greenish stuff like the dross of an iron-furnace, forming dark clefts and caves here and there, into which a ceaseless sea pours a fury of foam; overhanging them with a swirl of gray, haggard mist, amidst which sail screaming flights of unearthly birds heightening the dismal din. However calm the sea without, there is no rest for these swells and those rocks; they lash and are lashed, even when the outer ocean is most at peace with itself. On the oppressive, clouded days, such as are peculiar to this part of the watery Equator, the dark, vitrified masses, many of which raise themselves among white whirlpools and breakers in detached and perilous places off the shore, present a most Plutonian sight. In no world but a fallen one could such lands exist.

Those parts of the strand free from the marks of fire, stretch away in wide level beaches of multitudinous dead shells, with here and there decayed bits of sugar-cane, bamboos, and cocoanuts, washed upon this other and darker world from the charming palm isles to the westward and southward; all the way from Paradise to Tartarus; while mixed with the relics of distant beauty you will sometimes see fragments of charred wood and mouldering ribs of wrecks. Neither will any one be surprised at meeting these last, after observing the conflicting currents which eddy throughout nearly all the wide channels of the entire group. The capriciousness of the tides of air sympathizes with those of the sea. Nowhere is the wind so light, baffling, and every way unreliable, and so given to perplexing calms, as at the Encantadas. Nigh a month has been spent by a ship going from one isle to another, though but ninety miles between; for owing to the force of the current, the boats employed to tow barely suffice to keep the craft from sweeping upon the cliffs, but do nothing towards accelerating her voyage. Sometimes it is impossible for a vessel from afar to fetch up with the group itself, unless large allowances for prospective lee-way have been made ere its coming in sight. And yet, at other times, there is a mysterious indraft, which irresistibly draws a passing vessel among the isles, though not bound to them.

True, at one period, as to some extent at the present day, large fleets of whalemen cruised for spermaceti upon what some seamen call the Enchanted Ground. But this, as in due place will be described, was off the great outer isle of Albemarle, away from the intricacies of the smaller isles, where there is plenty of sea-room; and hence, to that vicinity, the above remarks do not altogether apply; though even there the current runs at times with singular force, shifting, too, with as singular a caprice.

Indeed, there are seasons when currents quite unaccountable prevail for a great distance round about the total group, and are so strong and irregular as to change a vessel's course against the helm, though sailing at the rate of four or five miles the hour. The difference in the reckonings of navigators, produced by these causes, along with the light and variable winds, long nourished a persuasion, that there existed two distinct clusters of isles in the parallel of the Encantadas, about a hundred leagues apart. Such was the idea of their earlier visitors, the Buccaneers; and as late as 1750, the charts of that part of the Pacific accorded with the strange delusion. And this apparent fleetingness and unreality of the locality of the isles was most probably one reason for the Spaniards calling them the Encantada, or Enchanted Group.

But not uninfluenced by their character, as they now confessedly exist, the modern voyager will be inclined to fancy that the bestowal of this name might have in part originated in that air of spell-bound desertness which so significantly invests the isles. Nothing can better suggest the aspect of once living things malignly crumbled from ruddiness into ashes. Apples of Sodom, after touching, seem these isles.

However wavering their place may seem by reason of the currents, they themselves, at least to one upon the shore, appear invariably the same: fixed, cast, glued into the very body of cadaverous death.

Nor would the appellation, enchanted, seem misapplied in still another sense. For concerning the peculiar reptile inhabitant of these wilds—whose presence gives the group its second Spanish name, Galapagos—concerning the tortoises found here, most mariners have long cherished a superstition, not more frightful than grotesque. They earnestly believe that all wicked sea-officers, more especially commodores and captains, are at death (and, in some cases, before death) transformed into tortoises; thenceforth dwelling upon these hot aridities, sole solitary lords of Asphaltum.

Doubtless, so quaintly dolorous a thought was originally inspired by the woebegone landscape itself; but more particularly, perhaps, by the tortoises. For, apart from their strictly physical features, there is something strangely self-condemned in the appearance of these creatures. Lasting sorrow and penal hopelessness are in no animal form so suppliantly expressed as in theirs; while the thought of their wonderful longevity does not fail to enhance the impression.

Nor even at the risk of meriting the charge of absurdly believing in enchantments, can I restrain the admission that sometimes, even now, when leaving the crowded city to wander out July and August among the Adirondack Mountains, far from the influences of towns and proportionally nigh to the mysterious ones of nature; when at such times I sit me down in the mossy head of some deep-wooded gorge, surrounded by prostrate trunks of blasted pines, and recall, as in a dream, my other and far-distant rovings in the baked heart of the charmed isles; and remember the sudden glimpses of dusky shells, and long languid necks protruded from the leafless thickets; and again have beheld the vitreous inland rocks worn down and grooved into deep ruts by ages and ages of the slow draggings of tortoises in quest of pools of scanty water; I can hardly resist the feeling that in my time I have indeed slept upon evilly enchanted ground.

Nay, such is the vividness of my memory, or the magic of my fancy, that I know not whether I am not the occasional victim of optical delusion concerning the Galapagos. For, often in scenes of social merriment, and especially at revels held by candle-light in old-fashioned mansions, so that shadows are thrown into the further recesses of an angular and spacious room, making them put on a look of haunted undergrowth of lonely woods, I have drawn the attention of my comrades by my fixed gaze and sudden change of air, as I have seemed to see, slowly emerging from those imagined solitudes, and heavily crawling along the floor, the ghost of a gigantic tortoise, with "Memento * * * * *" burning in live letters upon his back.

SKETCH SECOND

Two Sides to a Tortoise

Most ugly shapes and horrible aspects,
Such as Dame Nature selfe mote feare to see,
Or shame, that ever should so fowle defects
From her most cunning hand escaped bee;
All dreadfull pourtraicts of deformitee:
Ne wonder, if these do a man appall;
For all that here at home we dreadfull hold,
Be but as bugs to fearen babes withall,
Compared to the creatures in these isles' entrall.

"Feare nought," then saide the Palmer well aviz'd,
"For these same monsters are not these in deed,
But are into these fearfull shapes disguiz'd."
And lifting up his vertuous staffe on hye,
Then all that dreadfull armie fast can flye
Into great Tethys bosome, where they hidden lye.

In view of the description given, may one be gay upon the Encantadas? Yes: that is, find one the gaiety, and he will be gay. And, indeed, sackcloth and ashes as they are, the isles are not perhaps unmitigated gloom. For while no spectator can deny their claims to a most solemn and superstitious consideration, no more than my firmest resolutions can decline to behold the spectre-tortoise when emerging from its shadowy recess; yet even the tortoise, dark and melancholy as it is upon the back, still possesses a bright side; its calipee or breast-plate being sometimes of a faint yellowish or golden tinge. Moreover, every one knows that tortoises as well as turtles are of such a make, that if you but put them on their backs you thereby expose their bright sides without the possibility of their recovering themselves, and turning into view the other. But after you have done this, and because you have done this, you should not swear that the tortoise has no dark side. Enjoy the bright, keep it turned up perpetually if you can, but be honest, and don't deny the black. Neither should he, who cannot turn the tortoise from its natural position so as to hide the darker and expose his livelier aspect, like a great October pumpkin in the sun, for that cause declare the creature to be one total inky blot. The tortoise is both black and bright. But let us to particulars.

Some months before my first stepping ashore upon the group, my ship was cruising in its close vicinity. One noon we found ourselves off the South Head of Albemarle, and not very far from the land. Partly by way of freak, and partly by way of spying out so strange a country, a boat's crew was sent ashore, with orders to see all they could, and besides, bring back whatever tortoises they could conveniently transport.

It was after sunset, when the adventurers returned. I looked down over the ship's high side as if looking down over the curb of a well, and dimly saw the damp boat deep in the sea with some unwonted weight. Ropes were dropt over, and presently three huge antediluvian-looking tortoises, after much straining, were landed on deck. They seemed hardly of the seed of earth. We had been abroad upon the waters for five long months, a period amply sufficient to make all things of the land wear a fabulous hue to the dreamy mind. Had three Spanish custom-house officers boarded us then, it is not unlikely that I should have curiously stared at them, felt of them, and stroked them much as savages serve civilized guests. But instead of three custom-house officers, behold these really wondrous tortoises—none of your schoolboy mud-turtles—but black as widower's weeds, heavy as chests of plate, with vast shells medallioned and orbed like shields, and dented and blistered like shields that have breasted a battle, shaggy, too, here and there, with dark green moss, and slimy with the spray of the sea. These mystic creatures, suddenly translated by night from unutterable solitudes to our peopled deck, affected me in a manner not easy to unfold. They seemed newly crawled forth from beneath the foundations of the world. Yea, they seemed the identical tortoises whereon the Hindoo plants this total sphere. With a lantern I inspected them more closely. Such worshipful venerableness of aspect! Such furry greenness mantling the rude peelings and healing the fissures of their shattered shells. I no more saw three tortoises. They expanded—became transfigured. I seemed to see three Roman Coliseums in magnificent decay.

Ye oldest inhabitants of this, or any other isle, said I, pray, give me the freedom of your three walled towns.

The great feeling inspired by these creatures was that of age:—dateless, indefinite endurance. And, in fact, that any other creature can live and breathe as long as the tortoise of the Encantadas, I will not readily believe. Not to hint of their known capacity of sustaining life, while going without food for an entire year, consider that impregnable armor of their living mail. What other bodily being possesses such a citadel wherein to resist the assaults of Time?

As, lantern in hand, I scraped among the moss and beheld the ancient scars

of bruises received in many a sullen fall among the marly mountains of the isle
—scars strangely widened, swollen, half obliterate, and yet distorted like those
sometimes found in the bark of very hoary trees, I seemed an antiquary of a
geologist, studying the bird-tracks and ciphers upon the exhumed slates trod by
incredible creatures whose very ghosts are now defunct.

As I lay in my hammock that night, overhead I heard the slow weary draggings of the three ponderous strangers along the encumbered deck. Their stu-
pidity or their resolution was so great, that they never went aside for any
impediment. One ceased his movements altogether just before the mid-watch. At
sunrise I found him butted like a battering-ram against the immovable foot of
the foremast, and still striving, tooth and nail, to force the impossible passage.
That these tortoises are the victims of a penal, or malignant, or perhaps a downright diabolical enchanter, seems in nothing more likely than in that strange
infatuation of hopeless toil which so often possesses them. I have known them
in their journeyings ram themselves heroically against rocks, and long abide
there, nudging, wriggling, wedging, in order to displace them, and so hold on
their inflexible path. Their crowning curse is their drudging impulse to straight-
forwardness in a belittered world.

Meeting with no such hinderance as their companion did, the other tortoises
merely fell foul of small stumbling-blocks—buckets, blocks, and coils of rigging
—and at times in the act of crawling over them would slip with an astounding
rattle to the deck. Listening to these draggings and concussions, I thought me
of the haunt from which they came; an isle full of metallic ravines and gulches,
sunk bottomlessly into the hearts of splintered mountains, and covered for many
miles with inextricable thickets. I then pictured these three straightforward
monsters, century after century, writhing through the shades, grim as black-
smiths; crawling so slowly and ponderously, that not only did toadstools and all
fungous things grow beneath their feet, but a sooty moss sprouted upon their
backs. With them I lost myself in volcanic mazes; brushed away endless boughs
of rotting thickets; till finally in a dream I found myself sitting cross-legged
upon the foremost, a Brahmin similarly mounted upon either side, forming a
tripod of foreheads which upheld the universal cope.

Such was the wild nightmare begot by my first impression of the Encantadas
tortoise. But next evening, strange to say, I sat down with my shipmates, and
made a merry repast from tortoise steaks and tortoise stews; and supper over,
out knife, and helped convert the three mighty concave shells into three fanciful
soup-tureens, and polished the three flat yellowish calipees into three gorgeous
salvers.

SKETCH THIRD

Rock Rodondo

For thy this hight the Rock of vile Reproch,
A dangerous and dreadfull place;
To which nor fish nor fowle did once approch,
But yelling meawes, with seagulles hoars and bace,
And cormoyrants, with birds of ravenous race,
Which still sit waiting on that dreadful clift.

With that the rolling sea resounding soft,
In his big base them fitly answered;
And on the Rock the waves breaking aloft
A solemne meane unto them measured;
Then he the Boteman bad row easily,
And let him heare some part of that rare melody.

Suddeinly an innumerable flight
Of harmefull fowles about them fluttering cride,
And with their wicked wings them oft did smight,
And sore annoyed, groping in that griesly night.
Even all the nation of unfortunate
And fatall birds about them flocked were.

To go up into a high stone tower is not only a very fine thing in itself, but the very best mode of gaining a comprehensive view of the region round about. It is all the better if this tower stand solitary and alone, like that mysterious Newport one, or else be sole survivor of some perished castle.

Now, with reference to the Enchanted Isles, we are fortunately supplied with just such a noble point of observation in a remarkable rock, from its peculiar figure called of old by the Spaniards, Rock Rodondo, or Round Rock. Some two hundred and fifty feet high, rising straight from the sea ten miles from land, with the whole mountainous group to the south and east, Rock Rodondo occupies, on a large scale, very much the position which the famous Campanile or detached Bell-Tower of St. Mark does with respect to the tangled group of hoary edifices around it.

Ere ascending, however, to gaze abroad upon the Encantadas, this sea-tower itself claims attention. It is visible at the distance of thirty miles; and, fully participating in that enchantment which pervades the group, when first seen afar invariably is mistaken for a sail. Four leagues away, of a golden, hazy noon, it seems some Spanish Admiral's ship, stacked up with glittering canvas. *Sail ho! Sail ho! Sail ho!* from all three masts. But coming nigh, the enchanted frigate is transformed apace into a craggy keep.

My first visit to the spot was made in the gray of the morning. With a view of fishing, we had lowered three boats, and pulling some two miles from our vessel, found ourselves just before dawn of day close under the moon-shadow of Rodondo. Its aspect was heightened, and yet softened, by the strange double twilight of the hour. The great full moon burnt in the low west like a half-spent beacon, casting a soft mellow tinge upon the sea like that cast by a waning fire of embers upon a midnight hearth; while along the entire east the invisible sun sent pallid intimations of his coming. The wind was light; the waves languid; the stars twinkled with a faint effulgence; all nature seemed supine with the long night watch, and half-suspended in jaded expectation of the sun. This was the critical hour to catch Rodondo in his perfect mood. The twilight was just enough to reveal every striking point, without tearing away the dim investiture of wonder.

From a broken stair-like base, washed, as the steps of a water-palace, by the waves, the tower rose in entablatures of strata to a shaven summit. These uniform layers, which compose the mass, form its most peculiar feature. For at their lines of junction they project flatly into encircling shelves, from top to bottom, rising one above another in graduated series. And as the eaves of any old barn or abbey are alive with swallows, so were all these rocky ledges with unnumbered sea-fowl. Eaves upon eaves, and nests upon nests. Here and there were long birdlime streaks of a ghostly white staining the tower from sea to air, readily accounting for its sail-like look afar. All would have been bewitchingly quiescent, were it not for the demoniac din created by the birds. Not only were the eaves rustling with them, but they flew densely overhead, spreading themselves into a winged and continually shifting canopy. The tower is the resort of aquatic birds for hundreds of leagues around. To the north, to the east, to the west, stretches nothing but eternal ocean; so that the man-of-war hawk coming from the coasts of North America, Polynesia, or Peru, makes his first land at Rodondo. And yet though Rodondo be terra firma, no land-bird ever lighted on it. Fancy a red-robin or a canary there! What a falling into the hands of the Philistines, when the poor warbler should be surrounded by such locust-flights of strong bandit birds, with long bills cruel as daggers.

I know not where one can better study the Natural History of strange sea-fowl than at Rodondo. It is the aviary of Ocean. Birds light here which never touched mast or tree; hermit-birds, which ever fly alone; cloud-birds, familiar with unpierced zones of air.

Let us first glance low down to the lowermost shelf of all, which is the widest, too, and but a little space from high-water mark. What outlandish beings are these? Erect as men, but hardly as symmetrical, they stand all round the rock like sculptured caryatides, supporting the next range of eaves above. Their bodies are grotesquely misshapen; their bills short; their feet seemingly legless; while the members at their sides are neither fin, wing, nor arm. And truly neither fish, flesh, nor fowl is the penguin; as an edible, pertaining neither to Carnival nor Lent; without exception the most ambiguous and least lovely creature yet discovered by man. Though dabbling in all three elements, and indeed possessing some rudimental claims to all, the penguin is at home in none. On land it stumps; afloat it sculls; in the air it flops. As if ashamed of her failure, Nature keeps this ungainly child hidden away at the ends of the earth, in the Straits of Magellan, and on the abased sea-story of Rodondo.

But look, what are yon woe-begone regiments drawn up on the next shelf above? what rank and file of large strange fowl? what sea Friars of Orders Gray? Pelicans. Their elongated bills, and heavy leathern pouches suspended thereto, give them the most lugubrious expression. A pensive race, they stand for hours together without motion. Their dull, ashy plumage imparts an aspect as if they had been powdered over with cinders. A penitential bird, indeed, fitly haunting the shores of the clinkered Encantadas, whereon tormented Job himself might have well sat down and scraped himself with potsherds.

Higher up now we mark the gony, or gray albatross, anomalously so called, an unsightly, unpoetic bird, unlike its storied kinsman, which is the snow-white ghost of the haunted Capes of Hope and Horn.

As we still ascend from shelf to shelf, we find the tenants of the tower serially disposed in order of their magnitude:—gannets, black and speckled haglets, jays, sea-hens, sperm-whale-birds, gulls of all varieties:—thrones, princedoms, powers, dominating one above another in senatorial array; while, sprinkled over all, like an ever-repeated fly in a great piece of broidery, the stormy petrel or Mother Cary's chicken sounds his continual challenge and alarm. That this mysterious humming-bird of ocean—which, had it but brilliancy of hue, might, from its evanescent liveliness, be almost called its butterfly, yet whose chirrup under the stern is ominous to mariners as to the peasant the death-tick sounding from behind the chimney jamb—should have its special haunt at the Encantadas, contributes, in the seaman's mind, not a little to their dreary spell.

As day advances the dissonant din augments. With ear-splitting cries the wild birds celebrate their matins. Each moment, flights push from the tower, and join the aerial choir hovering overhead, while their places below are supplied by darting myriads. But down through all this discord of commotion, I hear clear, silver, bugle-like notes unbrokenly falling, like oblique lines of swift-slanting rain in a cascading shower. I gaze far up, and behold a snow-white angelic thing, with one long, lance-like feather thrust out behind. It is the bright, inspiriting chanticleer of ocean, the beauteous bird, from its bestirring whistle of musical invocation, fitly styled the "Boatswain's Mate."

The winged life clouding Rodondo had its full counterpart in the finny hosts which peopled the waters at its base. Below the waterline, the rock seemed one honey-comb of grottoes, affording labyrinthine lurking-places for swarms of fairy fish. All were strange; many exceedingly beautiful; and would have well graced the costliest glass globes in which gold-fish are kept for a show. Nothing was more striking than the complete novelty of many individuals of this multitude. Here hues were seen as yet unpainted, and figures which are unengraved.

To show the multitude, avidity, and nameless fearlessness and tameness of these fish, let me say, that often, marking through clear spaces of water—temporarily made so by the concentric dartings of the fish above the surface—certain larger and less unwary wights, which swam slow and deep, our anglers would cautiously essay to drop their lines down to these last. But in vain; there was no passing the uppermost zone. No sooner did the hook touch the sea, than a hundred infatuates contended for the honor of capture. Poor fish of Rodondo! in your victimized confidence, you are of the number of those who inconsiderately trust, while they do not understand, human nature.

But the dawn is now fairly day. Band after band, the sea-fowl sail away to forage the deep for their food. The tower is left solitary, save the fish-caves at its base. Its birdlime gleams in the golden rays like the whitewash of a tall lighthouse, or the lofty sails of a cruiser. This moment, doubtless, while we know it to be a dead desert rock, other voyagers are taking oaths it is a glad populous ship.

But ropes now, and let us ascend. Yet soft, this is not so easy.

SKETCH FOURTH

A Pisgah View from the Rock

That done, he leads him to the highest Mount,
From whence, far off he unto him did shew . . .

If you seek to ascend Rock Rodondo, take the following prescription. Go three voyages round the world as a main-royal-man of the tallest frigate that floats; then serve a year or two apprenticeship to the guides who conduct strangers up the Peak of Teneriffe; and as many more respectively to a rope-dancer, an Indian juggler, and a chamois. This done, come and be rewarded by the view from our tower. How we get there, we alone know. If we sought to tell others, what the wiser were they? Suffice it, that here at the summit you and I stand. Does any balloonist, does the outlooking man in the moon, take a broader view of space? Much thus, one fancies, looks the universe from Milton's celestial battlements. A boundless watery Kentucky. Here Daniel Boone would have dwelt content.

Never heed for the present yonder Burnt District of the Enchanted Isles. Look edgeways, as it were, past them, to the south. You see nothing; but permit me to point out the direction, if not the place, of certain interesting objects in the vast sea, which, kissing this tower's base, we behold unscrolling itself towards the Antarctic Pole.

We stand now ten miles from the Equator. Yonder, to the east, some six hundred miles, lies the continent; this Rock being just about on the parallel of Quito.

Observe another thing here. We are at one of three uninhabited clusters, which, at pretty nearly uniform distances from the main, sentinel, at long intervals from each other, the entire coast of South America. In a peculiar manner, also, they terminate the South American character of country. Of the unnumbered Polynesian chains to the westward, not one partakes of the qualities of the Encantadas or Galapagos, the isles of San Felix and San Ambrosio, the isles Juan Fernandez and Mas-a-Fuera. Of the first, it needs not here to speak. The second lie a little above the Southern Tropic; lofty, inhospitable, and uninhabitable rocks, one of which, presenting two round hummocks connected by a low reef, exactly resembles a huge double-headed shot. The last lie in the latitude of 33°; high, wild and cloven. Juan Fernandez is sufficiently famous without further description. Mas-a-Fuera is a Spanish name, expressive of the fact, that the isle so called lies *more without,* that is, further off the main than its neighbor Juan. This isle Mas-a-Fuera has a very imposing aspect at a distance of eight or ten miles. Approached in one direction, in cloudy weather, its great overhanging height and rugged contour, and more especially a peculiar slope of its broad summits, give it much the air of a vast iceberg drifting in tremendous poise. Its sides are split with dark cavernous recesses, as an old cathedral with its gloomy lateral chapels. Drawing nigh one of these gorges from sea, after a long voyage, and beholding some tatterdemalion outlaw, staff in hand, descending its steep rocks toward you, conveys a very queer emotion to a lover of the picturesque.

On fishing parties from ships, at various times, I have chanced to visit each of these groups. The impression they give to the stranger pulling close up in his boat under their grim cliffs is, that surely he must be their first discoverer, such, for the most part, is the unimpaired . . . . . . silence and solitude. And here, by the way, the mode in which these isles were really first lighted upon by Europeans is not unworthy of mention, especially as what is about to be said, likewise applies to the original discovery of our Encantadas.

Prior to the year 1563, the voyages made by Spanish ships from Peru to Chile, were full of difficulty. Along this coast, the winds from the South most generally prevail; and it had been an invariable custom to keep close in with the land, from a superstitious conceit on the part of the Spaniards, that were they to lose sight of it, the eternal trade-wind would waft them into unending waters, from whence would be no return. Here, involved among tortuous capes and headlands, shoals and reefs, beating, too, against a continual head wind, often light, and sometimes for days and weeks sunk into utter calm, the provincial vessels, in many cases, suffered the extremest hardships, in passages, which at the present day seem to have been incredibly protracted. There is on record in some collections of nautical disasters, an account of one of these ships, which, starting on a voyage whose duration was estimated at ten days, spent four months at sea, and indeed never again entered harbor, for in the end she was cast away. Singular to tell, this craft never encountered a gale, but was the vexed sport of malicious calms and currents. Thrice, out of provisions, she put back to an intermediate port, and started afresh, but only yet again to return. Frequent fogs enveloped her; so that no observation could be had of her place, and once, when all hands were joyously anticipating sight of their destination, lo! the vapors lifted and disclosed the mountains from which they had taken their first departure. In the like deceptive vapors she at last struck upon a reef, whence ensued a long series of calamities too sad to detail.

It was the famous pilot, Juan Fernandez, immortalized by the island named after him, who put an end to these coasting tribulations, by boldly venturing the experiment—as De Gama did before him with respect to Europe—of standing broad out from land. Here he found the winds favorable for getting to the South, and by running westward till beyond the influences of the trades, he regained the coast without difficulty; making the passage which, though in a high degree circuitous, proved far more expeditious than the nominally direct one. Now it was upon these new tracks, and about the year 1670, or thereabouts, that the Enchanted Isles, and the rest of the sentinel groups, as they may be called, were discovered. Though I know of no account as to whether any of them were found inhabited or no, it may be reasonably concluded that they have been immemorial solitudes. But let us return to Rodondo.

Southwest from our tower lies all Polynesia, hundreds of leagues away; but straight west, on the precise line of this parallel, no land rises till your keel is beached upon the Kingsmills, a nice little sail of, say 5000 miles.

Having thus by such distant references—with Rodondo the only possible ones —settled our relative place on the sea, let us consider objects not quite so remote. Behold the grim and charred Enchanted Isles. This nearest crater-shaped headland is part of Albemarle, the largest of the group, being some sixty miles or more long, and fifteen broad. Did you ever lay eye on the real genuine Equator? Have you ever, in the largest sense, toed the Line? Well, that identical crater-shaped headland there, all yellow lava, is cut by the Equator exactly as a knife cuts straight through the centre of a pumpkin pie. If you could only see so far, just to one side of that same headland, across yon low dikey ground, you would catch sight of the isle of Narborough, the loftiest land of the cluster; no soil whatever; one seamed clinker from top to bottom; abounding in black caves like smithies; its metallic shore ringing under foot like plates of iron; its central volcanoes standing grouped like a gigantic chimney-stack.

Narborough and Albemarle are neighbors after a quite curious fashion. A familiar diagram will illustrate this strange neighborhood:

Cut a channel at the above letter joint, and the middle transverse limb is Narborough, and all the rest is Albemarle. Volcanic Narborough lies in the black jaws of Albemarle like a wolf's red tongue in his open mouth.

If now you desire the population of Albemarle, I will give you, in round numbers, the statistics, according to the most reliable estimates made upon the spot:

Men, ...	none
Ant-eaters, ...	unknown
Man-haters, ...	unknown
Lizards, ...	500,000
Snakes, ...	500,000
Spiders, ...	10,000,000
Salamanders, ...	unknown
Devils, ...	do.
Making a clean total of	11,000,000

exclusive of an incomputable host of fiends, ant-eaters, man-haters, and sala-manders.

Albemarle opens his mouth towards the setting sun. His distended jaws form a great bay, which Narborough, his tongue, divides into halves, one whereof is called Weather Bay, the other Lee Bay; while the volcanic promontories, termi-nating his coasts, are styled South Head and North Head. I note this, because these bays are famous in the annals of the Sperm Whale Fishery. The whales come here at certain seasons to calve. When ships first cruised hereabouts, I am told, they used to blockade the entrance of Lee Bay, when their boats going round by Weather Bay, passed through Narborough channel, and so had the Leviathans very neatly in a pen.

The day after we took fish at the base of this Round Tower, we had a fine wind, and shooting round the north headland, suddenly descried a fleet of full thirty sail, all beating to windward like a squadron in line. A brave sight as ever man saw. A most harmonious concord of rushing keels. Their thirty kelsons hummed like thirty harp-strings, and looked as straight whilst they left their parallel traces on the sea. But there proved too many hunters for the game. The fleet broke up, and went their separate ways out of sight, leaving my own ship and two trim gentlemen of London. These last, finding no luck either, likewise vanished; and Lee Bay, with all its appurtenances, and without a rival, devolved to us.

The way of cruising here is this. You keep hovering about the entrance of the bay, in one beat and out the next. But at times—not always, as in other parts of the group—a race-horse of a current sweeps right across its mouth. So, with all sails set, you carefully ply your tacks. How often, standing at the foremast head at sunrise, with our patient prow pointed in between these isles, did I gaze upon that land, not of cakes, but of clinkers, not of streams of sparkling water, but arrested torrents of tormented lava.

As the ship runs in from the open sea, Narborough presents its side in one dark craggy mass, soaring up some five or six thousand feet, at which point it hoods itself in heavy clouds, whose lowest level fold is as clearly defined against the rocks as the snow-line against the Andes. There is dire mischief going on in that upper dark. There toil the demons of fire, who, at intervals, irradiate the nights with a strange spectral illumination for miles and miles around, but unaccompanied by any further demonstration; or else, suddenly announce themselves by terrific concussions, and the full drama of a volcanic eruption. The blacker that cloud by day, the more may you look for light by night. Often whalemen have found themselves cruising nigh that burning mountain when all aglow with a ballroom blaze. Or, rather, glass-works, you may call this same vitreous isle of Narborough, with its tall chimney-stacks.

Where we still stand, here on Rodondo, we cannot see all the other isles, but it is a good place from which to point out where they lie. Yonder, though, to the E.N.E., I mark a distant dusky ridge. It is Abington Isle, one of the most northerly of the group; so solitary, remote, and blank, it looks like No-Man's Land seen off our northern shore. I doubt whether two human beings ever touched upon that spot. So far as yon Abington Isle is concerned, Adam and his billions of posterity remain uncreated.

Ranging south of Abington, and quite out of sight behind the long spine of Albemarle, lies James's Isle, so called by the early Buccaneers after the luckless Stuart, Duke of York. Observe here, by the way, that, excepting the isles particularized in comparatively recent times, and which mostly received the names of famous Admirals, the Encantadas were first christened by the Spaniards; but these Spanish names were generally effaced on English charts by the subsequent christenings of the Buccaneers, who, in the middle of the seventeenth century, called them after English noblemen and kings. Of these loyal freebooters and the things which associate their name with the Encantadas, we shall hear anon. Nay, for one little item, immediately; for between James's Isle and Albemarle, lies a fantastic islet, strangely known as "Cowley's Enchanted Isle." But, as all the group is deemed enchanted, the reason must be given for the spell within a spell involved by this particular designation. The name was bestowed by that excellent Buccaneer himself, on his first visit here. Speaking in his published voyages of this spot, he says—"My fancy led me to call it Cowley's Enchanted Isle, for, we having had a Sight of it upon several Points of the Compass, it appear'd always in as many different Forms; sometimes like a ruined Fortification, upon another Point, like a great City, &c." No wonder though, that among the Encantadas all sorts of ocular deceptions and mirages should be met.

That Cowley linked his name with this self-transforming and bemocking isle, suggests the possibility that it conveyed to him some meditative image of himself. At least, as is not impossible, if he were any relative of the mildly-thoughtful and self-upbraiding poet Cowley, who lived about his time, the conceit might seem not unwarranted; for that sort of thing evinced in the naming of this isle runs in the blood, and may be seen in pirates as in poets.

Still south of James's Isle lie Jervis Isle, Duncan Isle, Crossman's Isle, Brattle Isle, Wood's Isle, Chatham Isle, and various lesser isles, for the most part an archipelago of aridities, without inhabitant, history, or hope of either in all time to come. But not far from these are rather notable isles—Barrington, Charles's, Norfolk, and Hood's. Succeeding chapters will reveal some ground for their notability.

SKETCH FIFTH

The Frigate, and Ship Flyaway

Looking far foorth into the ocean wide,
A goodly ship with banners bravely dight,
And flag in her top-gallant I espide
Through the maine sea making her merry flight.

Ere quitting Rodondo, it must not be omitted that here, in 1813, the U.S. frigate *Essex*, Captain David Porter, came near leaving her bones. Lying becalmed one morning with a strong current setting her rapidly towards the rock, a strange sail was descried, which—not out of keeping with alleged enchantments of the neighborhood—seemed to be staggering under a violent wind, while the frigate lay lifeless as if spell-bound. But a light air springing up, all sail was made by the frigate in chase of the enemy, as supposed—he being deemed an English whale-ship—but the rapidity of the current was so great, that soon all sight was lost of him; and, at meridian, the *Essex,* spite of her drags, was driven so close under the foam-lashed cliffs of Rodondo that, for a time, all hands gave her up. A smart breeze, however, at last helped her off, though the escape was so critical as to seem almost miraculous.

Thus saved from destruction herself, she now made use of that salvation to destroy the other vessel, if possible. Renewing the chase in the direction in which the stranger had disappeared, sight was caught of him the following morning. Upon being descried he hoisted American colors and stood away from the *Essex.* A calm ensued; when, still confident that the stranger was an Englishman, Porter dispatched a cutter, not to board the enemy, but drive back his boats engaged in towing him. The cutter succeeded. Cutters were subsequently sent to capture him; the stranger now showing English colors in place of American. But, when the frigate's boats were within a short distance of their hoped-for prize, another sudden breeze sprang up; the stranger, under all sail, bore off to the westward, and, ere night, was hull down ahead of the *Essex,* which, all this time, lay perfectly becalmed.

This enigmatic craft—American in the morning, and English in the evening— her sails full of wind in a calm—was never again beheld. An enchanted ship no doubt. So, at least, the sailors swore.

The cruise of the *Essex* in the Pacific during the war of 1812, is, perhaps, the strangest and most stirring to be found in the history of the American navy. She captured the furthest wandering vessels; visited the remotest seas and isles; long hovered in the charmed vicinity of the enchanted group; and, finally, valiantly gave up the ghost fighting two English frigates in the harbor of Valparaiso. Mention is made of her here for the same reason that the Buccaneers will like-wise receive record; because, like them, by long cruising among the isles, tortoise-hunting upon their shores, and generally exploring them; for these and other reasons, the *Essex* is peculiarly associated with the Encantadas.

Here be it said that you have but three eye-witness authorities worth men-tioning touching the Enchanted Isles:—Cowley, the Buccaneer (1684); Colnett, the whaling-ground explorer (1793); Porter, the post captain (1813). Other than these you have but barren, bootless allusions from some few passing voyagers or compilers.

SKETCH SIXTH

Barrington Isle and the Buccaneers

Let us all servile base subjection scorne;
And, as we bee sonnes of the earth so wide,
Let us our fathers heritage divide,
And chalenge to our selves our portions dew
Of all the patrimonie, which a few
Now hold in hugger-mugger in their hand . . .
Lords of the world, and so will wander free,
Where so us listeth, uncontrol'd of anie.

How bravely now we live, how jocund, how
near the first inheritance, without fear, how
free from little troubles!

Near two centuries ago Barrington Isle was the resort of that famous wing of the West Indian Buccaneers, which, upon their repulse from the Cuban waters, crossing the Isthmus of Darien, ravaged the Pacific side of the Spanish colonies, and, with the regularity and timing of a modern mail, waylaid the royal treasure-ships plying between Manila and Acapulco. After the toils of piratic war, here they came to say their prayers, enjoy their free-and-easies, count their crackers from the cask, their doubloons from the keg, and measure their silks of Asia with long Toledos for their yard-sticks.

As a secure retreat, and undiscoverable hiding-place, no spot in those days could have been better fitted. In the centre of a vast and silent sea, but very little traversed—surrounded by islands, whose inhospitable aspect might well drive away the chance navigator—and yet within a few days' sail of the opulent countries which they made their prey—the unmolested Buccaneers found here that tranquillity which they fiercely denied to every civilized harbor in that part of the world. Here, after stress of weather, or a temporary drubbing at the hands of their vindictive foes, or in swift flight with golden booty, those old marauders came, and lay snugly out of all harm's reach. But not only was the place a harbor of safety, and a bower of ease, but for utility in other things it was most admirable.

Barrington Isle is, in many respects, singularly adapted to careening, refitting, refreshing, and other seamen's purposes. Not only has it good water, and good anchorage, well sheltered from all winds by the high land of Albemarle, but it is the least unproductive isle of the group. Tortoises good for food, trees good for fuel, and long grass good for bedding, abound here, and there are pretty natural walks, and several landscapes to be seen. Indeed, though in its locality belonging to the Enchanted group, Barrington Isle is so unlike most of its neighbors, that it would hardly seem of kin to them.

"I once landed on its western side," says a sentimental voyager long ago, "where it faces the black buttress of Albemarle. I walked beneath groves of trees—not very lofty, and not palm trees, or orange trees, or peach trees, to be sure—but, for all that, after a long sea-faring, very beautiful to walk under, even though they supplied no fruit. And here, in calm spaces at the heads of glades, and on the shaded tops of slopes commanding the most quiet scenery— what do you think I saw? Seats which might have served Brahmins and presidents of peace societies. Fine old ruins of what had once been symmetric lounges of stone and turf, they bore every mark both of artificialness and age, and were, undoubtedly, made by the Buccaneers. One had been a long sofa, with back and arms, just such a sofa as the poet Gray might have loved to throw himself upon, his Crébillon in hand.

"Though they sometimes tarried here for months at a time, and used the spot for a storing-place for spare spars, sails, and casks; yet it is highly improbable that the Buccaneers ever erected dwelling-houses upon the isle. They never were here except their ships remained, and they would most likely have slept on board. I mention this, because I cannot avoid the thought, that it is hard to impute the construction of these romantic seats to any other motive than one of pure peacefulness and kindly fellowship with nature. That the Buccaneers perpetrated the greatest outrages is very true—that some of them were mere cut-throats is not to be denied; but we know that here and there among their host was a Dampier, a Wafer, and a Cowley, and likewise other men, whose worst reproach was their desperate fortunes—whom persecution, or adversity, or secret and unavengeable wrongs, had driven from Christian society to seek the melancholy solitude or the guilty adventures of the sea. At any rate, long as those ruins of seats on Barrington remain, the most singular monuments are furnished to the fact, that all of the Buccaneers were not unmitigated monsters.

"But during my ramble on the isle I was not long in discovering other tokens, of things quite in accordance with those wild traits, popularly, and no doubt truly enough, imputed to the freebooters at large. Had I picked up old sails and rusty hoops I would only have thought of the ship's carpenter and cooper. But I found old cutlasses and daggers reduced to mere threads of rust, which, doubtless, had stuck between Spanish ribs ere now. These were signs of the murderer and robber; the reveler likewise had left his trace. Mixed with shells, fragments of broken jars were lying here and there, high up upon the beach. They were precisely like the jars now used upon the Spanish coast for the wine and Pisco spirits of that country.

"With a rusty dagger-fragment in one hand, and a bit of a wine-jar in another, I sat me down on the ruinous green sofa I have spoken of, and bethought me long and deeply of these same Buccaneers. Could it be possible, that they robbed and murdered one day, reveled the next, and rested themselves by turning meditative philosophers, rural poets, and seat-builders on the third? Not very improbable, after all. For consider the vacillations of a man. Still, strange as it may seem, I must also abide by the more charitable thought; namely, that among these adventurers were some gentlemanly, companionable souls, capable of genuine tranquillity and virtue."

SKETCH SEVENTH

Charles's Isle and the Dog-King

Loe with outragious cry
A thousand villeins round about him swarmd
Out of the rockes and caves adjoyning nye;
Vile caitive wretches, ragged, rude, deformd,
All threatning death, all in straunge manner armd;
Some with unweldy clubs, some with long speares,
Some rusty knives, some staves in fier warmd.

We will not be of anie occupation,
Let such vile vassalls borne to base vocation
Drudge in the world, and for their living droyle,
Which have no wit to live withouten toyle.

Southwest of Barrington lies Charles's Isle. And hereby hangs a history which I gathered long ago from a shipmate learned in all the lore of outlandish life.

During the successful revolt of the Spanish provinces from Old Spain, there fought on behalf of Peru a certain Creole adventurer from Cuba, who, by his bravery and good fortune, at length advanced himself to high rank in the patriot army. The war being ended, Peru found itself like many valorous gentlemen, free and independent enough, but with few shot in the locker. In other words, Peru had not wherewithal to pay off its troops. But the Creole—I forget his name—volunteered to take his pay in lands. So they told him he might have his pick of the Enchanted Isles, which were then, as they still remain, the nominal appanage of Peru. The soldier straightway embarks thither, explores the group, returns to Callao, and says he will take a deed of Charles's Isle. Moreover, this deed must stipulate that thenceforth Charles's Isle is not only the sole property of the Creole, but is forever free of Peru, even as Peru of Spain. To be short, this adventurer procures himself to be made in effect Supreme Lord of the Island, one of the princes of the powers of the earth.*

He now sends forth a proclamation inviting subjects to his as yet unpopulated kingdom. Some eighty souls, men and women, respond; and being provided by their leader with necessaries, and tools of various sorts, together with a few cattle and goats, take ship for the promised land; the last arrival on board, prior to sailing, being the Creole himself, accompanied, strange to say, by a disciplined cavalry company of large grim dogs. These, it was observed on the passage, refusing to consort with the emigrants, remained aristocratically grouped around their master on the elevated quarter-deck, casting disdainful glances forward upon the inferior rabble there; much as, from the ramparts, the soldiers of a garrison, thrown into a conquered town, eye the inglorious citizen-mob over which they are set to watch.

Now Charles's Isle not only resembles Barrington Isle in being much more inhabitable than other parts of the group, but it is double the size of Barrington, say forty or fifty miles in circuit.

Safely debarked at last, the company, under direction of their lord and patron, forthwith proceeded to build their capital city. They make considerable advance in the way of walls of clinkers, and lava floors, nicely sanded with cinders. On the least barren hills they pasture their cattle, while the goats, adventurers by nature, explore the far inland solitudes for a scanty livelihood of lofty herbage. Meantime, abundance of fish and tortoises supply their other wants.

The disorders incident to settling all primitive regions, in the present case were heightened by the peculiarly untoward character of many of the pilgrims. His Majesty was forced at last to proclaim martial law, and actually hunted and shot with his own hand several of his rebellious subjects, who, with most questionable intentions, had clandestinely encamped in the interior, whence they stole by night, to prowl barefooted on tiptoe round the precincts of the lava-palace. It is to be remarked, however, that prior to such stern proceedings, the more reliable men had been judiciously picked out for an infantry body-guard, subordinate to the cavalry body-guard of dogs. But the state of politics in this unhappy nation may be somewhat imagined, from the circumstance that all who were not of the body-guard were downright plotters and malignant traitors. At length the death penalty was tacitly abolished, owing to the timely thought, that were strict sportsman's justice to be dispensed among such subjects, ere

* The American Spaniards have long been in the habit of making presents of islands to deserving individuals. The pilot Juan Fernandez procured a deed of the isle named after him, and for some years resided there before Selkirk came. It is supposed, however, that he eventually contracted the blues upon his princely property, for after a time he returned to the main, and as report goes, became a very garrulous barber in the city of Lima.

long the Nimrod King would have little or no remaining game to shoot. The human part of the life-guard was now disbanded, and set to work cultivating the soil, and raising potatoes; the regular army now solely consisting of the dog-regiment. These, as I have heard, were of a singularly ferocious character, though by severe training rendered docile to their master. Armed to the teeth, the Creole now goes in state, surrounded by his canine janizaries, whose terrific bayings prove quite as serviceable as bayonets in keeping down the surgings of revolt.

But the census of the isle, sadly lessened by the dispensation of justice, and not materially recruited by matrimony, began to fill his mind with sad mistrust. Some way the population must be increased. Now, from its possessing a little water, and its comparative pleasantness of aspect, Charles's Isle at this period was occasionally visited by foreign whalers. These His Majesty had always levied upon for port charges, thereby contributing to his revenue. But now he had additional designs. By insidious arts he, from time to time, cajoles certain sailors to desert their ships, and enlist beneath his banner. Soon as missed, their captains crave permission to go and hunt them up. Whereupon His Majesty first hides them very carefully away, and then freely permits the search. In consequence, the delinquents are never found, and the ships retire without them.

Thus, by a two-edged policy of this crafty monarch, foreign nations were crippled in the number of their subjects, and his own were greatly multiplied. He particularly petted these renegado strangers. But alas for the deep-laid schemes of ambitious princes, and alas for the vanity of glory. As the foreign-born Praetorians, unwisely introduced into the Roman state, and still more unwisely made favorites of the Emperors, at last insulted and overturned the throne, even so these lawless mariners, with all the rest of the body-guard and all the populace, broke out into a terrible mutiny, and defied their master. He marched against them with all his dogs. A deadly battle ensued upon the beach. It raged for three hours, the dogs fighting with determined valor, and the sailors reckless of everything but victory. Three men and thirteen dogs were left dead upon the field, many on both sides were wounded, and the king was forced to fly with the remainder of his canine regiment. The enemy pursued, stoning the dogs with their master into the wilderness of the interior. Discontinuing the pursuit, the victors returned to the village on the shore, stove the spirit casks, and proclaimed a Republic. The dead men were interred with the honors of war, and the dead dogs ignominiously thrown into the sea. At last, forced by stress of suffering, the fugitive Creole came down from the hills and offered to treat for peace. But the rebels refused it on any other terms than his unconditional banishment. Accordingly, the next ship that arrived carried away the ex-king to Peru.

The history of the king of Charles's Island furnishes another illustration of the difficulty of colonizing barren islands with unprincipled pilgrims.

Doubtless for a long time the exiled monarch, pensively ruralizing in Peru, which afforded him a safe asylum in his calamity, watched every arrival from the Encantadas, to hear news of the failure of the Republic, the consequent penitence of the rebels, and his own recall to royalty. Doubtless he deemed the Republic but a miserable experiment which would soon explode. But no, the insurgents had confederated themselves into a democracy neither Grecian, Roman, nor American. Nay, it was no democracy at all, but a permanent *Riotocracy,* which gloried in having no law but lawlessness. Great inducements being offered to deserters, their ranks were swelled by accessions of scamps from every ship which touched their shores. Charles's Island was proclaimed the asylum of the oppressed of all navies. Each runaway tar was hailed as a martyr in the cause of freedom, and became immediately installed a ragged citizen of this universal nation. In vain the captains of absconding seamen strove to regain them. Their new compatriots were ready to give any number of ornamental eyes in their behalf. They had few cannon, but their fists were not to be trifled with. So at last it came to pass that no vessels acquainted with the character of that country durst touch there, however solely in want of refreshment. It became Anathema— a sea Alsatia—the unassailed lurking-place of all sorts of desperadoes, who in the name of liberty did just what they pleased. They continually fluctuated in their numbers. Sailors, deserting ships at other islands, or in boats at sea any- where in that vicinity, steered for Charles's Isle, as to their sure home of refuge; while, sated with the life of the isle, numbers from time to time crossed the water to the neighboring ones, and there presenting themselves to strange cap- tains as shipwrecked seamen, often succeeded in getting on board vessels bound to the Spanish coast, and having a compassionate purse made up for them on landing there.

One warm night during my first visit to the group, our ship was floating along in languid stillness, when some one on the forecastle shouted "Light ho!" We looked and saw a beacon burning on some obscure land off the beam. Our third mate was not intimate with this part of the world. Going to the captain he said, "Sir, shall I put off in a boat? These must be shipwrecked men."

The captain laughed rather grimly, as, shaking his fist towards the beacon, he rapped out an oath, and said—"No, no, you precious rascals, you don't juggle one of my boats ashore this blessed night. You do well, you thieves—you do benevolently to hoist a light yonder as on a dangerous shoal. It tempts no wise man to pull off and see what's the matter, but bids him steer small and keep off shore—that is Charles's Island; brace up, Mr. Mate, and keep the light astern."

SKETCH EIGHTH

Norfolk Isle and the Chola Widow

At last they in an Island did espy
A seemely woman, sitting by the shore,
That with great sorrow and sad agony
Seemed some great misfortune to deplore,
And lowd to them for succour called evermore.

Blacke hys eye as the midnyghte sky,
Whyte hys neck as the driven snowe,
Redde hys cheek as the mornynge lyghte,
Cold he lys ynne the ground belowe;
  Mie love ys dedde,
  Gon to hys deathe-bedde,
  All under the cactus tree.

Each lonely scene shall thee restore,
  For thee the tear be duly shed;
Belov'd till life can charm no more,
  And mourn'd till Pity's self be dead.

Far to the northeast of Charles's Isle, sequestered from the rest, lies Norfolk Isle; and, however insignificant to most voyagers, to me, through sympathy, that lone island has become a spot made sacred by the strangest trials of humanity.

It was my first visit to the Encantadas. Two days had been spent ashore in hunting tortoises. There was not time to capture many; so on the third afternoon we loosed our sails. We were just in the act of getting under way, the uprooted anchor yet suspended and invisibly swaying beneath the wave, as the good ship gradually turned her heel to leave the isle behind, when the seaman who heaved with me at the windlass paused suddenly, and directed my attention to something moving on the land, not along the beach, but somewhat back, fluttering from a height.

In view of the sequel of this little story, be it here narrated how it came to pass, that an object which partly from its being so small was quite lost to every other man on board, still caught the eye of my handspike companion. The rest of the crew, myself included, merely stood up to our spikes in heaving, whereas, unwontedly exhilarated, at every turn of the ponderous windlass, my belted comrade leaped atop of it, with might and main giving a downward, thewy, perpendicular heave, his raised eye bent in cheery animation upon the slowly receding shore. Being high lifted above all others was the reason he perceived the object, otherwise unperceivable; and this elevation of his eye was owing to the elevation of his spirits; and this again—for truth must out—to a dram of Peruvian pisco, in guerdon for some kindness done, secretly administered to him that morning by our mulatto steward. Now, certainly, pisco does a deal of mischief in the world; yet seeing that, in the present case, it was the means, though indirect, of rescuing a human being from the most dreadful fate, must we not also needs admit that sometimes pisco does a deal of good?

Glancing across the water in the direction pointed out, I saw some white thing hanging from an inland rock, perhaps half a mile from the sea.

"It is a bird; a white-winged bird; perhaps a——no; it is——it is a handkerchief!"

"Aye, a handkerchief!" echoed my comrade, and with a louder shout apprised the captain.

Quickly now—like the running out and training of a great gun—the long cabin spy-glass was thrust through the mizzen-rigging from the high platform of the poop; whereupon a human figure was plainly seen upon the inland rock, eagerly waving towards us what seemed to be the handkerchief.

Our captain was a prompt, good fellow. Dropping the glass, he lustily ran forward, ordering the anchor to be dropped again; hands to stand by a boat, and lower away.

In a half-hour's time the swift boat returned. It went with six and came with seven; and the seventh was a woman.

It is not artistic heartlessness, but I wish I could but draw in crayons; for this woman was a most touching sight; and crayons, tracing softly melancholy lines, would best depict the mournful image of the dark-damasked Chola widow.

Her story was soon told, and though given in her own strange language was as quickly understood; for our captain, from long trading on the Chilean coast, was well versed in the Spanish. A Chola, or half-breed Indian woman of Payta in Peru, three years gone by, with her young new-wedded husband Felipe, of pure Castilian blood, and her one only Indian brother, Truxill, Hunilla had taken passage on the main in a French whaler, commanded by a joyous man; which vessel, bound to the cruising grounds beyond the Enchanted Isles, proposed passing close by their vicinity. The object of the little party was to procure tortoise oil, a fluid which for its great purity and delicacy is held in high estimation wherever known; and it is well known all along this part of the Pacific coast. With a chest of clothes, tools, cooking utensils, a rude apparatus for trying out the oil, some casks of biscuit, and other things, not omitting two favorite dogs, of which faithful animal all the Cholos are very fond, Hunilla and her companions were safely landed at their chosen place; the Frenchman, according to the contract made ere sailing, engaged to take them off upon returning from a four months' cruise in the westward seas; which interval the three adventurers deemed quite sufficient for their purposes.

On the isle's lone beach they paid him in silver for their passage out, the stranger having declined to carry them at all except upon that condition; though willing to take every means to insure the due fulfillment of his promise. Felipe had striven hard to have this payment put off to the period of the ship's return. But in vain. Still they thought they had, in another way, ample pledge of the good faith of the Frenchman. It was arranged that the expenses of the passage home should not be payable in silver, but in tortoises; one hundred tortoises ready captured to the returning captain's hand. These the Cholos meant to secure after their own work was done, against the probable time of the French-man's coming back; and no doubt in prospect already felt, that in those hundred tortoises—now somewhere ranging the isle's interior—they possessed one hundred hostages. Enough: the vessel sailed; the gazing three on shore answered the loud glee of the singing crew; and ere evening, the French craft was hull down in the distant sea, its masts three faintest lines which quickly faded from Hunilla's eye.

The stranger had given a blithesome promise, and anchored it with oaths; but oaths and anchors equally will drag; naught else abides on fickle earth but unkept promises of joy. Contrary winds from out unstable skies, or contrary moods of his more varying mind, or shipwreck and sudden death in solitary waves; whatever was the cause, the blithe stranger never was seen again.

Yet, however dire a calamity was here in store, misgivings of it ere due time never disturbed the Cholos' busy minds, now all intent upon the toilsome matter which had brought them hither. Nay, by swift doom coming like the thief at night, ere seven weeks went by, two of the little party were removed from all anxieties of land or sea. No more they sought to gaze with feverish fear, or still more feverish hope, beyond the present's horizon line; but into the furthest future their own silent spirits sailed. By persevering labor beneath that burning sun, Felipe and Truxill had brought down to their hut many scores of tortoises, and tried out the oil, when, elated with their good success, and to reward themselves for such hard work, they, too hastily, made a catamaran, or Indian raft, much used on the Spanish main, and merrily started on a fishing trip, just without a long reef with many jagged gaps, running parallel with the shore, about half a mile from it. By some bad tide or hap, or natural negligence of joyfulness (for though they could not be heard, yet by their gestures they seemed singing at the time), forced in deep water against that iron bar, the ill-made catamaran was overset, and came all to pieces; when dashed by broad-chested swells between their broken logs and the sharp teeth of the reef, both adventurers perished before Hunilla's eyes.

Before Hunilla's eyes they sank. The real woe of this event passed before her sight as some sham tragedy on the stage. She was seated in a rude bower among the withered thickets, crowning a lofty cliff, a little back from the beach. The thickets were so disposed, that in looking upon the sea at large she peered out from among the branches as from the lattice of a high balcony. But upon the day we speak of here, the better to watch the adventure of those two hearts she loved, Hunilla had withdrawn the branches to one side, and held them so. They formed an oval frame, through which the bluely boundless sea rolled like a painted one. And there, the invisible painter painted to her view the wave-tossed and disjointed raft, its once level logs slantingly upheaved, as raking masts, and the four struggling arms undistinguishable among them; and then all subsided into smooth-flowing creamy waters, slowly drifting the splintered wreck; while first and last, no sound of any sort was heard. Death in a silent picture; a dream of the eye; such vanishing shapes as the mirage shows.

So instant was the scene, so trance-like its mild pictorial effect, so distant from her blasted bower and her common sense of things, that Hunilla gazed and gazed, nor raised a finger or a wail. But as good to sit thus dumb, in stupor staring on that dumb show, for all that otherwise might be done. With half a mile of sea between, how could her two enchanted arms aid those four fated ones? The distance long, the time one sand. After the lightning is beheld, what fool shall stay the thunder-bolt? Felipe's body was washed ashore, but Truxill's never came; only his gay, braided hat of golden straw—that same sunflower thing he waved to her, pushing from the strand—and now, to the last gallant, it still saluted her. But Felipe's body floated to the marge, with one arm encirclingly outstretched. Lock-jawed in grim death, the lover-husband softly clasped his bride, true to her even in death's dream. Ah, Heaven, when man thus keeps his faith, wilt Thou be faithless who created the faithful one? But they cannot break faith who never plighted it.

It needs not to be said what nameless misery now wrapped the lonely widow. In telling her own story she passed this almost entirely over, simply recounting the event. Construe the comment of her features as you might, from her mere words little would you have weened that Hunilla was herself the heroine of her tale. But not thus did she defraud us of our tears. All hearts bled that grief could be so brave.

She but showed us her soul's lid, and the strange ciphers thereon engraved; all within, with pride's timidity, was withheld. Yet was there one exception. Holding out her small olive hand before her captain, she said in mild and slowest Spanish, "Señor, I buried him," then paused, struggled as against the writhed coilings of a snake, and cringing suddenly, leaped up, repeating in im-passioned pain, "I buried him, my life, my soul!"

Doubtless, it was by half-unconscious, automatic motions of her hands, that this heavy-hearted one performed the final office for Felipe, and planted a rude cross of withered sticks—no green ones might be had—at the head of that lonely grave, where rested now in lasting uncomplaint and quiet haven he whom untranquil seas had overthrown.

But some dull sense of another body that should be interred, of another cross that should hallow another grave—unmade as yet—some dull anxiety and pain touching her undiscovered brother, now haunted the oppressed Hunilla. Her hands fresh from the burial earth, she slowly went back to the beach, with unshaped purposes wandering there, her spell-bound eye bent upon the incessant waves. But they bore nothing to her but a dirge, which maddened her to think that murderers should mourn. As time went by, and these things came less dreamingly to her mind, the strong persuasions of her Romish faith, which sets peculiar store by consecrated urns, prompted her to resume in waking earnest that pious search which had but been begun as in somnambulism. Day after day, week after week, she trod the cindery beach, till at length a double motive edged every eager glance. With equal longing she now looked for the living and the dead; the brother and the captain; alike vanished, never to return. Little accurate note of time had Hunilla taken under such emotions as were hers, and little, outside herself, served for calendar or dial. As to poor Crusoe in the self-same sea, no saint's bell pealed forth the lapse of week or month; each day went by unchallenged; no chanticleer announced those sultry dawns, no lowing herds those poisonous nights. All wonted and steadily recurring sounds, human, or humanized by sweet fellowship with man, but one stirred that torrid trance—the cry of dogs; save which naught but the rolling sea invaded it, an all-pervad-ing monotone; and to the widow that was the least loved voice she could have heard.

No wonder, that as her thoughts now wandered to the unreturning ship, and were beaten back again, the hope against hope so struggled in her soul, that at length she desperately said, "Not yet, not yet; my foolish heart runs on too fast." So she forced patience for some further weeks. But to those whom earth's sure indraft draws, patience or impatience is still the same.

Hunilla now sought to settle precisely in her mind, to an hour, how long it was since the ship had sailed; and then, with the same precision, how long a space remained to pass. But this proved impossible. What present day or month it was she could not say. Time was her labyrinth, in which Hunilla was entirely lost.

And now follows——

Against my own purposes a pause descends upon me here. One knows not whether nature doth not impose some secrecy upon him who has been privy to certain things. At least, it is to be doubted whether it be good to blazon such. If some books are deemed most baneful and their sale forbid, how, then, with deadlier facts, not dreams of doting men? Those whom books will hurt will not be proof against events. Events, not books, should be forbid. But in all things man sows upon the wind, which bloweth just there whither it listeth; for ill or good, man cannot know. Often ill comes from the good, as good from ill.

When Hunilla——

Dire sight it is to see some silken beast long dally with a golden lizard ere she devour. More terrible, to see how feline Fate will sometimes dally with a human soul, and by a nameless magic make it repulse a sane despair with a hope which is but mad. Unwittingly I imp this cat-like thing, sporting with the heart of him who reads; for if he feel not he reads in vain.

—"The ship sails this day, to-day," at last said Hunilla to herself; "this gives me certain time to stand on; without certainty I go mad. In loose ignorance I have hoped and hoped; now in firm knowledge I will but wait. Now I live and no longer perish in bewilderings. Holy Virgin, aid me! Thou wilt waft back the ship. Oh, past length of weary weeks—all to be dragged over—to buy the certainty of to-day, I freely give ye, though I tear ye from me!"

As mariners, tost in tempest on some desolate ledge, patch them a boat out of the remnants of their vessel's wreck, and launch it in the self-same waves, see here Hunilla, this lone shipwrecked soul, out of treachery invoking trust. Humanity, thou strong thing, I worship thee, not in the laureled victor, but in this vanquished one.

Truly Hunilla leaned upon a reed, a real one; no metaphor: a real Eastern reed. A piece of hollow cane, drifted from unknown isles, and found upon the beach, its once jagged ends rubbed smoothly even as by sand-paper; its golden glazing gone. Long ground between the sea and land, upper and nether stone, the unvarnished substance was filed bare, and wore another polish now, one with itself, the polish of its agony. Circular lines at intervals cut all round this surface, divided it into six panels of unequal length. In the first were scored the days, each tenth one marked by a longer and deeper notch; the second was scored for the number of sea-fowl eggs for sustenance, picked out from the rocky nests; the third, how many fish had been caught from the shore; the fourth, how many small tortoises found inland; the fifth, how many days of sun; the sixth, of clouds; which last, of the two, was the greater one. Long night of busy numbering, misery's mathematics, to weary her too-wakeful soul to sleep; yet sleep for that was none.

The panel of the days was deeply worn—the long tenth notches half effaced, as alphabets of the blind. Ten thousand times the longing widow had traced her finger over the bamboo—dull flute, which played on, gave no sound—as if counting birds flown by in air would hasten tortoises creeping through the woods.

After the one hundred and eightieth day no further mark was seen; that last one was the faintest, as the first the deepest.

"There were more days," said our Captain; "many, many more; why did you not go on and notch them, too, Hunilla?"

"Señor, ask me not."

"And meantime, did no other vessel pass the isle?"

"Nay, Señor;—but——"

"You do not speak; but *what,* Hunilla?"

"Ask me not, Señor."

"You saw ships pass, far away; you waved to them; they passed on;—was that it, Hunilla?"

"Señor, be it as you say."

Braced against her woe, Hunilla would not, durst not trust the weakness of her tongue. Then when our Captain asked whether any whale-boats had——

But no, I will not file this thing complete for scoffing souls to quote, and call it firm proof upon their side. The half shall here remain untold. Those two un-named events which befell Hunilla on this isle, let them abide between her and her God. In nature, as in law, it may be libelous to speak some truths.

Still, how it was that, although our vessel had lain three days anchored nigh the isle, its one human tenant should not have discovered us till just upon the point of sailing, never to revisit so lone and far a spot, this needs explaining ere the sequel come.

The place where the French captain had landed the little party was on the further and opposite end of the isle. There, too, it was that they had afterwards built their hut. Nor did the widow in her solitude desert the spot where her loved ones had dwelt with her, and where the dearest of the twain now slept his last long sleep, and all her plaints awaked him not, and he of husbands the most faithful during life.

Now, high broken land rises between the opposite extremities of the isle. A ship anchored at one side is invisible from the other. Neither is the isle so small, but a considerable company might wander for days through the wilderness of one side, and never be seen, or their halloos heard, by any stranger holding aloof on the other. Hence Hunilla, who naturally associated the possible coming of ships with her own part of the isle, might to the end have remained quite ignorant of the presence of our vessel, were it not for a mysterious presentiment, borne to her, so our mariners averred, by this isle's enchanted air. Nor did the widow's answer undo the thought.

"How did you come to cross the isle this morning, then, Hunilla?" said our Captain.

"Señor, something came flitting by me. It touched my cheek, my heart, Señor."

"What do you say, Hunilla?"

"I have said, Señor, something came through the air."

It was a narrow chance. For when in crossing the isle Hunilla gained the high land in the centre, she must then for the first have perceived our masts, and also marked that their sails were being loosed, perhaps even heard the echoing chorus of the windlass song. The strange ship was about to sail, and she behind. With all haste she now descends the height on the hither side, but soon loses sight of the ship among the sunken jungles at the mountain's base. She struggles on through the withered branches, which seek at every step to bar her path, till she comes to the isolated rock, still some way from the water. This she climbs, to reassure herself. The ship is still in plainest sight. But now, worn out with over-tension, Hunilla all but faints; she fears to step down from her giddy perch; she is fain to pause, there where she is, and as a last resort catches the turban from her head, unfurls and waves it over the jungles towards us.

During the telling of her story the mariners formed a voiceless circle round Hunilla and the Captain; and when at length the word was given to man the fastest boat, and pull round to the isle's thither side, to bring away Hunilla's chest and the tortoise oil, such alacrity of both cheery and sad obedience seldom before was seen. Little ado was made. Already the anchor had been recommitted to the bottom, and the ship swung calmly to it.

But Hunilla insisted upon accompanying the boat as indispensable pilot to her hidden hut. So being refreshed with the best the steward could supply, she started with us. Nor did ever any wife of the most famous admiral, in her husband's barge, receive more silent reverence of respect than poor Hunilla from this boat's crew.

Rounding many a vitreous cape and bluff, in two hours' time we shot inside the fatal reef; wound into a secret cove, looked up along a green many-gabled lava wall, and saw the island's solitary dwelling.

It hung upon an impending cliff, sheltered on two sides by tangled thickets, and half-screened from view in front by juttings of the rude stairway, which climbed the precipice from the sea. Built of canes, it was thatched with long, mildewed grass. It seemed an abandoned hay-rick, whose haymakers were now no more. The roof inclined but one way; the eaves coming to within two feet of the ground. And here was a simple apparatus to collect the dews, or rather doubly-distilled and finest winnowed rains, which, in mercy or in mockery, the night-skies sometimes drop upon these blighted Encantadas. All along beneath the eaves, a spotted sheet, quite weather-stained, was spread, pinned to short, upright stakes, set in the shallow sand. A small clinker, thrown into the cloth, weighed its middle down, thereby straining all moisture into a calabash placed below. This vessel supplied each drop of water ever drunk upon the isle by the

Cholos. Hunilla told us the calabash would sometimes, but not often, be half filled overnight. It held six quarts, perhaps. "But," said she, "we were used to thirst. At sandy Payta, where I live, no shower from heaven ever fell; all the water there is brought on mules from the inland vales."

Tied among the thickets were some twenty moaning tortoises, supplying Hunilla's lonely larder; while hundreds of vast tableted black bucklers, like displaced, shattered tomb-stones of dark slate, were also scattered round. These were the skeleton backs of those great tortoises from which Felipe and Truxill had made their precious oil. Several large calabashes and two goodly kegs were filled with it. In a pot near by were the caked crusts of a quantity which had been permitted to evaporate. "They meant to have strained it off next day," said Hunilla, as she turned aside.

I forgot to mention the most singular sight of all, though the first that greeted us after landing.

Some ten small, soft-haired, ringleted dogs, of a beautiful breed, peculiar to Peru, set up a concert of glad welcomings when we gained the beach, which was responded to by Hunilla. Some of these dogs had, since her widowhood, been born upon the isle, the progeny of the two brought from Payta. Owing to the jagged steeps and pitfalls, tortuous thickets, sunken clefts and perilous intricacies of all sorts in the interior, Hunilla, admonished by the loss of one favorite among them, never allowed these delicate creatures to follow her in her occasional birds'-nests climbs and other wanderings; so that, through long habituation, they offered not to follow, when that morning she crossed the land, and her own soul was then too full of other things to heed their lingering behind. Yet, all along she had so clung to them, that, besides what moisture they lapped up at early daybreak from the small scoop-holes among the adjacent rocks, she had shared the dew of her calabash among them; never laying by any considerable store against the prolonged and utter droughts which, in some disastrous seasons, warp these isles.

Having pointed out, at our desire, what few things she would like transported to the ship—her chest, the oil, not omitting the live tortoises which she intended for a grateful present to our Captain—we immediately set to work, carrying them to the boat down the long, sloping stair of deeply-shadowed rock. While my comrades were thus employed, I looked and Hunilla had disappeared.

It was not curiosity alone, but, it seems to me, something different mingled with it, which prompted me to drop my tortoise, and once more gaze slowly around. I remembered the husband buried by Hunilla's hands. A narrow pathway led into a dense part of the thickets. Following it through many mazes, I came out upon a small, round, open space, deeply chambered there.

The mound rose in the middle; a bare heap of finest sand, like that unverdured heap found at the bottom of an hour-glass run out. At its head stood the cross of withered sticks; the dry, peeled bark still fraying from it; its transverse limb tied up with rope, and forlornly adroop in the silent air.

Hunilla was partly prostrate upon the grave; her dark head bowed, and lost in her long, loosened Indian hair; her hands extended to the cross-foot, with a little brass crucifix clasped between; a crucifix worn featureless, like an ancient graven knocker long plied in vain. She did not see me, and I made no noise, but slid aside, and left the spot.

A few moments ere all was ready for our going, she reappeared among us. I looked into her eyes, but saw no tear. There was something which seemed strangely haughty in her air, and yet it was the air of woe. A Spanish and an Indian grief, which would not visibly lament. Pride's height in vain abased to proneness on the rack; nature's pride subduing nature's torture.

Like pages the small and silken dogs surrounded her, as she slowly descended towards the beach. She caught the two most eager creatures in her arms—"*Tita mia! Tomotita mia!*"—and fondling them, inquired how many could we take on board.

The mate commanded the boat's crew; not a hard-hearted man, but his way of life had been such that in most things, even in the smallest, simple utility was his leading motive.

"We cannot take them all, Hunilla; our supplies are short; the winds are unreliable; we may be a good many days going to Tumbez. So take those you have, Hunilla; but no more."

She was in the boat; the oarsmen, too, were seated, all save one, who stood ready to push off and then spring himself. With the sagacity of their race, the dogs now seemed aware that they were in the very instant of being deserted upon a barren strand. The gunwales of the boat were high; its prow—presented inland—was lifted; so owing to the water, which they seemed instinctively to shun, the dogs could not well leap into the little craft. But their busy paws hard scraped the prow, as it had been some farmer's door shutting them out from shelter in a winter storm. A clamorous agony of alarm. They did not howl, or whine; they all but spoke.

"Push off! Give way!" cried the mate. The boat gave one heavy drag and lurch, and next moment shot swiftly from the beach, turned on her heel, and sped. The dogs ran howling along the water's marge; now pausing to gaze at the flying boat, then motioning as if to leap in chase, but mysteriously withheld themselves; and again ran howling along the beach. Had they been human beings, hardly would they have more vividly inspired the sense of desolation. The oars were plied as confederate feathers of two wings. No one spoke. I looked back upon the beach, and then upon Hunilla, but her face was set in a stern dusky calm. The dogs crouching in her lap vainly licked her rigid hands. She never looked behind her, but sat motionless, till we turned a promontory of the coast and lost all sights and sounds astern. She seemed as one who, having experienced the sharpest of mortal pangs, was henceforth content to have all lesser heart-strings riven, one by one. To Hunilla, pain seemed so necessary, that pain in other beings, though by love and sympathy made her own, was unrepiningly to be borne. A heart of yearning in a frame of steel. A heart of earthly yearning, frozen by the frost which falleth from the sky.

The sequel is soon told. After a long passage, vexed by calms and baffling winds, we made the little port of Tumbez in Peru, there to recruit the ship. Payta was not very distant. Our captain sold the tortoise oil to a Tumbez merchant; and adding to the silver a contribution from all hands, gave it to our silent passenger, who knew not what the mariners had done.

The last seen of lone Hunilla she was passing into Payta town, riding upon a small gray ass; and before her on the ass's shoulders, she eyed the jointed workings of the beast's armorial cross.

SKETCH NINTH

Hood's Isle and the Hermit Oberlus

That darkesome glen they enter, where they find
That cursed man, low sitting on the ground,
Musing full sadly in his sullein mind;
His griesie lockes, long growen and unbound,
Disordred hong about his shoulders round,
And hid his face; through which his hollow eyne
Lookt deadly dull, and stared as astound;
His raw-bone cheekes, through penurie and pine,
Were shronke into his jawes, as he did never dine.
His garment nought but many ragged clouts,
With thornes together pind and patched was,
The which his naked sides he wrapt abouts.

Southeast of Crossman's Isle lies Hood's Isle, or McCain's Beclouded Isle; and upon its south side is a vitreous cove with a wide strand of dark pounded black lava, called Black Beach, or Oberlus's Landing. It might fitly have been styled Charon's.

It received its name from a wild white creature who spent many years here; in the person of a European bringing into this savage region qualities more diabolical than are to be found among any of the surrounding cannibals.

About half a century ago, Oberlus deserted at the above-named island, then, as now, a solitude. He built himself a den of lava and clinkers, about a mile from the Landing, subsequently called after him, in a vale, or expanded gulch, containing here and there among the rocks about two acres of soil capable of rude cultivation; the only place on the isle not too blasted for that purpose. Here he succeeded in raising a sort of degenerate potatoes and pumpkins, which from time to time he exchanged with needy whalemen passing, for spirits or dollars.

His appearance, from all accounts, was that of the victim of some malignant sorceress; he seemed to have drunk of Circe's cup; beast-like; rags insufficient to hide his nakedness; his befreckled skin blistered by continual exposure to the sun; nose flat; countenance contorted, heavy, earthy; hair and beard unshorn, profuse, and of fiery red. He struck strangers much as if he were a volcanic creature thrown up by the same convulsion which exploded into sight the isle. All bepatched and coiled asleep in his lonely lava den among the mountains, he looked, they say, as a heaped drift of withered leaves, torn from autumn trees, and so left in some hidden nook by the whirling halt for an instant of a fierce night-wind, which then ruthlessly sweeps on, somewhere else to repeat the capricious act. It is also reported to have been the strangest sight, this same Oberlus, of a sultry, cloudy morning, hidden under his shocking old black tarpaulin hat, hoeing potatoes among the lava. So warped and crooked was his strange nature, that the very handle of his hoe seemed gradually to have shrunk and twisted in his grasp, being a wretched bent stick, elbowed more like a savage's war-sickle than a civilized hoe-handle. It was his mysterious custom upon a first encounter with a stranger ever to present his back; possibly, because that was his better side, since it revealed the least. If the encounter chanced in his garden, as it sometimes did—the new-landed strangers going from the sea-side straight through the gorge, to hunt up the queer green-grocer reported doing business here—Oberlus for a time hoed on, unmindful of all greeting, jovial or bland; as the curious stranger would turn to face him, the recluse, hoe in hand, as diligently would avert himself; bowed over, and sullenly revolving round his murphy hill. Thus far for hoeing. When planting, his whole aspect and all his gestures were so malevolently and uselessly sinister and secret, that he seemed rather in act of dropping poison into wells than potatoes into soil. But among his lesser and more harmless marvels was an idea he ever had, that his visitors came equally as well led by longings to behold the mighty hermit Oberlus in his royal state of solitude, as simply to obtain potatoes, or find whatever company might be upon a barren isle. It seems incredible that such a being should possess such vanity; a misanthrope be conceited; but he really had his notion; and upon the strength of it, often gave himself amusing airs to captains. But after all, this is somewhat of a piece with the well-known eccentricity of some convicts, proud of that very hatefulness which makes them notorious. At other times, another unaccountable whim would seize him, and he would long dodge advancing strangers round the clinkered corners of his hut; sometimes like a stealthy bear, he would slink through the withered thickets up the mountains, and refuse to see the human face.

Except his occasional visitors from the sea, for a long period, the only companions of Oberlus were the crawling tortoises; and he seemed more than degraded to their level, having no desires for a time beyond theirs, unless it were for the stupor brought on by drunkenness. But sufficiently debased as he appeared, there yet lurked in him, only awaiting occasion for discovery, a still further proneness. Indeed, the sole superiority of Oberlus over the tortoises was his possession of a larger capacity of degradation; and along with that, something like an intelligent will to it. Moreover, what is about to be revealed, perhaps will show, that selfish ambition, or the love of rule for its own sake, far from being the peculiar infirmity of noble minds, is shared by beings which have no mind at all. No creatures are so selfishly tyrannical as some brutes; as any one who has observed the tenants of the pasture must occasionally have observed.

"This island's mine by Sycorax my mother," said Oberlus to himself, glaring round upon his haggard solitude. By some means, barter or theft—for in those days ships at intervals still kept touching at his Landing—he obtained an old musket, with a few charges of powder and ball. Possessed of arms, he was stimulated to enterprise, as a tiger that first feels the coming of its claws. The long habit of sole dominion over every object round him, his almost unbroken solitude, his never encountering humanity except on terms of misanthropic independence, or mercantile craftiness, and even such encounters being comparatively but rare; all this must have gradually nourished in him a vast idea of his own importance, together with a pure animal sort of scorn for all the rest of the universe.

The unfortunate Creole, who enjoyed his brief term of royalty at Charles's Isle was perhaps in some degree influenced by not unworthy motives; such as prompt other adventurous spirits to lead colonists into distant regions and assume political pre-eminence over them. His summary execution of many of his Peruvians is quite pardonable, considering the desperate characters he had to deal with; while his offering canine battle to the banded rebels seems under the circumstances altogether just. But for this King Oberlus and what shortly follows, no shade of palliation can be given. He acted out of mere delight in tyranny and cruelty, by virtue of a quality in him inherited from Sycorax his mother. Armed now with that shocking blunderbuss, strong in the thought of being master of that horrid isle, he panted for a chance to prove his potency upon the first specimen of humanity which should fall unbefriended into his hands.

Nor was he long without it. One day he spied a boat upon the beach, with one man, a negro, standing by it. Some distance off was a ship, and Oberlus immediately knew how matters stood. The vessel had put in for wood, and the boat's crew had gone into the thickets for it. From a convenient spot he kept watch of the boat, till presently a straggling company appeared loaded with billets. Throwing these on the beach, they again went into the thickets, while the negro proceeded to load the boat.

Oberlus now makes all haste and accosts the negro, who, aghast at seeing any living being inhabiting such a solitude, and especially so horrific a one, immediately falls into a panic, not at all lessened by the ursine suavity of Oberlus, who begs the favor of assisting him in his labors. The negro stands with several billets on his shoulder, in act of shouldering others; and Oberlus, with a short cord concealed in his bosom, kindly proceeds to lift those other billets to their place. In so doing, he persists in keeping behind the negro, who, rightly suspicious of this, in vain dodges about to gain the front of Oberlus; but Oberlus dodges also; till at last, weary of this bootless attempt at treachery, or fearful of being surprised by the remainder of the party, Oberlus runs off a little space to a bush, and fetching his blunderbuss, savagely commands the negro to desist work and follow him. He refuses. Whereupon, presenting his piece, Oberlus snaps at him. Luckily the blunderbuss misses fire; but by this time, frightened out of his wits, the negro, upon a second intrepid summons, drops his billets, surrenders at discretion, and follows on. By a narrow defile familiar to him, Oberlus speedily removes out of sight of the water.

On their way up the mountains, he exultingly informs the negro that henceforth he is to work for him, and be his slave, and that his treatment would entirely depend on his future conduct. But Oberlus, deceived by the first impulsive cowardice of the black, in an evil moment slackens his vigilance. Passing through a narrow way, and perceiving his leader quite off his guard, the negro, a powerful fellow, suddenly grasps him in his arms, throws him down, wrests his musketoon from him, ties his hands with the monster's own cord, shoulders him, and returns with him down to the boat. When the rest of the party arrive, Oberlus is carried on board the ship. This proved an Englishman, and a smuggler; a sort of craft not apt to be over-charitable. Oberlus is severely whipped, then handcuffed, taken ashore, and compelled to make known his habitation and produce his property. His potatoes, pumpkins, and tortoises, with a pile of dollars he had hoarded from his mercantile operations were secured on the spot. But while the too vindictive smugglers were busy destroying his hut and garden, Oberlus makes his escape into the mountains, and conceals himself there in impenetrable recesses, only known to himself, till the ship sails, when he ventures back, and by means of an old file which he sticks into a tree, contrives to free himself from his handcuffs.

Brooding among the ruins of his hut, and the desolate clinkers and extinct volcanoes of this outcast isle, the insulted misanthrope now meditates a signal revenge upon humanity, but conceals his purposes. Vessels still touch the Landing at times; and by and by Oberlus is enabled to supply them with some vegetables.

Warned by his former failure in kidnapping strangers, he now pursues a quite different plan. When seamen come ashore, he makes up to them like a free-and-easy comrade, invites them to his hut, and with whatever affability his red-haired grimness may assume, entreats them to drink his liquor and be merry. But his guests need little pressing; and so, soon as rendered insensible, are tied hand and foot, and pitched among the clinkers, are there concealed till the ship departs, when, finding themselves entirely dependent upon Oberlus, alarmed at his changed demeanor, his savage threats, and above all, that shocking blunderbuss, they willingly enlist under him, becoming his humble slaves, and Oberlus the most incredible of tyrants. So much so, that two or three perish beneath his initiating process. He sets the remainder—four of them—to breaking the caked soil; transporting upon their backs loads of loamy earth, scooped up in moist clefts among the mountains; keeps them on the roughest fare; presents his piece at the slightest hint of insurrection; and in all respects converts them into reptiles at his feet—plebeian garter-snakes to this Lord Anaconda.

At last, Oberlus contrives to stock his arsenal with four rusty cutlasses, and an added supply of powder and ball intended for his blunderbuss. Remitting in good part the labor of his slaves, he now approves himself a man, or rather devil, of great abilities in the way of cajoling or coercing others into acquiescence with his own ulterior designs, however at first abhorrent to them. But indeed, prepared for almost any eventual evil by their previous lawless life, as a sort of ranging Cow-Boys of the sea, which had dissolved within them the whole moral man, so that they were ready to concrete in the first offered mold of baseness now; rotted down from manhood by their hopeless misery on the isle; wonted to cringe in all things to their lord, himself the worst of slaves; these wretches were now become wholly corrupted to his hands. He used them as creatures of an inferior race; in short, he gaffles his four animals, and makes murderers of them; out of cowards fitly manufacturing bravoes.

Now, sword or dagger, human arms are but artificial claws and fangs, tied on like false spurs to the fighting cock. So, we repeat, Oberlus, czar of the isle, gaffles his four subjects; that is, with intent of glory, puts four rusty cutlasses into their hands. Like any other autocrat, he had a noble army now.

It might be thought a servile war would hereupon ensue. Arms in the hands of trodden slaves? how indiscreet of Emperor Oberlus! Nay, they had but cutlasses—sad old scythes enough—he a blunderbuss, which by its blind scatterings of all sorts of boulders, clinkers, and other scoria would annihilate all four mutineers, like four pigeons at one shot. Besides, at first he did not sleep in his accustomed hut; every lurid sunset, for a time, he might have been seen wending his way among the riven mountains, there to secrete himself till dawn in some sulphurous pitfall, undiscoverable to his gang; but finding this at last too troublesome, he now each evening tied his slaves hand and foot, hid the cutlasses, and thrusting them into his barracks, shut to the door, and lying down before it, beneath a rude shed lately added, slept out the night, blunderbuss in hand.

It is supposed that not content with daily parading over a cindery solitude at the head of his fine army, Oberlus now meditated the most active mischief; his probable object being to surprise some passing ship touching at his dominions, massacre the crew, and run away with her to parts unknown. While these plans were simmering in his head, two ships touch in company at the isle, on the opposite side to his; when his designs undergo a sudden change.

The ships are in want of vegetables, which Oberlus promises in great abundance, provided they send their boats round to his Landing, so that the crews may bring the vegetables from his garden; informing the two captains, at the same time, that his rascals—slaves and soldiers—had become so abominably lazy and good-for-nothing of late, that he could not make them work by ordinary inducements, and did not have the heart to be severe with them.

The arrangement was agreed to, and the boats were sent and hauled upon the beach. The crews went to the lava hut; but to their surprise nobody was there. After waiting till their patience was exhausted, they returned to the shore, when lo, some stranger—not the Good Samaritan either—seems to have very recently passed that way. Three of the boats were broken in a thousand pieces, and the fourth was missing. By hard toil over the mountains and through the clinkers, some of the strangers succeeded in returning to that side of the isle where the ships lay, when fresh boats are sent to the relief of the rest of the hapless party.

However amazed at the treachery of Oberlus, the two captains, afraid of new and still more mysterious atrocities—and indeed, half imputing such strange events to the enchantments associated with these isles—perceive no security but in instant flight; leaving Oberlus and his army in quiet possession of the stolen boat.

On the eve of sailing they put a letter in a keg, giving the Pacific Ocean intelligence of the affair, and moored the keg in the bay. Some time subsequent, the keg was opened by another captain chancing to anchor there, but not until after he had dispatched a boat round to Oberlus's Landing. As may be readily surmised, he felt no little inquietude till the boat's return; when another letter was handed him, giving Oberlus's version of the affair. This precious document had been found pinned half-mildewed to the clinker wall of the sulphurous and deserted hut. It ran as follows: showing that Oberlus was at least an accomplished writer, and no mere boor; and what is more, was capable of the most tristful eloquence.

"Sir: I am the most unfortunate ill-treated gentleman that lives. I am a patriot, exiled from my country by the cruel hand of tyranny.

"Banished to these Enchanted Isles, I have again and again besought captains of ships to sell me a boat, but always have been refused, though I offered the handsomest prices in Mexican dollars. At length an opportunity presented of possessing myself of one, and I did not let it slip.

"I have been long endeavoring, by hard labor and much solitary suffering, to accumulate something to make myself comfortable in a virtuous though unhappy old age; but at various times have been robbed and beaten by men professing to be Christians.

"To-day I sail from the Enchanted group in the good boat Charity bound to the Feejee Isles.

FATHERLESS OBERLUS

"P.S.—Behind the clinkers, nigh the oven, you will find the old fowl. Do not kill it; be patient; I leave it setting; if it shall have any chicks, I hereby bequeath them to you, whoever you may be. But don't count your chicks before they are hatched."

The fowl proved a starveling rooster, reduced to a sitting posture by sheer debility.

Oberlus declares that he was bound to the Feejee Isles; but this was only to throw pursuers on a false scent. For, after a long time, he arrived, alone in his open boat, at Guayaquil. As his miscreants were never again beheld on Hood's Isle, it is supposed, either that they perished for want of water on the passage to Guayaquil, or, what is quite as probable, were thrown overboard by Oberlus, when he found the water growing scarce.

From Guayaquil Oberlus proceeded to Payta; and there, with that nameless witchery peculiar to some of the ugliest animals, wound himself into the affections of a tawny damsel; prevailing upon her to accompany him back to his Enchanted Isle; which doubtless he painted as a Paradise of flowers, not a Tartarus of clinkers.

But unfortunately for the colonization of Hood's Isle with a choice variety of animated nature, the extraordinary and devilish aspect of Oberlus made him to be regarded in Payta as a highly suspicious character. So that being found concealed one night, with matches in his pocket, under the hull of a small vessel just ready to be launched, he was seized and thrown into jail.

The jails in most South American towns are generally of the least wholesome sort. Built of huge cakes of sunburnt brick, and containing but one room, without windows or yard, and but one door heavily grated with wooden bars, they present both within and without the grimmest aspect. As public edifices they conspicuously stand upon the hot and dusty Plaza, offering to view, through the gratings, their villainous and hopeless inmates, burrowing in all sorts of tragic squalor. And here, for a long time, Oberlus was seen; the central figure of a mongrel and assassin band; a creature whom it is religion to detest, since it is philanthropy to hate a misanthrope.

Note.—They who may be disposed to question the possibility of the character above depicted, are referred to the 2d vol. of Porter's *Voyage into the Pacific,* where they will recognize many sentences, for expedition's sake derived verbatim from thence, and incorporated here; the main difference—save a few passing reflections—between the two accounts being, that the present writer has added to Porter's facts accessory ones picked up in the Pacific from reliable sources; and where facts conflict, has naturally preferred his own authorities to Porter's. As, for instance, *his* authorities place Oberlus on Hood's Isle: Porter's, on Charles's Isle. The letter found in the hut is also somewhat different; for while at the Encantadas he was informed that, not only did it evince a certain clerkiness, but was full of the strangest satiric effrontery which does not adequately appear in Porter's version. I accordingly altered it to suit the general character of its author.

SKETCH TENTH

Runaways, Castaways, Solitaries, Grave-Stones, Etc.

And all about old stockes and stubs of trees,
Whereon nor fruit nor leafe was ever seen,
Did hang upon the ragged rocky knees;
On which had many wretches hanged beene.

Some relics of the hut of Oberlus partially remain to this day at the head of the clinkered valley. Nor does the stranger, wandering among other of the Enchanted Isles, fail to stumble upon still other solitary abodes, long abandoned to the tortoise and the lizard. Probably few parts of earth have, in modern times, sheltered so many solitaries. The reason is, that these isles are situated in a distant sea, and the vessels which occasionally visit them are mostly all whalers, or ships bound on dreary and protracted voyages, exempting them in a good degree from both the oversight and the memory of human law. Such is the character of some commanders and some seamen, that under these untoward circumstances, it is quite impossible but that scenes of unpleasantness and discord should occur between them. A sullen hatred of the tyrannic ship will seize the sailor, and he gladly exchanges it for isles, which, though blighted as by a continual sirocco and burning breeze, still offer him, in their labyrinthine interior, a retreat beyond the possibility of capture. To flee the ship in any Peruvian or Chilean port, even the smallest and most rustical, is not unattended with great risk of apprehension, not to speak of jaguars. A reward of five pesos sends fifty dastardly Spaniards into the wood, who, with long knives, scour them day and night in eager hopes of securing their prey. Neither is it, in general, much easier to escape pursuit at the isles of Polynesia. Those of them which have felt a civilizing influence present the same difficulty to the runaway with the Peruvian ports, the advanced natives being quite as mercenary and keen of knife and scent as the retrograde Spaniards; while, owing to the bad odor in which all Europeans lie, in the minds of aboriginal savages who have chanced to hear aught of them, to desert the ship among primitive Polynesians, is, in most cases, a hope not unforlorn. Hence the Enchanted Isles become the voluntary tarrying places of all sorts of refugees; some of whom too sadly experience the fact, that flight from tyranny does not of itself insure a safe asylum, far less a happy home.

Moreover, it has not seldom happened that hermits have been made upon the isles by the accidents incident to tortoise-hunting. The interior of most of them is tangled and difficult of passage beyond description; the air is sultry and stifling; an intolerable thirst is provoked, for which no running stream offers its kind relief. In a few hours, under an equatorial sun, reduced by these causes to entire exhaustion, woe betide the straggler at the Enchanted Isles! Their extent is such as to forbid an adequate search, unless weeks are devoted to it. The impatient ship waits a day or two; when, the missing man remaining undiscovered, up goes a stake on the beach, with a letter of regret, and a keg of crackers and another of water tied to it, and away sails the craft.

Nor have there been wanting instances where the inhumanity of some captains has led them to wreak a secure revenge upon seamen who have given their caprice or pride some singular offense. Thrust ashore upon the scorching marl, such mariners are abandoned to perish outright, unless by solitary labors they succeed in discovering some precious driblets of moisture oozing from a rock or stagnant in a mountain pool.

I was well acquainted with a man, who, lost upon the Isle of Narborough, was brought to such extremes by thirst, that at last he only saved his life by taking that of another being. A large hair-seal came upon the beach. He rushed upon it, stabbed it in the neck, and then throwing himself upon the panting body quaffed at the living wound; the palpitations of the creature's dying heart injected life into the drinker.

Another seaman, thrust ashore in a boat upon an isle at which no ship ever touched, owing to its peculiar sterility and the shoals about it, and from which all other parts of the group were hidden—this man, feeling that it was sure death to remain there, and that nothing worse than death menaced him in quitting it, killed two seals, and inflating their skins, made a float, upon which he transported himself to Charles's Island, and joined the republic there.

But men, not endowed with courage equal to such desperate attempts, find their only resource in forthwith seeking some watering-place, however precarious or scanty; building a hut; catching tortoises and birds; and in all respects preparing for a hermit life, till tide of time, or a passing ship arrives to float them off.

At the foot of precipices on many of the isles, small rude basins in the rocks are found, partly filled with rotted rubbish or vegetable decay, or overgrown with thickets, and sometimes a little moist; which, upon examination, reveal plain tokens of artificial instruments employed in hollowing them out, by some poor castaway or still more miserable runaway. These basins are made in places where it was supposed some scanty drops of dew might exude into them from the upper crevices.

The relics of hermitages and stone basins are not the only signs of vanishing humanity to be found upon the isles. And, curious to say, that spot which of all others in settled communities is most animated, at the Enchanted Isles presents the most dreary of aspects. And though it may seem very strange to talk of post-offices in this barren region, yet post-offices are occasionally to be found there. They consist of a stake and a bottle. The letters being not only sealed, but corked. They are generally deposited by captains of Nantucketers for the benefit of passing fishermen, and contain statements as to what luck they had in whaling or tortoise-hunting. Frequently, however, long months and months, whole years glide by and no applicant appears. The stake rots and falls, presenting no very exhilarating object.

If now it be added that grave-stones, or rather grave-boards, are also discovered upon some of the isles, the picture will be complete.

Upon the beach of James's Isle, for many years, was to be seen a rude finger-post, pointing inland. And, perhaps, taking it for some signal of possible hospitality in this otherwise desolate spot—some good hermit living there with his maple dish—the stranger would follow on in the path thus indicated, till at last he would come out in a noiseless nook, and find his only welcome, a dead man—his sole greeting the inscription over a grave. Here, in 1813, fell, in a daybreak duel, a lieutenant of the U.S. frigate *Essex,* aged twenty-one: attaining his majority in death.

It is but fit that, like those old monastic institutions of Europe, whose inmates go not out of their own walls to be inurned, but are entombed there where they die, the Encantadas, too, should bury their own dead, even as the great general monastery of earth does hers.

It is known that burial in the ocean is a pure necessity of sea-faring life, and that it is only done when land is far astern, and not clearly visible from the bow.

Hence, to vessels cruising in the vicinity of the Enchanted Isles, they afford a convenient Potter's Field. The interment over, some good-natured forecastle poet and artist seizes his paint-brush, and inscribes a doggerel epitaph. When, after a long lapse of time, other good-natured seamen chance to come upon the spot, they usually make a table of the mound, and quaff a friendly can to the poor soul's repose.

As a specimen of these epitaphs, take the following, found in a bleak gorge of Chatham Isle:

> *Oh, Brother Jack, as you pass by,*
> *As you are now, so once was I.*
> *Just so game, and just so gay,*
> *But now, alack, they've stopped my pay.*
> *No more I peep out of my blinkers,*
> *Here I be—tucked in with clinkers!*

PART VIII

A LECTURE ON
THE SOUTH SEAS
(1859)

❀ ❀ ❀

INTRODUCTION

To eke out the family income, Melville turned to the career of lecturer, a common resort of authors of that day.[1] As one might expect, reticent Herman was not a highly appealing figure on the platform, but he supplemented his earnings by lecturing for several years.

At his first appearance, at a charity affair at Lawrence, Massachusetts, on November 23, 1857, he talked about Roman statuary—a topic soon changed for one closer to his heart. His essay on "The South Seas" was tried out at Auburn, New York, on January 5, 1858, and became his mainstay. No full text has been found, but a "phonographist" was present from the Baltimore *American* on February 8, 1859, and the following newspaper account reflects Melville's recollections of youthful adventure. The title was preferred to that of "The Pacific" because "The South Seas" evoked a more romantic picture and because that ocean is not always as peaceful as its name might suggest.[2] One part of his address that is topical today concerns his prediction, exactly a century before the event, that the Hawaiian or Sandwich Islands would eventually be annexed to the American Union.

❀   ❀   ❀

Mr. M. began by saying:

The subject of our lecture this evening, "the South Seas" may be thought perhaps a theme if not ambitious, at least somewhat expansive, covering, according to the authorities, I am afraid to say how much of the earth's surface—in short more than one-half. We have, therefore, a rather spacious field before us, and I hardly think we shall be able, in a thorough way, to go over the whole of it to-night.

And here (to do away with any erroneous anticipations as to our topic) I hope you do not expect me to repeat what has long been in print touching my own casual adventures in Polynesia. I propose to treat of matters of more general interest, and, in a random way, discuss the South Seas at large and under various aspects, introducing, as occasion may serve, any little incident, personal or other, fitted to illustrate the point in hand.

South Seas is simply an equivalent term for Pacific Ocean. Then why not say Pacific Ocean at once?—Because one may have a lingering regard for certain old associations, linking the South Seas as a name with many pleasant and venerable books of voyages, full of well-remembered engravings.

To be sure those time-worn tomes are pretty nearly obsolete but none the less are they, with the old name they enshrine, dear to the memory of their reader; in much the same way too that the old South Sea House in London was dear to the heart of Charles Lamb.—Who that has read it can forget that quaint sketch, the introductory essay of Elia, where he speaks of the Balclutha-like desolation of those haunted old offices of the once famous South Sea Company—the old oaken wainscots hung with the dusty maps of Mexico and soundings of the Bay of Panama—the vast cellarages under the whole pile where Mexican dollars and doubloons once lay heaped in huge bins for Mammon to solace his solitary heart withal?

But besides summoning up the memory of brave old books, Elia's fine sketch, and the great South Sea Bubble, originating in the institution there celebrated—the words South Seas are otherwise suggestive, yielding to the fancy an indefinable odor of sandalwood and cinnamon. In the adventures of Captain Dampier (that eminent and excellent buccaneer) you read only of South Seas. In Harris'

274

old voyages, and many others, the title is the same, and even as late as 1803 we find that Admiral Burney prefers the old title to the new, Pacific, which appellation has in the present century only become the popular one—notwithstanding which we occasionally find the good old name first bestowed still employed by writers of repute.

But since these famous waters lie on both sides of the Equator and wash the far northern shores of Kamchatka as well as the far southern ones of Tierra del Fuego, how did they ever come to be christened with such a misnomer as *South* Seas? The way it happened was this: The Isthmus of Darien runs not very far from east and west; if you stand upon its further shore the ocean will appear to the *south* of you, and were you ignorant of the general direction of the coastline you would infer that it rolled away wholly toward that quarter. Now Balboa, the first white man who laid eyes upon these waters, stood in just this position; drew just this inference and bestowed its name accordingly.

The circumstances of Balboa's discovery are not uninteresting. In the earliest days of the Spanish dominion on this continent, he commanded a petty post on the northern shore of the Isthmus, and hearing it rumored that there was a vast sea on the other side of the land—its beach not distant, but of difficult approach, owing to a range of steep mountain wall and other obstruction, he resolved to explore in that direction. His hardships may be imagined by recalling the narrative a few years since of the adventures of Lieut. Strain and party who in like manner with the Spaniard, undertook [in 1854] to cross from sea to sea, through the primeval wilderness. A party of buccaneers also likewise crossed the Isthmus under suffering, the utmost that nature is capable of sustaining. Balboa and the buccaneers, though not more courageous, were certainly more hardy or more fortunate than the American officer, since, after all they underwent, their efforts were at last successful.

The thronging Indians opposed Balboa's passage, demanding who he was, what he wanted, and whither he was going. The reply is a model of Spartan directness. "I am a Christian, my errand is to spread true religion and to seek gold, and I am going in search of the sea."

Coming at last to the foot of a mountain, he was told that from its summit he could see the object of his search. He ordered a halt, and, like Moses, the devout Spaniard "went up into the mountain alone." When he beheld the sea he fell upon his knees and thanked God for the sight. The next day with sword and target, wading up to his waist in its waters, he called upon his troop and the assembled Indians to bear witness that he took possession of that whole ocean with all the lands and kingdoms pertaining to it for his soverign master the King of Castile and Leon. A large-minded gentleman, of great latitude of sentiment, was Vasco Nuñez de Balboa, commander of that petty post of Darien.

The tempests off Cape Horn were here described by the lecturer, with allu-

sion to the rapid run often made up the west coast of South America, sometimes leaving but a few days between the latitudes of icebergs and oranges.

The European who first sailed upon those waters had this experience intensified. True, Magellan passed not round the yet undiscovered Horn, but through the straits which bear his name. But this only made the matter worse. For, in these straits, narrow, tortuous, and rock-bound, dense fogs prevail and antarctic squalls, and the navigation is peculiarly dangerous. Magellan worked through, however, and when he beheld ahead a fine open ocean, by good fortune smooth and serene, in his excess of emotion he burst into tears, stout sailor as he was, and this was the man who gave to this sea its second name—Pacific. The great sea then was in a happy humor, and hence received a name which will forever be called Pacific, even by the sailor destined to perish in one of its terrible typhoons.

Although the Pacific covers half the surface of the planet, yet with all its dotted isles and people it remained almost unknown to even a recent period. Captain Cook's account of his visit to Tahiti could produce, as late as 1780, upon the English people almost the full thrill of novelty. Indeed, but little was known of the whole region till Cook's time. It was California that first brought the Pacific home to the great body of Anglo-Saxons.

The world of water here is so broad and its living races so various, that one is puzzled where to choose his matter for a lecture.

We might tell of tribes of sharks that populate some parts of the Pacific as thickly as the celestials do the Chinese Empire, or we might introduce that gallant chevalier, the swordfish—the Hector of the seas—and tell of his martial exploits; the tilts he runs at the great ships; the duels he fights with them—sometimes leaving his weapon in their ribs, or by withdrawing it, leaving an open wound, to the great peril of the craft and crew, as in the case of the English ship *Foxhound*. We might tell of the devil-fish, which sailors say, dives to the profoundest abyss and comes up roaring with mouths as many and as wide open as the Mississippi.

The pelican, with his pouch stuffed with game like a sportsman's bag; the melancholy penguin standing on one spot all day with a fit of the blues; the man-of-war hawk, that fierce black bandit; and the storied albatross, with white and arching wing like an archangel's, his haughty beak curved like a scimetar. Yes, a whole hour might be spent in telling about either the fishes or the birds.

Furthermore, there are exceptional phenomena, such as the peculiar phosphoric aspect of the water sometimes. I have been in a whale-boat at midnight when, having lost the ship, we would keep steering through the lonely night for her, while the sea that weltered by us would present the pallid looks of the face of a corpse, and lit by its spectral gleam we men in the boat showed to each other like so many weather-beaten ghosts. Then to mark Leviathan come wallowing along, dashing the pale sea into sparkling cascades of fire, showering it all over him till the monster would look like Milton's Satan, riding the flame billows of the infernal world. We might fill night after night with that fertile theme, the whaling voyage. The adventurous sailors, either on the blank face of the waters, where often for months together their ship floats lonely as the ark of Noah, or in their intercourse with the natives of coasts reached by few or none but themselves. The islands, too, are an endless theme; thick as the stars in the milky way. The name bestowed upon their swarming clusters— Polynesia—not inaptly hints at their numberlessness.

The most noted of these are the Sandwich and Society groups; the Friendly, Navigator, and Feejee clusters; the Pelew, Ladrone, Mulgrave, Kingsmills, and Radack chains—but there are more than Briareus could number on all his finger ends.

The popular notion, from the early vague accounts, imagines them to hold enameled plains, with groves of shadowing palms, watered by purling brooks and the country but little elevated. The reverse of this is true: bold rock-bound coasts—a beating surf—lofty and craggy cliffs, split here and there into deep inlets opening to the view deeper valleys parted by masses of emerald mountains sweeping seaward from an interior of lofty peaks.

But, would you get the best water view of a Polynesian island, select one with a natural breakwater of surf-beaten coral all around it, leaving within a smooth, circular canal, broad and deep, entrance to which is had through natural sea-gates. Lounging in a canoe, there is nothing more pleasant than to float along—especially where Boraborra, and Otaha, the glorious twins of the Society group, rear their lofty masses to the ever vernal heights, belted about by the same zone of reef—the reef itself being dotted with small islets perpetually thick and green with grass.

The virgin freshness of these unviolated wastes, the exemption of those far-off archipelagoes from the heat and dust of civilization, acts sometimes as the last provocative to those jaded tourists to whom even Europe has become hackneyed, and who look upon the Parthenon and the Pyramids with a yawn.

Why don't the English yachters give up the prosy Mediterranean and sail out here? Any one who treats the natives fairly is just as safe as if he were on the Nile or Danube. But I am sorry to say we whites have a sad reputation among many of the Polynesians. They esteem us, with rare exceptions, such as *some* of the missionaries, the most barbarous, treacherous, irreligious, and devilish creatures on the earth. It may be a mere prejudice of these unlettered savages, for have not our traders always treated them with brotherly affection? Who has ever heard of a vessel sustaining the honor of a Christian flag and the spirit of the Christian Gospel by opening its batteries in indiscriminate massacre upon some poor little village on the seaside—splattering the torn bamboo huts with blood and brains of women and children, defenceless and innocent?

We have not space to follow the speaker fully in the remainder of his lecture, in which he graphically described the boundless expanse of the Pacific and its myriad islands as a hiding place as far removed from the life of the great world as though its people dwelt upon another planet. This mantle of mystery long hid the Buccaneers, who plundered the Spanish commerce; and covered for years Christian, the mutineer of the *Bounty,* who, after a life of exile and immunity from European law, was found, bent with age, amid a thriving colony of half-breed children and grand-children, whom his savage wives had reared for him amid ever-green woods, under ever-healthful skies, and through the plenty of perpetual harvests. *There is no such hiding place on earth, said the lecturer, except the solitude of London.*

The lecturer then spoke of the projects of some reformers who, despairing of civilized Europe or America according to their rule, projected establishments in the Pacific where they hoped to find a fitting place for the good time coming. The Polynesians themselves, he said, were not without their dream, their ideal, their Utopia. As Ponce de Leon hoped to find in Florida the fountain of perpetual youth, so the mystic Kamapuhai [Kamapiikai] left the western shore of the island where he suffered with his restless philosophy and, hoping to find the joy-giving fountain and the people like to the Gods, sailed after the sinking sun, and has not yet returned to cheer mankind with his discoveries.

Another strange quest was that of Alvaro, a bold Spanish captain, who stirred up such enthusiasm among the courtly Dons and Donnas of his time that many of them joined his expedition, in which he was sure he would find the Phœnician Ophir of King Hiram and bring from it more than the treasure stores with which Solomon had beautified his temple. After months and months of voyaging with hope deferred, the mines of Mammon were not found, and the poor Captain, dying, was buried in the solitude of an unfathomed sea.

Graphic descriptions were given of the graceful forms of the Polynesian women, and the splendid figures of the men, with their symmetrical and columnar legs.

The rapid advance, in the externals only, of civilized life was then spoken of, and the prospect of annexing the Sandwich Islands to the American Union commented on, with the remark that the whalemen of Nantucket and the Westward ho! of California were every day getting them more and more annexed.

The lecturer closed with an earnest wish that adventurers from our soil and from the lands of Europe would abstain from those brutal and cruel vices which disgust even savages with our manners, while they turn an earthly paradise into a pandemonium. And as for annexation he begged, as a general philanthropist, to offer up an earnest prayer, and he entreated all present to join him in it, that the banns of that union should be forbidden until we had found for ourselves a civilization moral, mental, and physical, higher than one which has culminated in almshouses, prisons, and hospitals.

PART IX

FOUR POEMS

❁ ❁ ❁

INTRODUCTION

Later in life, Melville took to writing verse. His lengthy narrative poem, *Clarel* (1876), represents a young seeker on a tour of the Holy Land. There he encounters other pilgrims, including a simple man of nature, an aged sailor named Agath. Asked if any place where this "timoneer" had traveled might compare with Judea, Agath replies with a description of another desert— a far island, clearly in the Galápagos group, where a sea hawk had snatched cooking meat from his campfire. Urged by the group, the pilot continues with lyric commentary on this island, where the giant tortoise, like a convict condemmed ("lagged") to a rocky prison, labors all its life.

Rolfe, the cynic in *Clarel,* is compared (III, xxix) with a bird in a cave at Cape Horn, and he himself is reminded by the landscape of a place

> *Where Eden, isled, impurpled, glows*
> *In old Mendanna's sea.*

"Mendanna" is, of course, Álvaro de Mendaña, discoverer of the Solomon and Marquesas Islands.

"A Sketch" in *Clarel* reports a colloquy on the road to the Dead Sea. It was inspired by Melville's years of pondering on the wreck in the equatorial Pacific of the *Essex,* sunk by two smashing blows from a whale in 1820, an attack that inspired the denouement of *Moby Dick.* The main character of this canto is modeled on Captain George Pollard, master at the time of the *Essex* disaster. Pollard decided, instead of risking cannibalism at the Marquesas group, that the boats should head for South America (the "Spanish Main"), some three thousand miles to the east. The horrible three-month voyage that followed led to cannibalism among the survivors themselves. "Being returned home," runs the account in Chapter 45 of *Moby Dick,* "Captain Pollard once more sailed for the Pacific in command of another ship, but the gods shipwrecked him again upon unknown rocks and breakers; for the second

283

time his ship was utterly lost, and forthwith forswearing the sea, he has never tempted it since." Melville not only read Owen Chase's account of the *Essex* tragedy while voyaging in the *Acushnet* but later owned a copy during the writing of *Moby Dick*. In it he inserted a memoir of the author and added an account of his meeting with George Pollard. "I—sometime about 1850–53 [July, 1852]—saw Capt. Pollard on the island of Nantucket, and exchanged some words with him. To the islanders he was a nobody—to me, the most impressive man, tho' wholly unassuming, even humble—that I ever encountered."[1] To add reader interest in the poem, Melville put Pollard's second command earlier and used the whale attack as a culmination. He changed the voyage from whaling to sealing; he also made Pollard the sole survivor of his first command. Pollard died in 1870, having served in lowly shore posts on Nantucket. Melville's interest in this man ties in closely with the author's lifelong concern with the conflict between Calvinistic predestination and the possibility of defying fate through exercise of the will.

"The Enviable Isles" was planned to appear in an uncompleted sketch, "Rammon," wherein a despondent prince, son of Solomon, addresses a Tyrian trader, Zardi:

> *Fable me, then, those Enviable Isles*
> *Whereof King Hiram's tars used to tell . . .*

The sonnet portrays more lovely isles than the Galápagos, and may fit the title of "The Tahiti Islands," found among Melville's manuscripts of "Rammon." "The Enviable Isles" was later included in *John Marr and Other Sailors* (1888). The lyric rpresents a refuge from storm in a lotos-eating paradise, a setting reflected in other Melville works. Tomo remarks, it will be remembered, at the end of Chapter 20 in *Typee* that sleep was among the Marquesans "the great business of life," and that to many of them life was little else than "an often interrupted and luxurious nap." And toward the conclusion of *Mardi*, safe from a great storm, the philosopher Babbalanja decides to remain on Serenia, a languorous paradise, even though his friend, the quester Taji, continues the voyage.

Included also in *John Marr* is "To Ned," wherein Melville's companion in the valley of Taipi, Toby Greene, is addressed under the name of "Ned Bunn," recalling:

> *Marquesas and glenned isles that be*
> *Authentic Edens in a pagan sea.*

Melville's rough meter keeps him from being a great poet, but he was serious in his attempt to achieve power in this kind of writing. Nor did he wish to have his poems trade upon any earlier success in prose. In the directions to his brother Allan in 1860 concerning the publication of a collection of verses he wrote: "For God's sake don't have *By the author of 'Typee' 'Piddledee' &c* on the title page."

THE ISLAND

           ... Vine's watchful eye,
While none perceived where bent his view,
Had fed on Agath sitting by;
He seemed to like him, one whose print
The impress bore of Nature's mint.
Authentic; man of nature true,
If simple; naught that slid between
Him and the elemental scene—
Unless it were that thing indeed
Uplooming from his ancient creed;
Yet that but deepen might the sense
Of awe, and serve dumb reverence
And resignation—"Anywhere,"
Asked Vine—here now to converse led—
"In those far regions, strange or rare,
Where thou hast been, may aught compare
With Judah here?"
           "Sooth, sir," he said,
"Some chance comparison I've made
In mind between this stricken land
And one far isle forever banned
I camped on in life's early days:
I view it now—but through a haze:
Our boats I view, reversed, turned down
For shelter by the midnight sea;
The very slag comes back to me.
I raked for shells, but found not one;
That harpy sea-hawk—him I view
Which, pouncing, from the red coal drew
Our hissing meat—we lounging nigh—

An instant's dash—and with it flew
To his sea-rock detached, his cry
Thence sent, to mock the marl we threw—
I hear, I see; return those days
Again—but 'tis through deepening haze:
How like a flash that life is gone—
So brief the youth by sailors known!"

      "But tell us, tell," now others cried,
And grouped them as by hearthstone wide.
The timoneer, at hazard thrown
With men of order not his own,
Evinced abashment, yes, proved shy.
They urged; and he could but comply.

    But, more of clearness to confer—
Less dimly to express the thing
Rude outlined by this mariner,
Licence is claimed in rendering;
And tones he felt but scarce might give,
The verse essays to interweave.
"In waters where no charts avail,
The lonely spout of hermit-whale,
God set that isle which haunteth me.
There clouds hang low, but yield no rain—
For ever hang, since wind is none
Or light; nor ship-boy's eye may gain
The smoke-wrapped peak, the inland one
Volcanic; this, within its shroud
Streaked black and red, burns unrevealed;
It burns by night—by day the cloud
Shows leaden all, and dull and sealed.
The beach is cinders.   With the tide
Salt creek and ashy inlet bring
More loneness from the outer ring
Of ocean."

      Pause he made, and sighed.—
"But take the way cross the marl,
A broken field of tumbled slabs
Like ice-cakes frozen in a snarl
After the break-up in a sound;
So win the thicket's upper ground
Where silence like a poniard stabs,

Since there the low throb of the sea
Not heard is, and the sea-fowl flee
Far off the shore, all the long day
Hunting the flying-fish their prey.
Haply in bush ye find a path:
Of man or beast it scarce may be;
And yet a wasted look it hath,
As it were travelled ceaselessly—
Century after century—
The rock in places much worn down
Like to some old, old kneeling-stone
Before a shrine.   But naught's to see,
At least naught there was seen by me,
Of any moving, creeping one.
No berry do those thickets bear,
Nor many leaves. Yet even there,
Some sailor from the steerage den
Put sick ashore—alas, by men
Who weary of him thus abjure—
The way may follow, in pursuit
Of apples red—the homestead-fruit
He dreams of in his calenture.
He drops, lost soul; but we go on—
Advance, until in end be won
The terraced orchard's mysteries,
Which well do that imp-isle beseem;
Paved with jet blocks those terraces,
The surface rubbed to unctuous gleam
By something which has life, you feel:
And yet, the shades but death reveal;
For under cobwebbed cactus trees,
White by their trunks—what hulks be these
Which, like old skulls of Anaks, are
Set round as in a Golgotha?
But, list—a sound!   Dull, dull it booms—
Dull as the jar in vaulted tombs
When urns are shifted. With amaze
Into the dim retreats ye gaze.
Lo, 'tis the monstrous tortoise drear!
Of huge humped arch, the ancient shell
Is trenched with seams where lichens dwell,

Or some adhesive growth and sere:
A lumpish languor marks the pace—
A hideous, harmless look, with trace
Of hopelessness; the eyes are dull
As in the bog the dead black pool:
Penal his aspect; all is dragged,
As he for more than years had lagged—
A convict doomed to bide the place;
A soul transformed—for earned disgrace
Degraded, and from higher race.
Ye watch him—him so woebegone:
Searching, he creeps with labouring neck,
Each crevice tries, and long may seek:
Water he craves, where rain is none—
Water within the parching zone,
Where only dews of midnight fall
And dribbling lodge in chinks of stone.
For meat the bitter tree is all—
The cactus, whose nipped fruit is shed
On those bleached skull-like hulks below,
Which, when by life inhabited,
Crept hither in last journey slow
After a hundred years of pain
And pilgrimage here to and fro,
For other hundred years to reign
In hollow of white armour so—
Then perish piecemeal.   You advance:
Instant, more rapid than a glance,
Long neck and four legs are drawn in,
Letting the shell down with report
Upon the stone; so falls in court
The clattering buckler with a din.
There leave him, since for hours he'll keep
That feint of death.—But for the isle—
Much seems it like this barren steep:
As here, few there would think to smile."
    So, paraphrased in lines sincere
Which still similitude would win,
The sketch ran of that timoneer.
He ended, and how passive sate:
Nature's own look, which might recall

Dumb patience of mere animal,
Which better may abide life's fate
Than comprehend. . . .

A SKETCH

For ease upon the ground they sit;
And Rolfe, with eye still following
Where Nehemiah slow footed it,
Asked Clarel: "Know you anything
Of this man's prior life at all?"
"Nothing," said Clarel.—"I recall,"
Said Rolfe, "a mariner like him."
"A mariner?"—"Yes; one whom grim
Disaster made as meek as he
There plodding." Vine here showed the zest
Of a deep human interest:
"We crave of you his history."
      And Rolfe began: "Scarce would I tell
Of what this mariner befell—
So much is it with cloud o'ercast—
Were he not now gone home at last
Into the green land of the dead,
Where he encamps and peace is shed.
Hardy he was, sanguine and bold,
The master of a ship. His mind
In night-watch frequent he unrolled—
As seamen sometimes are inclined—
On serious topics, to his mate
A man to creed austere resigned.
The master ever spurned at fate,
Calvin's or Zeno's. Always still
Man-like he stood by man's free will
And power to effect each thing he would,
Did reason but pronounce it good.
The subaltern held in humble way
That still heaven's over-rulings sway
Will and event.
                "On waters far,
Where map-man never made survey,

Gliding along in easy plight,
The strong one brake the lull of night
Emphatic in his willful war—
But staggered, for there came a jar
With fell arrest to keel and speech:
A hidden rock. The pound—the grind—
Collapsing sails o'er deck declined—
Sleek billows curling in the breach,
And nature with her neutral mind.
A wreck. 'Twas in the former days,
Those waters then obscure; a maze;
The isles were dreaded—every chain;
Better to brave the immense of sea,
And venture for the Spanish Main,
Beating and rowing against the trades,
Than float to valleys 'neath the lee,
Nor far removed, and palmy shades.
So deemed he, strongly erring there.
To boats they take; the weather fair—
Never the sky a cloudlet knew;
A temperate wind unvarying blew
Week after week; yet came despair;
The bread tho' doled, and water stored,
Ran low and lower—ceased. They burn—
They agonize till crime abhorred
Lawful might be. O trade-wind, turn!
    "We may some items sleep unrolled—
Never by the one survivor told.
Him they picked up, where, cuddled down,
They saw the jacketed skeleton,
Lone in the only boat that lived—
His signal frittered to a shred.
    " 'Strong need'st thou be,' the rescuers said,
'Who hast such trial sole survived.'
'I *willed* it,' gasped he. And the man,
Renewed ashore, pushed off again.
How bravely sailed the pennoned ship
Bound outward on her sealing trip
Antarctic. Yes; but who returns
Too soon, regaining port by land
Who left it by the bay? What spurns

Were his that so could countermand?
Nor mutineer, nor rock, nor gale
Nor leak had foiled him. No; a whale
Of purpose aiming, stove the bow:
They foundered. To the master now
Owners and neighbors all impute
An inauspiciousness. His wife—
Gentle, but unheroic—she,
Poor thing, at heart knew bitter strife
Between her love and her simplicity:
A Jonah is he?—And men bruit
The story. None will give him place
In a third venture. Came the day
Dire need constrained the man to pace
A night patrolman on the quay
Watching the bales till the morning hour
Through fair and foul. Never he smiled;
Call him, and he would come; not sour
In spirit, but meek and reconciled;
Patient he was, he none withstood;
Oft on some secret thing would brood.
He ate what came, though but a crust;
In Calvin's creed he put his trust;
Praised heaven, and said that God was good,
And his calamity but just.
So Silvio Pellico from cell-door
Forth tottering, after dungeoned years,
Crippled and bleached, and dead his peers:
'Grateful, I thank the Emperor.' "

THE ENVIABLE ISLES

Through storms you reach them and from storms are free.
  Afar descried, the foremost drear in hue,
But, nearer, green; and, on the marge, the sea
  Makes thunder low and mist of rainbowed dew.

But, inland, where the sleep that folds the hills
A dreamier sleep, the trance of God, instills—
  On uplands hazed, in wandering airs aswoon,

Slow-swaying palms salute love's cypress tree
  Adown in vale where pebbly runlets croon
A song to lull all sorrow and all glee.

Sweet-fern and moss in many a glade are here,
  Where, strown in flocks, what cheek-flushed myriads lie
Dimpling in dream—unconscious slumberers mere,
  While billows endless round the beaches die.

TO NED

  Where is the world we roved, Ned Bunn?
    Hollows thereof lay rich in shade
  By voyagers old inviolate thrown
    Ere Paul Pry cruised with Pelf and Trade.
  To us old lads some thoughts come home
  Who roamed a world young lads no more shall roam.

  Nor less the satiate year impends
    When, wearying of routine-resorts,
  The pleasure-hunter shall break loose,
    Ned, for our Pantheistic ports:—
  Marquesas and glenned isles that be
  Authentic Edens in a Pagan sea.

  The charm of scenes untried shall lure,
    And, Ned, a legend urge the flight—
  The Typee-truants under stars
    Unknown to Shakespere's *Midsummer-Night;*
  And man, if lost to Saturn's Age,
  Yet feeling life no Syrian pilgrimage.

  But, tell, shall he, the tourist, find
    Our isles the same in violet-glow
  Enamoring us what years and years—
    Ah, Ned, what years and years ago!
  Well, Adam advances, smart in pace,
  But scarce by violets that advance you trace.

  But we, in anchor-watches calm,
    The Indian Psyche's languor won,

And, musing, breathed primeval balm
  From Edens ere yet overrun;
Marveling mild if mortal twice,
Here and hereafter, touch a Paradise.

NOTES

❈ ❈ ❈

PREFACE

[1] John Freeman, *Herman Melville* (London and New York: Macmillan, 1926).

[2] The sea-loving British did not forget Melville during the years of American neglect. W. Clark Russell was his most ardent propagandist in Melville's last years; writing to an American in an attempt to arrange a biography, Russell called Melville "the greatest genius your country has produced." Louis Becke, an Australian writer then in London, contributed a glowing introduction to a 1901 reprint of *Moby Dick* in that city. Becke, who had spent twenty years in the South Seas as a trader, sailor, and beachcomber, commended Melville as "the one man who knew his subject and knew how to write about it. . . . He was of the sea; he loved it. Its hardships, its miseries, its starvation, its brutalities, and the grossness and wickedness that everywhere surrounded him in his wanderings through the two Pacifics, held but little place in the mind of a man who, ragged and unkempt as was too often his condition, had a soul as deep and wide and pure as the ocean itself, a soul that forever lifted him up above all mean and squalid things." Becke referred to Melville as "a born whaleman, a sailor and a 'perfect gentleman,'" and regarded *Moby Dick* as one of the best sea books ever written.

[3] Newton Arvin, *Herman Melville* (New York: Viking Press, 1950), p. 176.

[4] Jay Leyda, *The Melville Log* (New York: Harcourt, Brace & World, 1951), I, p. 393.

PART I—HERMAN MELVILLE IN THE PACIFIC

[1] An article, "Mocha-Dick; or the White Whale of the Pacific," by Jeremiah N. Reynolds, had appeared in the *Knickerbocker Magazine* in May, 1839, and had been reprinted for sailors to read.

[2] Jay Leyda, *The Melville Log* (New York: Harcourt, Brace & World, 1951), I, p. 119. A quotation from Chase's book, *Narrative of the Most Extraordinary and Distressing Shipwreck of the Whale-Ship "Essex," of Nantucket* (New York: W. B. Gilley, 1821), appears in the "Extracts" prefacing *Moby Dick*. In Chapter 45 of this novel entitled "The Affidavit," Melville gives recorded instances of attacks by whales, and in a note quotes Chase at length.

[3] Wilson L. Heflin has shown that Melville's statement in Chapter 45 that he had

seen Owen Chase was in error, for Chase was home in Nantucket at this time. The captain of the *Charles Carroll* was Thomas Andrews.

4 Melville claims in Sketch Second of *Las Encantadas* to have cruised off the south head of Albemarle at a time when the *Acushnet* was five months out from her port. The log of the *Acushnet* shows, however, that the ship was near the longitude of 130 ° W., far to westward, in May and June. Melville does not say that he landed, but only that a boat's crew was sent ashore, with orders to "bring back whatever tortoises they could conveniently transport."

5 Sandusky, Ohio, *Register,* Dec. 7, 1854.

6 The Reverend Titus Coan, who visited Nuku-Hiva in 1867, minimizes the dangers by stating that during Melville's romantic captivity, he was only four or five miles by land from the harbor whence he had fled. See Coan's *Life in Hawaii* (New York: R. D. F. Randolf, 1882), pp. 199–200.

7 See R. S. Forsythe, "Herman Melville in the Marquesas," *Philological Quarterly,* XV (Jan., 1936), pp. 1–15. An American naval officer, Henry A. Wise, mentioned in his book *Los Gringos* (New York, 1849) that during a visit at Nuku-Hiva in 1848 he saw a damsel named Fayaway who was ironing the pants of a French commissary while a "young *oui oui*" [a part-French baby] was tumbling about on the mats in their home. Clarence Gohdes, in "Gossip about Melville in the South Seas," *New England Quarterly,* X (Sept., 1937), pp. 526–31, prints a letter from the London *Athenaeum* of April 25, 1868, by a British naval officer, "R.S.," which reports that he had visited the Marquesas at the end of 1867 and states: "Melville's account of Typee (they always spoke of him as 'Shore') was well known; and we were told that Fa-a-wa and a daughter of Melville's were still living, the former an old woman."

8 See Mabel Weaks, "Long Ago and 'Faraway': Traces of Melville in the Marquesas in the Journal of A. G. Jones, 1845–55," *New York Public Library Bulletin,* LII (1948), pp. 362–369.

9 *The Hidden Worlds of Polynesia* (New York: New American Library, 1962), Chapter 9. The sailor's escape differs somewhat from that told in *Typee;* according to Suggs's informant: "Finally, after much pleading, he was carried to the beach to see an American [Australian] ship that had stopped there, and managed to reach the visitors' longboat while his native guards were occupied picking up trinkets that the American seamen had scattered in the water to attract their attention. Once in the longboat, he was borne safely to the waiting whaler under a shower of spears and slingstones hurled by his former captors, who were furious at losing their half-god." Dr. Suggs comments: "It was difficult to see how a story could have been passed on intact, by word of mouth over the years, yet it was as difficult to believe that so many details could check so well if it had been but a recently introduced tale. Perhaps future research in the field of Melvilleana will produce some facts that will support or disprove the tale of Heiku'a, but for the present, the strangely accurate tale cannot be labeled true or false." Possibly this is a sample of anthropological feedback, comparable to that found by Dr. Suggs's mentor, Dr. Harry Shapiro, on Pitcairn Island, where descendants of the *Bounty* mutineers told him as tradition what they had read in the standard accounts of the settlement (*The Heritage of the "Bounty,"* rev. ed., New York: Doubleday, 1962, p.15).

10 R. T. Greene, "Toby's Own Story," Buffalo, New York, *Commercial Advertiser,* July 11, 1846.

11 Melville's daughter Elizabeth noted that "whatever might have been his suspicions, he never had evidence that it was the custom of the tribe." See Leyda, I, p. 137.

[12] *Herman Melville: A Biography* (Berkeley and Los Angeles: University of California Press, 1951), p. 54.

[13] See Ida Leeson, "The Mutiny on the *Lucy Ann*," *Philological Quarterly*, XIX (Oct., 1940), pp. 370–79, and Leyda, I, pp. 141–50.

[14] See R. S. Forsythe, "Herman Melville's Father Murphy," *Notes and Queries*, XLXXII (April 10 and 17, 1937), pp. 254–58 and 272–76.

[15] *Rovings in the Pacific, from 1837 to 1849 . . . by a Merchant Long Resident at Tahiti* (London: Longman, Brown, Green, & Longmans, 1851), pp. 287–90.

[16] See Wilson L. Heflin, "Melville's Third Whaler," *Modern Languages Notes*, LXIV (April, 1949), pp. 241–245.

[17] Whale ship arrivals in 1843 numbered 247 at Lahaina and 136 at Honolulu (R. S. Kuykendall, *The Hawaiian Kingdom*, Honolulu: University of Hawaii Press, 1938, I, p. 307). Most of these, however, came in spring and fall.

[18] William H. Gilman, "A Note on Herman Melville in Honolulu," *American Literature*, XIX (May, 1947), p. 169. The letter was printed in the March 14, 1850, issue of the *Democrat* of Lansingburgh, New York, where the Melvilles had lived.

[19] Melville's many references in *Typee* to the Sandwich Islands reflect his strong animosity toward mission activity and the domination of the monarchy by American Congregationalists.

[20] R. S. Forsythe, "Herman Melville in Honolulu," *New England Quarterly*, VIII (March, 1935), p. 102.

[21] See Charles R. Anderson, *Melville in the South Seas* (New York: Columbia University Press, 1939; Dover, 1966), 349 ff., as well as Anderson, C. R. (ed.), *Journal of a Cruise to the Pacific Ocean, 1842–44, in the Frigate "United States"* (Durham, N.C.: Duke University Press, 1937).

[22] *Journal*, p. 62.

[23] *Journal*, p. 62–63.

[24] *Melville in the South Seas*, 395 ff.

[25] Nathaniel Ames, *A Mariner's Sketches* (Providence, R.I.: Long, Marshall & Hammond, 1830), pp. 227–30.

[26] *Ishmael* (Baltimore: Johns Hopkins University Press, 1956), pp. 92, 104.

[27] *Herman Melville* (New York: American Book Co., 1938), pp. xviii, xx.

[28] *Ishmael*, p. 121.

PART II—A PASSAGE TO THE MARQUESAS: *Typee*

[1] In his opening chapter, Melville mentions Captain David Porter's *Journal of a Cruise Made to the Pacific Ocean, in the U.S. Frigate "Essex," in the Years 1812, 1813, and 1814*, 2 vols. (Philadelphia: Bradford & Inskeep, 1815); C. S. Stewart's *A Visit to the South Seas, in the U.S. Ship "Vincennes" . . . 1829–30*, 2 vols. (New York: J. P. Haven, 1831); and William Ellis's *Polynesian Researches*, 2 vols. (London: Peter Jackson, 1829). He probably also used Edmund Fanning's *Voyages Round the World* (New York: Collins & Hannay, 1833) and Georg H. von Langsdorff's *Voyages and Travels in Various Parts of the World . . . 1803–1807*, 2 vols. (London: H. Colburn, 1813–14).

[2] Melville's spelling and punctuation were never standard. He cannot be seriously blamed, however, for his brave efforts in trying to write Polynesian words in an

American alphabet. A word like *ava,* when he wrote it as "arva," would come out close to the proper sounds when pronounced by his Eastern friends.

3 The Marquesans of Melville's Arcadia had an almost Greek cult of personal beauty. The sailors with Mendaña, discoverer of Polynesia, said that the olive-skinned girls of the Marquesas were prettier than those of Lima, who were famed for their beauty. Melville shows that both the women and the men of the valley of Taipi gave much time to cleanliness, personal grooming, and the tasteful selection of garlands and tunics, as well as to elaborate tattooing. This, he implies, revealed a frank worship of unashamed sensuality and innocent eroticism.

4 William Ellery Sedgwick, *Herman Melville, the Tragedy of Mind* (Cambridge, Mass.: Harvard University Press, 1944), pp. 28–30.

5 *Typee: A Peep at Polynesian Life,* edited by Harrison Hayford *et al.* (Evanston and Chicago: Northwestern University Press and The Newberry Library, 1968). Five professors contribute a 100-page appendix, collating all the editions that Melville might have seen and choosing variants judged to be closest to his intentions. The common paperback editions of Melville contain many gross errors.

PART III—A PASSAGE TO TAHITI: *Omoo*

1 In addition to the sources used for *Typee* (see Part II *ante*), Melville drew in *Omoo* upon The Right Reverend M. M. Russell's *Polynesia* (Edinburgh: Oliver & Boyd, 1843) and *Memoirs of the Life and Gospel Labors of the Late Daniel Wheeler* (London: Harvey & Darton, 1842). He also acknowledges Captain Otto von Kotzebue's *A New Voyage Round the World in the Years 1823-24-25-26,* 2 vols. (London: H. Colburn & R. Bentley, 1830); John Turnbull's *A Voyage Round the World . . . 1800-1804,* 3 vols. (Philadelphia: Benjamin & Thomas Kite, 1810); Captain F. W. Beechey's *Narrative of a Voyage to the Pacific and Bering Straits,* 2 vols. (London: H. Colburn & R. Bentley, 1831); Captain James Wilson's *A Missionary Voyage to the Southern Pacific Ocean . . . 1796, 1797, 1798* (London: S. Gosnell for T. Chapman, 1799); and *Narrative of the United States Exploring Expedition* (Philadelphia: C. Sherman, 1844), commanded by Lieut. Charles Wilkes.

2 *Omoo: A Narrative of Adventures in the South Seas,* edited by Harrison Hayford *et al.* (Evanston and Chicago: Northwestern University Press and The Newberry Library, 1968), p. 335.

3 *Studies in Classic American Literature* (New York: T. Seltzer, 1923), p. 207.

PART IV—A PASSAGE TO ALLEGORY: *Mardi*

1 See A. Grove Day, "Hawaiian Echoes in Melville's *Mardi,*" *Modern Language Quarterly,* XVIII (March, 1957), pp. 3–8, which continues the searches of Willard Thorp (*Herman Melville,* New York: American Book Company, 1938, lxvi, n. 103) and David Jaffé, "Some Sources of Melville's *Mardi,*" *American Literature,* IX (1937), pp. 60–62. The Day article shows that a number of references are made in *Mardi* to Hawaiian places, customs, and characters. The probability is offered that Melville used as sources not only William Ellis's *Polynesian Researches,* 2nd ed., 4 vols. (London: Peter Jackson, 1831) and C. S. Stewart's *A Visit to the South Seas in the U.S. Ship*

"*Vincennes*" (New York: J. P. Haven, 1831) but also Stewart's *Journal of a Residence in the Sandwich Islands,* 5th ed. (London and Boston: Weeks, Jordan, 1836).

[2] She has "A snow-white skin; blue, firmanent eyes: Golconda locks" (Chapter 43). The narrator speculates (Chapter 49) that she is an albino of the Tulla race of the Pacific. Association of Yillah with whiteness suggests the famous chapter in *Moby Dick* on "The Whiteness of the Whale," in which the unattainable truth is symbolized by this color that is no color. A number of other images of whiteness in *Mardi* anticipate those in *Moby Dick*.

[3] *Ishmael*, p. 192.

[4] *The English Notebooks* (London: Oxford University Press, 1941), p. 433.

[5] Melville, in turn, probably inspired other writers to use a Pacific archipelago as a setting for satirical romance. One follower was "Godfrey Sweven" [J. Macmillan Brown], author of *Riallaro, the Archipelago of Exiles* (London: Oxford University Press, 1897) and *Limanora, the Island of Progress* (London: Oxford University Press, 1903).

[6] Newton Arvin, *Herman Melville* (New York: Viking Press, 1950), p. 94.

[7] Sources cited by Charles R. Anderson are: [Daniel Tyerman and George Bennet] *Journal of Voyages and Travels . . .* 2 vols. (Boston: Crocker & Brewster, 1832); Frederick D. Bennett, *Narrative of a Whaling Voyage Round the Globe . . . 1833 to 1836,* 2 vols. (London: H. Bentley, 1840); William Ellis, *Polynesian Researches,* 2nd ed., 4 vols. (London: Peter Jackson, 1831); and Commodore Charles Wilkes, *Narrative of the U.S. Exploring Expedition . . . 1838–1842,* 5 vols. (Philadelphia: C. Sherman, 1844). To these may be added the two books by C. S. Stewart (see Note 1).

[8] *Op. cit.,* pp. 92–93.

[9] IV, p. 149.

[10] Melville's use in *Mardi* of legends from worldwide sources can be found in Merrell R. Davis, *Melville's "Mardi": A Chartless Voyage* (New Haven, Conn.: Yale University Press, 1952) and H. Bruce Franklin, *The Wake of the Gods: Melville's Mythology* (Stanford, Calif.: Stanford University Press, 1963).

[11] Leon Howard, *Herman Melville* (Berkeley and Los Angeles: University of California Press, 1951), p. 129.

PART V—A PASSAGE BEFORE THE MAST: *White Jacket*

[1] Despite Melville's statement that he was writing "an impartial account . . . inventing nothing" (p. 59), all the comic incidents in *White Jacket* appear to be taken from Henry James Mercier's *Life in a Man-of-War, or Scenes from "Old Ironsides"* (Philadelphia: L. R. Bailey, 1841). Other sources were Tobias Smollett's *Roderick Random,* 2 vols., 10th ed. (London: Gardner, 1778); Nathaniel Ames's *A Mariner's Sketches* (Providence, R.I.: Long, Marshall & Hammond, 1830); Samuel Leech's *Thirty Years from Home, or a Voice from the Main Deck,* 15th ed. (Boston: J. M. Whittemore, 1847), and *Tales of the Ocean and Essays for the Forecastle,* by "Hawser Martingale" [John S. Sleeper] (Boston: G. W. Cottrell, 1840). As usual, Herman improved on his borrowings through a greater sense of drama.

[2] Charles R. Anderson, ed., *Journal of a Cruise in the Frigate "United States",* *1842–1844* (Durham, N.C.: Duke University Press, 1937), p. 7.

[3] See A. Grove Day, "American Naval Slang a Hundred Years Ago," U.S. Naval Institute *Proceedings*, LXVIII (March, 1942), pp. 376–384.

PART VI—A PASSAGE TO INFINITY: *Moby Dick*

[1] If Queequeg had a prototype in Melville's experience, he may have been Marnoo, the traveled tabu warrior, with spear in hand, who appears in Chapter 18 of *Typee*. Another candidate is the Marquesan named Marbonna, whom the rover met in Eimeo (*Omoo*, Chapter 81); see the edition of *Moby Dick* edited by Luther S. Mansfield and Howard P. Vincent (New York: Hendricks House, 1952), p. 608. The same edition notes (p. 621) that the relationship between Ishmael and Queequeg probably derived from the South Sea custom whereby an islander would choose a *tayo* or special friend among visiting sailors—a custom discussed in *Omoo*, Chapter 39.

PART VII—A PASSAGE TO THE ENCHANTED ISLES: *Las Encantadas*

[1] *The Encantadas or, Enchanted Isles,* with an introduction, critical epilogue, and bibliographical notes by Victor Wolfgang von Hagen (Burlingame, Calif.: W. P. Wreden, 1940), pp. viii–ix.
[2] Raymond Weaver, *Herman Melville, Mariner and Mystic* (New York: George H. Doran, 1921), p. 348.
[3] Michael Sadlier, *Excursions in Victorian Bibliography* (London: Chaundry & Cox, 1922).
[4] Captain David Porter, *Journal of a Cruise Made to the Pacific Ocean, in the U.S. Frigate "Essex,"* . . . 2 vols. (Philadelphia: Bradford & Inskeep, 1815).
[5] James Colnett, *A Voyage to the South Atlantic and Round Cape Horn into the Pacific Ocean . . . in the Ship "Rattler"* (London: W. Bennett, 1798).
[6] *Narrative of the Surveying Voyages of H.M.S. "Adventure" and "Beagle"* . . . *1826–36,* 4 vols. (London: Henry Colburn, 1839). The set was part of the library of the frigate *United States*. Melville purchased "1 copy of Darwin's Voyage" from Harper & Brothers on April 10, 1847, for the notable sum of seventy-two cents.
[7] Melville's main knowledge of the buccaneers came from James Burney, *Chronological History of the Discoveries in the South Sea or Pacific Ocean,* 5 vols. (London: L. Hansard, 1803–1817).

PART VIII—A LECTURE ON THE SOUTH SEAS

[1] For a full account see Merton M. Sealts, Jr., *Melville as a Lecturer* (Cambridge, Mass.: Harvard University Press, 1937). He includes a composite and annotated version of "The South Seas" based upon twenty-five newspaper accounts, which agrees in general with that here taken from the Baltimore *American*.
[2] "He adopts 'The South Seas' as a title for his lecture in preference to 'The Pacific'; he finds it more relishing of the old, antique exploring and buccaneering adventures of the fresh, imaginative days of voyaging in those waters; and he, prob-

ably from old experience, has a lurking distrust of the pacific qualities of the great ocean. It got its name up at a favorable moment, and in spite of pouting, storms, tempests, and hurricanes, has lain abed upon it ever since."—Unidentified New York newspaper, February 8, 1859.

PART IX—FOUR POEMS

[1] Charles Olson, *Call Me Ishmael* (New York: Reynal & Hitchcock, 1947), pp. 26–32.